Investigating the Ocean

Illustrated Concepts & Classroom Inquiry

R. Mark Leckie

Richard Yuretich

Boston Burr Ridge, IL Dubuque, IA New York San Francisco St. Louis
Bangkok Bogotá Caracas Lisbon London Madrid
Mexico City Milan New Delhi Seoul Singapore Sydney Taipei Toronto

The McGraw-Hill Companies

INVESTIGATING THE OCEAN
Illustrated Concepts & Classroom Inquiry

10 11 12 13 14 15 SCI SCI 17 16 15

ISBN-13: 978-0-07-804588-2
ISBN-10: 0-07-804588-6

Learning Solutions Consultant: Jessica Watts
Learning Solutions Representative: Nikki Schmitt
Production Editor: Nina Meyer
Cover Photos: Front: NASA; Back: NOAA (Walter F. Smith); Inside Front: US Coast and Geodetic Survey; Inside Back: NASA/JPL and U.S. Geological Survey
Printer/Binder: Quad/Graphics

INVESTIGATING THE OCEAN: ILLUSTRATED CONCEPTS AND CLASSROOM INQUIRY

About this book

Educational research has shown that "experience is the best teacher," that is, our most memorable and long-lasting learning comes out of things we have done ourselves. Many colleges have recognized this in recent years and have encouraged senior projects or honors theses in an increasing number of academic programs. However, introductory courses, especially those designed for the general student population, are only rarely provided with the tools for active learning. The traditional lecture and laboratory (or lecture only) is the way most students at colleges and universities fulfill their science requirements, and it is not about to change anytime soon. However, studies have shown that by making students engaged participants during the time they spend in class, their level of learning increases notably. This book is specifically designed to support constructivist and exploratory learning in the teaching of introductory oceanography.

Most modern textbooks are packed with information and contain beautiful pictures, but their encyclopedic and descriptive approach often makes it difficult for students to separate basic principles from supporting information. As a result, they use the book only sparingly, deriving most of the information from the class meetings. Despite the relative brevity of the text, this book is a complete survey of the science of oceanography. It is built upon a concise overview of the major concepts in oceanography, with all the major principles of this science digested into a two-page format. The combination of brief text and graphical summaries complement and support each other so that both textual and visual learners can benefit equally, while keeping the content focused and manageable. The text and illustrations are designed so that instructors can use these as the basis for their own planning and class sessions, which encourages students to actually use the book during class time. In our experience, students often follow along and annotate the diagrams with their own remarks and interpretations, which aids in their learning of the scientific concepts. In this revised version, we have also added a wide variety of photographs to help illustrate the processes, and several sections entitled *Oceanography in Action*, which provides perspectives on particular problems, events, and case studies.

A unique feature of our book is the inclusion of numerous student-active investigations as part of each chapter. Most of these exercises are designed for short collaborative investigations during class, but others are equally suitable as extended homework assignments. These investigations are interpretive and not "cookbook", in order to give students the time to contemplate the problem and deduce reasonable answers. They comprise a variety of active pedagogical approaches including think-pair-share, minute papers, data plotting and interpretation, brainstorming, debates, map interpretations, and simple calculations. In many cases, the questions or discussion points are sufficiently flexible so that the instructor can use his or her favorite resources as a lead-in or follow-up to them. At the University of Massachusetts, Introductory Oceanography has 300 students in each class that meets twice a week for 75 minutes. There are no laboratories or discussion sections. The investigations in this book have been used successfully in this setting for a number of years. We often use the "bookends" approach in our teaching: a brief (15-minute) lecture outlining some introductory concepts, then perhaps 10 minutes devoted to the investigation with a five-minute wrap-up before continuing onto the next segment. Our approach in designing these investigations has been deliberately "low-tech", access to the internet or sophisticated instrumentation is not required for any exercise, although some of the investigations are easily adaptable to the use of student-response technology (such as PRS®) and on-line learning management systems (such as Blackboard®). In fact, the authors have successfully migrated some of these investigations to Blackboard® as part of a move toward a "blended-learning" environment for this course. New features of the present edition are shorter, less involved questions and explorations that are scattered throughout the narrative pages as *Food for Thought* or *Follow-up*.

Although we initially developed this book for a very large class, it can be used equally well in smaller settings. The questions in the investigations can be discussed more thoroughly in smaller classes, many of the activities can be expanded, and the students can receive more extensive feedback on their responses. Many are amenable to extended homework problems. Whether the course is "lecture" only, or includes a separate laboratory section, this book is designed to be used intensively during class in order to engage the students and encourage their active participation in classroom discussions. We hope that this book will stimulate more college instructors to use an investigative approach to teaching introductory oceanography.

We wish to acknowledge the contributions of our colleagues Laurie Brown and Julie Brigham-Grette of the University of Massachusetts, Amherst, who also use these techniques in teaching this course and have contributed to the development of the in-class investigations. The development of this book has benefited from the comments of many individuals including Charles Bahr, Cindy Fisher, Michael McCormic, Desiree Polyak, Nicole Ramocki, and Lynda Vallejo. Steve Nathan (University of Massachusetts, Amherst), Gretchen Andreasen (University of California at Santa Cruz), and Glenn Jones (Texas A&M University-Galveston) provided thorough reviews of earlier editions. In addition, we wish to thank the many reviewers who were recruited by McGraw-Hill to provide comments during the writing process of the current version. These include Patricia Yager (University of Georgia), Donna L. Witter (Kent State University), Tessa Hill (University of California, Davis), Elizabeth Simmons (Metropolitan State College of Denver), June R. P. Ross (Western Washington University), Scott Snyder (East Carolina University), Ronald E. Johnson (Old Dominion University), Istvan Csato (Collin College), Michael E. Lane (University of Hawaii—Leeward Community College), Senjie Lin (University of Connecticut), Hans G. Dam (University of Connecticut), Dennis Hilbert (Everett Community College), Joseph Ortiz (Kent Staet University), Cynthia Venn (Bloomsburg University of Pennsylvania), Asil M. Wadia (University of Akron, Wayne College), Michele Arniboldi (University of Michigan), Annelie Skoog (University of Connecticut), Ed Laine (Bowdoin College), Sara Harris (University of British Columbia), Karl M. Chauff (St. Louis University), and Felix Rizk (Manatee Community College). The STEMTEC Project, a Collaborative for Excellence in Teacher Preparation of the National Science Foundation (DUE 9653966), supported the initial production of these resources and the student-active approach to learning oceanography.

R. Mark Leckie
Richard F. Yuretich
University of Massachusetts
Amherst, MA 01003
May 2011

To the student

This book is different from the textbooks that you use in most of your other science courses. It is primarily a resource manual and guide that will help you learn about the ocean, explore some of the major phenomena that occur on our home planet, and experience the way that scientific investigation of the Earth proceeds. Although most of the information can also be found in more traditional textbooks, our presentation allows you to see the "big ideas" at a glance, and will help you in grasping the essential points of a topic. In addition to the informational material that provides the necessary facts about the ocean system, this book contains a series of short investigations that are designed to help you learn about a particular topic. Scientific knowledge is gained by exploration and discovery, that is, by individuals and teams working together to solve problems and pursue ideas. Accordingly, you really can't appreciate or understand the process by which we gather scientific information simply by listening to lectures and reading a standard textbook. You can engage in the discovery process by becoming involved in in-class discussions, experiments and video "field trips" as guided by the questions and problems contained in this volume. Some of these will be used as investigations during class time; others may be used as a basis for homework assignments. Still others will accompany videos or films, so that you can maximize your understanding of the concepts that are presented in them. Furthermore, you will find that the investigations not used in class may also help you in studying the topic.

To make effective use of this volume, **BRING THIS BOOK TO EVERY CLASS!!** You will frequently turn in completed investigations from the book at the end of a class meeting. We have deliberately kept the book small so you should have no problem carrying it in your backpack!

INVESTIGATING THE OCEAN: ILLUSTRATED CONCEPTS AND CLASSROOM INQUIRY

Table of Contents

PART 1

Introducing the Ocean

Earth is the water planet, as any photograph from space will show, with about 71% of the surface of the globe covered by the ocean. As a result, the ocean has a large influence on the environment of our planet. The mass of the ocean helps to keep the Earth livable by moderating the surface temperature and providing the source of water that flows on the continents. The ocean also has a significant place in the human context. From the earliest days of recorded history, civilizations have used the sea in various ways, for trade, for food, and as a means to expand their reach. Periodically, violent storms, undersea volcanic explosions, and tsunami devastate coastal areas and these events have even led to the collapse of once-powerful civilizations. Over the centuries, we have come to realize that is in our own best interest to learn how the ocean works so that we can use it to our advantage and avoid damaging this essential part of the planet. We have not yet achieved these goals, but our knowledge of the sea grows with continuing study of the geology, biology, physics, and chemistry of the ocean. Before we explore these scientific pursuits, let's step back and take a look at the importance of the sea to our way of life, and become familiar with some of the basic tools we need for investigating the expanse of the ocean.

In this chapter you will learn:

- How the ocean is an essential part of planet Earth
- The history of ocean exploration and discovery
- The essentials of latitude and longitude
- Basic principles of navigation
- How to determine the depth of the ocean
- The value of the ocean in the modern world

1.1 The Earth as a Habitable Planet

A view of the Earth from space shows the abundance of water on our home planet.

As mentioned in the introduction, seawater covers nearly 71% of the Earth's surface. The Earth is unique among the other planets in our solar system because of temperatures and pressures at the surface and in the atmosphere that allow water to occur in the liquid state. No other planet in our solar system has so much water in its environment. In fact, Earth is the only planet where water is known to occur naturally in all three states: gaseous, liquid, and solid. It is the presence of such a large volume of water, and the ease by which it can change state, that moderates the extremes of climate and sustains life.

The Earth functions as a series of interconnected "systems", which include the geosphere, biosphere, atmosphere, hydrosphere, and cryosphere (Fig. 1.1). The hydrosphere, of which the ocean is a principal part, plays a fundamental role in the processes that make Earth habitable. For example, the rain and snow that sustains life on land is derived from the ocean, and water helps break down rocks on land to form soil and allows rivers to carry sediment and dissolved nutrients to the sea. The evaporation of water from the ocean surface and its later condensation into rainfall helps transfer heat from the ocean to the atmosphere, and from the tropics to the poles, thereby regulating the temperature at the Earth's surface.

The geosphere interacts with the ocean through processes that are taking place at the sea floor. Submarine volcanoes emit **magma** and fluids (primarily water and carbon dioxide) and cause seawater to circulate through the ocean crust. The volcanic activity on the sea floor also contributes to the movement of the continents around the Earth. A large part of the biosphere lives in the ocean and survives by extracting carbon dioxide and other nutrients from seawater. After death, the remains of these organisms are either cycled back into the water or incorporated into the sediments that accumulate on the sea floor. In general, Earth's interconnected systems are linked by the flow of water and the recycling of carbon. This occurs through volcanic activity, plate tectonics, the hydrologic cycle, climate, as well as the processes of life itself.

Earth systems are driven by two power plants: an external source of energy and an internal source. The energy from the sun, **solar radiation,** is the external source, responsible for heating the atmosphere and ocean, generating the winds and ocean currents, creating our weather and the erosion of the land, and powering photosynthesis and the many webs of life.

Internal energy is the result of **radioactive decay**. Many elements, such as hydrogen, have two or more naturally occurring **isotopes**. Isotopes of the same element differ slightly in atomic mass, or weight, because of differing numbers of **neutrons**. Most isotopes are stable but some are not. For example, the element uranium (U) has two unstable isotopes (^{235}U and ^{238}U). These unstable isotopes spontaneously change to stable isotopes of a different element, in this case lead (Pb), by radioactive decay. The heat generated by radioactive decay has built up within the interior of the Earth but over geologic time, Earth has been slowly losing this heat. Heat is transferred from deep within the Earth to the surface by way of **conduction**, the transfer of heat from one atom to another, and **convection**, which is differential heat loss that causes movement of mass. As we shall learn in our explorations, the ocean floor is in constant motion, with new crust being formed from molten lava at the ocean ridges, and old crust being returned to the Earth's

A more complete investigation of radioactive decay can be found in section 2.2

interior in the deep-sea trenches. These processes help to perpetuate an ever-changing landscape, atmospheric composition, climate, and biodiversity.

The Earth is dynamic; it's exterior is constantly being reshaped by geological processes, the hydrologic cycle, and biotic evolution. The ocean is a key component of all the principal "spheres" of the Earth, and consequently the ocean plays a major role in maintaining a livable environment on our home planet. A knowledge of the workings of the ocean is essential to evaluate the cause of many of the environmental changes we are experiencing today.

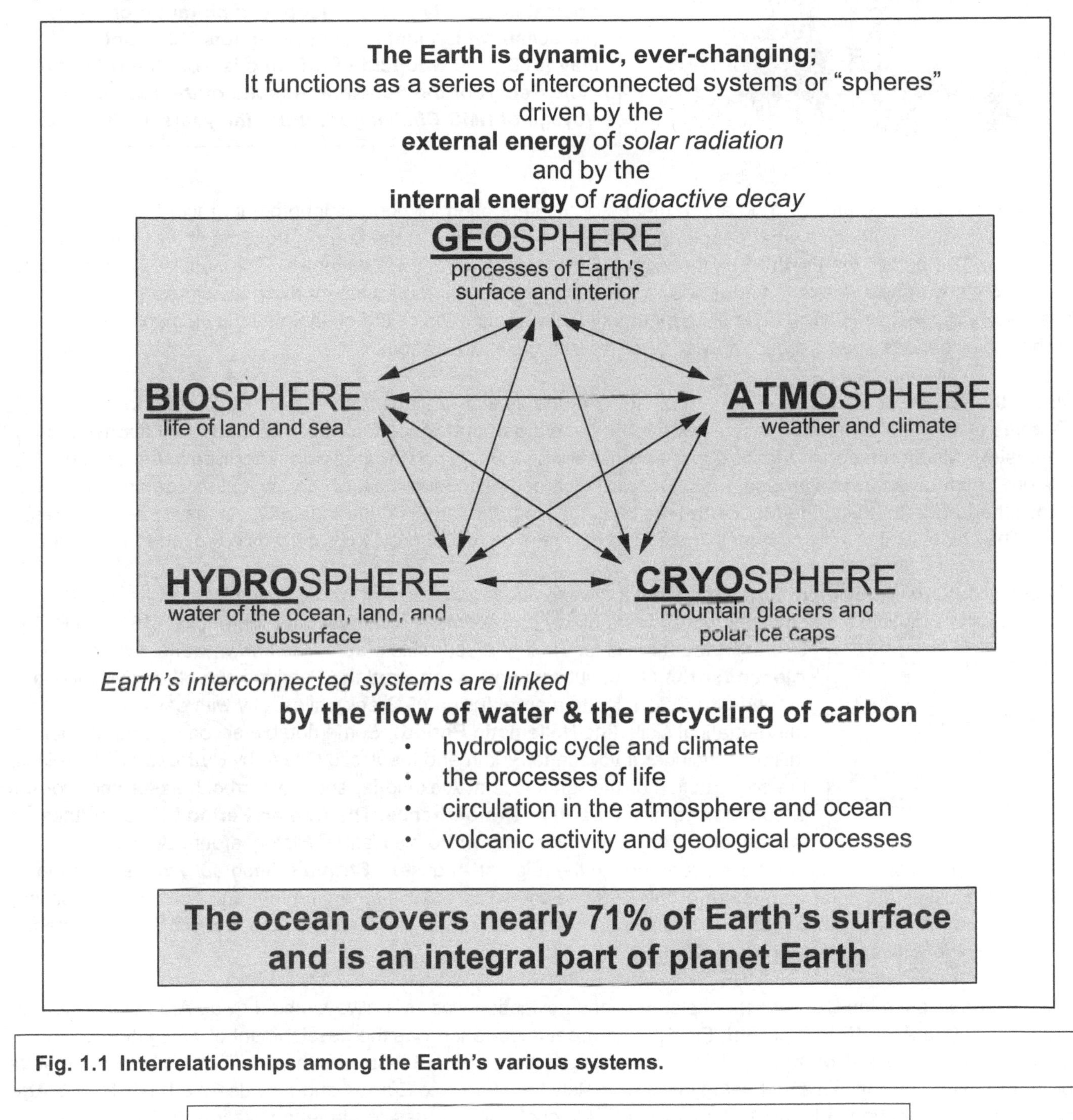

Fig. 1.1 Interrelationships among the Earth's various systems.

Investigation 1.1 explores the relationships among the parts of the Earth system using another approach.

■1.2 A Brief History of Ocean Exploration

The HMS Challenger embarked on the first cruise dedicated entirely to the scientific exploration of the ocean, which lasted from December, 1872 until May,1876. This woodcut of the ship is from the original *"The Report of the Scientific Results of the Exploring Voyage of HMS Challenger during the years 1873-1876."*

The sea has been a source of food and a means of transportation for peoples long before recorded history began. We can only imagine what people thought as they gazed out at the horizon from the shore. What was out there? The end of the Earth? Sea monsters? Other places with riches unknown? The earliest explorers were more likely driven by a desire to find new and more productive fishing grounds, or more hospitable places to live. The history of western civilization is linked strongly to the exploration of the ocean, so let us look briefly at some of the major periods and how our knowledge of the sea grew within them.

During the **"Dawn of Civilization"** (Fig. 1.2) some of the earliest writings from ancient Egypt refer to the "Peoples of the Sea", who are now believed to be the **Minoan and Mycenaean civilizations** that flourished in the eastern Mediterranean in the third and second millennia B.C. The **Phoenicians**, who lived in the area of modern Lebanon and Syria around 1,200 B.C. are regarded as the foremost of the ancient navigators. They established trade routes in the Mediterranean Sea, the Red Sea, and into the Indian Ocean as far as southeast Asia. They also successfully circumnavigated the continent of Africa, proving that it was surrounded by ocean.

We will learn more about latitude, longitude and navigation techniques in sections 1.3 to 1.5.

Although the **Greek Classical Period** was not known for its development of trade, their intellectual exploration led to several significant accomplishments, most notably a description of the world by Herodotus (484-425 B.C.) that provided a basis for the first reasonable map of the known world. When **Alexander the Great** subsequently conquered the Persians and other civilizations around 330 B.C., it led to a great fusion of Greek philosophy with eastern mathematical skills (the **Hellenistic Period**). Some notable accomplishments during this time include: a voyage to Britain and the Arctic Ocean by **Pytheas** of Marseilles; the construction of the lighthouse at Alexandria; and the correct measurement of the circumference of the Earth by **Eratosthenes**. The **Roman Period** built upon these foundations. **Pliny the Elder**, who wrote his *Natural History* around A.D. 77, recorded explorations of the northern ocean during the reign of Augustus. **Strabo**'s *Geography* written around A.D. 25, discusses the spherical nature of the Earth as shown by objects emerging from the horizon while sailing towards them. **Ptolemy** (2nd century A.D.) also published a Geography that included the first coordinate system for establishing a location anywhere in the known world.

While Europe was in the **Dark Ages**, exploration and navigation was kept alive by the thriving Arab culture in the Middle East (the **Arab Development**, Fig 1.2). Of great importance was the development of navigational techniques using the **astrolabe**, a predecessor of the modern **sextant** that uses the position of the sun and stars for determining location. This technology was ultimately transferred to Europe and provided the basis for the **Age of Exploration** that began in the 15th century A.D. Although the voyages of **Magellan**, **Vasco da Gama**, and **Columbus** were not concerned with scientific knowledge, their observations and experiences provided the foundation for the oceanographic expeditions of the 18th and 19th centuries (**Scientific Explorations**).

*By the **fall of the Roman Empire** (A.D. 476) the following was known:*

1. *The actual size and shape of the Earth,*
2. *The ocean surrounded all the continents,*
3. *Basic navigational techniques, and*
4. *The essential principles of making maps.*

Captain James Cook sailed as far south as possible at that time investigating the possible existence of a continent (now known as Antarctica). He also charted many islands in the South Pacific, during his three voyages from 1768-1779. **Charles Darwin**, during the voyage of the *Beagle* (1831-1836), researched the origin of coral atolls in addition to his famous observations on natural selection.

Modern oceanography or the **"Age of Big Science"** (Fig. 1.2) began in 1873 with the *H.M.S. Challenger*, which sailed the seas for four years collecting abundant information on the physics, chemistry, and biology of the ocean. The scientific reports filled 50 volumes of data and illustrations that greatly increased our knowledge of the sea. From this point until the beginnings of Word War II, many other nations followed on the heels of Britain and funded national expeditions to explore various parts of the ocean. The dominance of the United States in the post-war period led to the growth of the large oceanographic institutions (Lamont-Doherty, Woods Hole, and Scripps), a multiplication of research vessels dedicated exclusively to ocean research, and the development of a fleet of submersible vehicles, both manned (such as *Alvin*) and remotely operated (ROV such as *Jason*).

We will examine scientific ocean drilling and the discoveries made about the nature of the ocean floor in Part 2 of this book.

The era of scientific ocean drilling began in 1968, with the first voyage of the *Glomar Challenger*. This drilling ship bored over 600 holes into the seafloor, the results of which were instrumental in documenting the processes of seafloor spreading and plate tectonics. After its retirement in 1983, the work of this ship was transferred to the *JOIDES Resolution*, which continues today as the premier research platform criss-crossing the ocean.

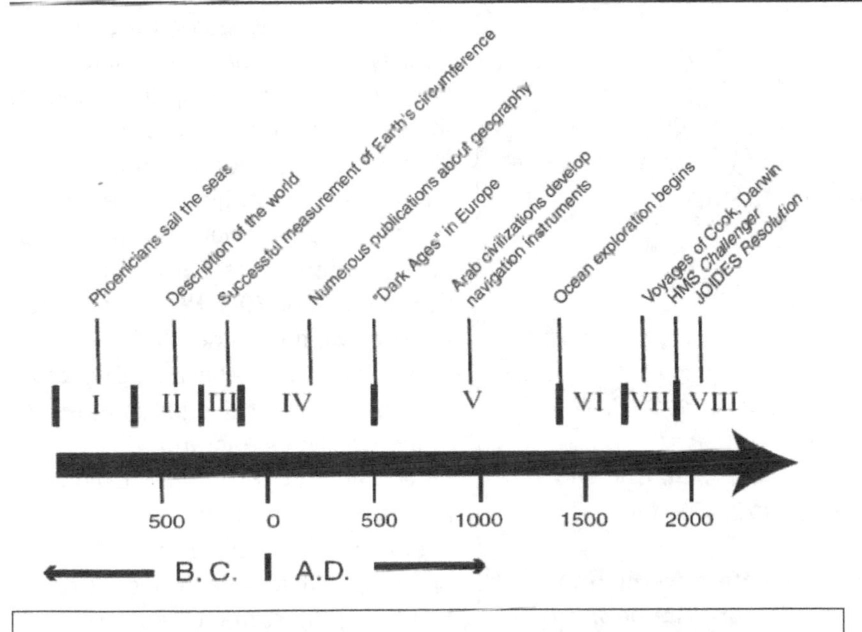

Fig. 1.2 The growth of scientific study of the ocean over time. I. The Dawn of Civilization; II. The Greek Classical Period; III. The Hellenistic Period; IV. The Romans; V. The Arab Development; VI. The Age of Exploration; VII. Scientific Explorations; VIII. The Age of "Big Science".

Food for Thought

Suppose that you were living in the Middle Ages, long before there were satellites that could observe the Earth from space, or any other modern technology. What observations could you make that would lead to the conclusion, as some did in those days, that the Earth was round?

■1.3 Latitude and Longitude

Location, location, location! There is arguably nothing more important when studying the ocean than being able to locate yourself precisely on the Earth's surface. On land, the task is relatively easy. Most of us can determine where we are very well by referring to known landmarks such as mountains, roads, and buildings, which are represented on an accurate map. Early seafarers stayed within sight of the coast in order to determine where they were. In the open ocean there are no landmarks; one stretch of ocean in the Atlantic looks just like one in the Pacific. But suppose that you are in a boat that has ventured out into the middle of the Pacific Ocean far from any coastline. Your engines have failed and you need to radio for help. How could you tell your rescuers where to locate you? To help in identifying a unique location on the ocean (or anywhere on Earth, for that matter) the **latitude** and **longitude** system was developed. The ancient Greeks beginning with Hipparchus in the 2nd century B.C. are credited with initiating a coordinate system for specifying locations on the Earth's surface, although it has been refined and developed over many centuries. The present system of latitude and longitude as we use it today was not standardized until well into the 18th century.

1 nautical mile = 1.15 statute mile = 1.85 km
1 km = 0.62 statute mile = 0.54 nautical mile

Getting back to your predicament in the Pacific, if you know your latitude and longitude precisely, this will help in directing rescuers to your boat. On a map, lines of latitude and longitude appear as a grid system that pinpoints each location on the Earth's surface with a unique set of coordinates (Fig.1.3) Since the Earth is a sphere, these reference "lines" are actually based on angular relationships between the surface of the Earth and its center (Fig. 1.4). For latitude, the Equator can be visualized as a plane that passes through the Earth at its mid-section. If we are located north or south of the Equator, we can specify our location as the angle between a line drawn to the center of the Earth and the plane of the Equator. In a similar fashion, longitude is the angle between our position and the imaginary plane that passes through the Earth at the Prime Meridian (0°). By international convention, the Prime Meridian is drawn through Greenwich, England. The other side of this plane emerges in the Pacific Ocean and is designated as 180°. Latitude lines are parallel to one another everywhere on the Earth so the distance between each degree of latitude is the same. Lines of longitude converge at the poles so that the distance between degrees of longitude decreases as you travel north or south of the equator.

Latitude Terminology

- "Parallels" = east-west grid lines that are parallel to the equator (Fig. 1.5)
- 0° at the **Equator**, 90°N at the **North Pole**, and 90°S at the **South Pole**
- 0°–90°N = **Northern Hemisphere**
- 0°–90°S = **Southern Hemisphere**
- Distances between latitudes are the same everywhere on Earth's surface. At all locations:

  1° latitude = 60 nautical miles = (111.32 km)
  1' latitude = 1 nautical mile

Longitude Terminology

- "meridians" = north-south grid lines that intersect at the poles (Fig. 1.5)
- 0° = **"Prime Meridian"** (passes through Greenwich, England)
- 180° = halfway around Earth (roughly approximates the international dateline)
- 0°–180° to the west of Greenwich is the **Western Hemisphere**
- 0°–180° to the east of Greenwich is the **Eastern Hemisphere**
- Longitudinal distances vary with distance from the equator:

  at 0° latitude, 1° longitude = 60 nautical miles (= 111.32 km)
  at 30° latitude, 1° longitude = 52 nautical mile (= 96.49 km)
  at 60° latitude, 1° longitude = 30 nautical miles (= 55.80 km)
  at 90° latitude, 1° longitude = 0 km

Latitude and longitude are measured with the same units as angles, namely degrees (°). Each degree is divided into 60 minutes ('), and each minute is further subdivided into 60 seconds(").

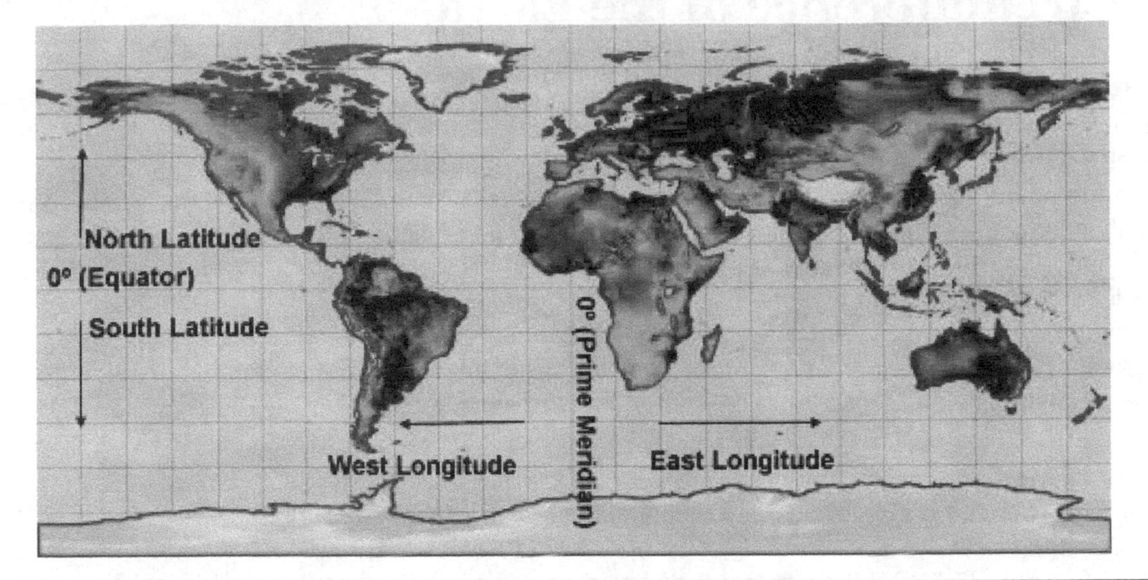

Fig. 1.3 Lines of latitude and longitude together comprise a grid system that uniquely identifies any point on the surface of the Earth.

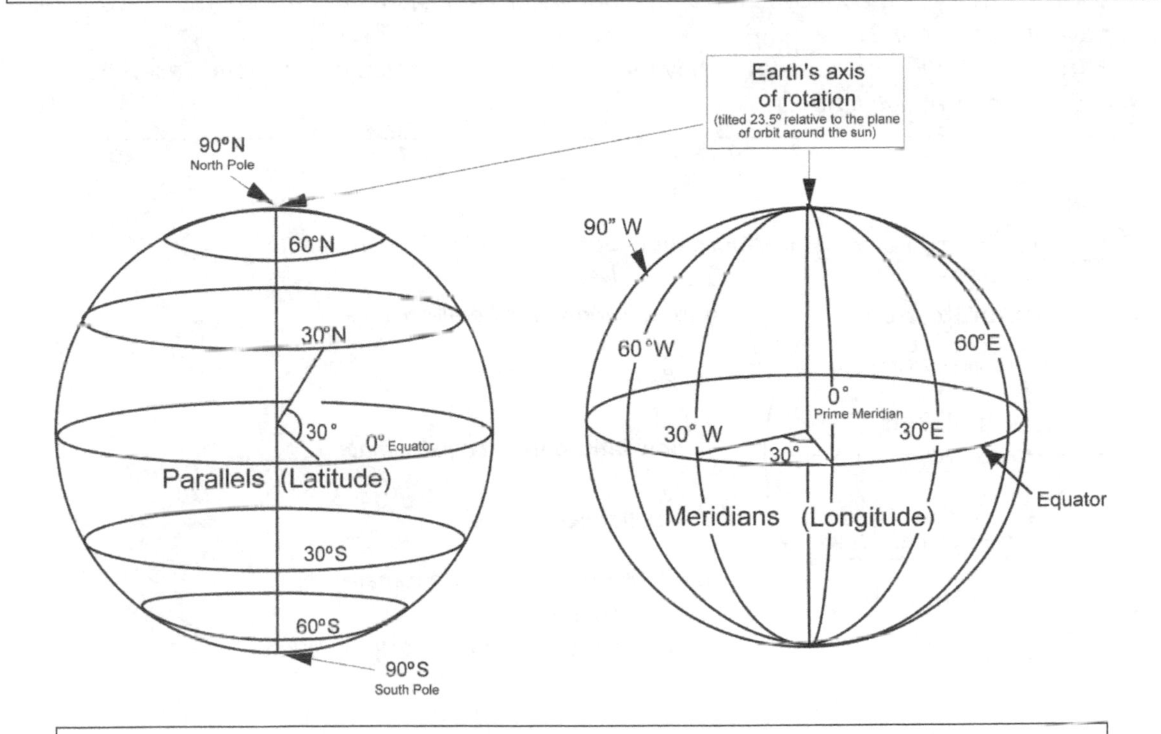

Fig. 1.4 Latitude and longitude represent the angles made between a perpendicular line that passes through the center of the Earth and a perpendicular line in a reference plane, either the Equator (latitude) or Prime Meridian (longitude).

Investigation 1.2 provides additional insight into determining latitude and longitude.

1.4 Latitude, Climate Zones, and the Circumference of the Earth

Latitude divides the Earth into the Northern and Southern Hemispheres, but it also has an exceedingly practical application in helping to define the different climatic regions on Earth. Because Earth's axis of rotation is tilted at an angle of 23.5° to its plane of orbit around the sun, we experience seasonal changes in the amount of solar radiation received at all latitudes. The most intense solar radiation is received in the tropical zone, which lies between 23.5°N and 23.5°S of the Equator. These latitudes mark the northern and southern limits where the sun will be directly overhead at some point during the year, and define the tropical climatic zone (Fig. 1.5). Similarly, at latitudes above 66.5°N or S, the sun will not rise or set at all for at least one day during the year; this is the polar climatic zone. The region in between these two extremes is the temperate zone.

We will examine the Earth's orbit around the sun and its effects on the seasons and the ocean temperature in section 3.11.

Equator (0°) – *the sun is directly overhead on or about March 21 (N. Hemisphere "spring") and September 21 (N. Hemisphere "fall").*
Tropic of Cancer (23.5°N) – *the sun is directly overhead on or about June 21 (N. Hemisphere "summer").*
Tropic of Capricorn (23.5°S) – *the sun is directly overhead on or about December 21 (N. Hemisphere "winter").*
Arctic Circle (66.5°N) – *the sun stays above the horizon for 24 hours on or about June 21, and doesn't rise at all on or about December 21.*
Antarctic Circle (66.5°S) – *the sun stays above the horizon for 24 hours on or about December 21, and doesn't rise at all on or about June 21.*

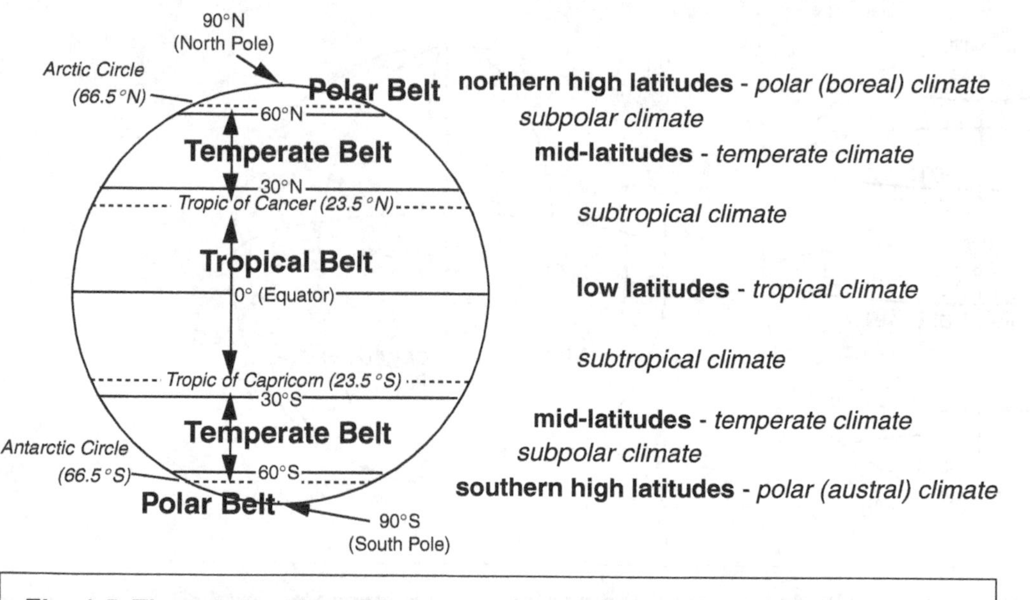

Fig. 1.5 The relationship of latitude to climate zones on the Earth.

Calculating the Size of the Earth

The concept of latitude, together with the seasonal changes in the angle of solar radiation, provides a method for calculating the size of the Earth. The most famous of these, and possibly the earliest, was accomplished by Eratosthenes of Cyrene (ca. 235 B.C., Hellenistic Egypt). He lived in the capital city of Alexandria on the Nile

Delta, which today we know has a latitude of 31.2° North. He noticed that at high noon on June 21, the sun was directly overhead in the city of Syene in southern Egypt,(near the modern city of Aswan at 24°N) However, in Alexandria where he lived, the sun cast a shadow of a tall monument that made an angle of 7.2° with the top of the actual monument. He knew the distance between the two cities (about 500 miles or 800 km in modern distance units) and so he was able to use this information to accurately estimate the circumference of the Earth using trigonometry (Fig. 1.6).

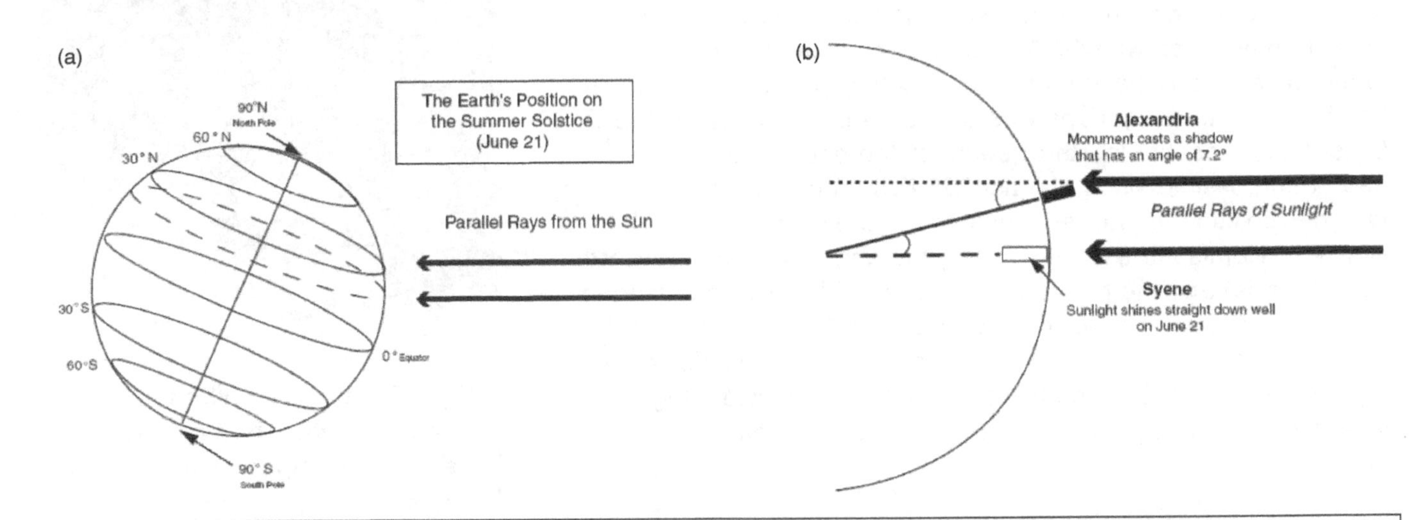

Fig. 1.6 Eratosthenes' measurement of the circumference of the Earth. a) On the summer solstice, June 21, the sun is directly overhead at a latitude of 23.5°N. b) The sun's light rays are parallel lines, and these can be drawn projecting into the interior of the Earth. The angle that the shadow makes with the monument is the same as the angle that the line from the monument makes with line from the well projected to the Earth's center. This is the trigonometric relationship of a line cutting two parallel lines. This angle at the Earth's interior is the same number of degrees as the arc of the circle it intersects. Eratosthenes knew that the distance along this arc from Syene to Alexandria was 5,000 stades (approximately 500 milesor 800 km). The distance around the Earth is a total of 360°, so that tho total distance can be found by the relationship:

$$\frac{360^\circ}{7.2^\circ} = \frac{x}{5{,}000}$$

In this calculation, the result is 250,000 stades. This is equivalent to 40,000 kilometers (24,000 miles) in modern measurement systems, which is very close to the actual circumference of the Earth.

Earth's Circumference and Exploration

Eratosthenes' calculations were well-known during the European "Age of Exploration," although there were competing measurements that underestimated the circumference of the Earth at 180,000 stades, and the actual length of the stade was a matter of some debate. For reasons that are not fully clear, Christopher Columbus convinced Queen Isabella of Spain that the smaller values were correct and received her support for his attempt to reach India by sailing west. If the Americas hadn't been there, Columbus' three tiny ships would almost surely have perished trying to cross the enormous expanse of the Atlantic and Pacific Ocean! If you would like to learn more about this subject, you can look at the interesting information that NASA has on one of it's web sites: http://www-istp.gsfc.nasa.gov/stargaze/Scolumb.htm.

■1.5 Navigation: Finding Your Way at Sea

Latitude and longitude provide a way of identifying unique points on the surface of the globe, but they are of no use in the task of navigation unless we can actually determine their values at the place we are located. Today almost all ships are outfitted with a radio navigation system, such as Omega or Loran, and satellite navigation with GPS (Global Positioning System), but in the days before these inventions locating your position on Earth or constructing maps was based on **celestial navigation**. Determining location north or south of the equator, or latitude, had been possible since at least 325 B.C. You can calculate latitude (position, in degrees, minutes, and seconds) in the Northern Hemisphere by measuring the angle between the North Star (Polaris) and the horizon. The hand-held instrument used to measure this angle is called a **sextant** (Fig 1.7). At the North Pole, the North Star is directly above you, or 90° north latitude. At the equator, the North Star is on the horizon, or 0° latitude. Fig.1.8 illustrates the principle behind the use of the sextant.

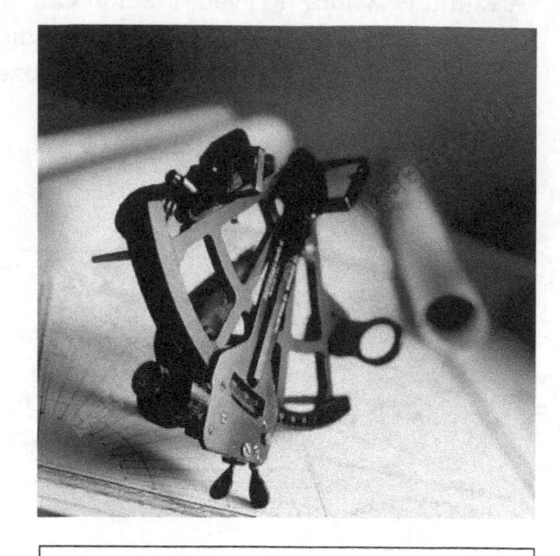

Fig 1.7 A typical sextant and navigation chart that can be used for finding locations at sea.

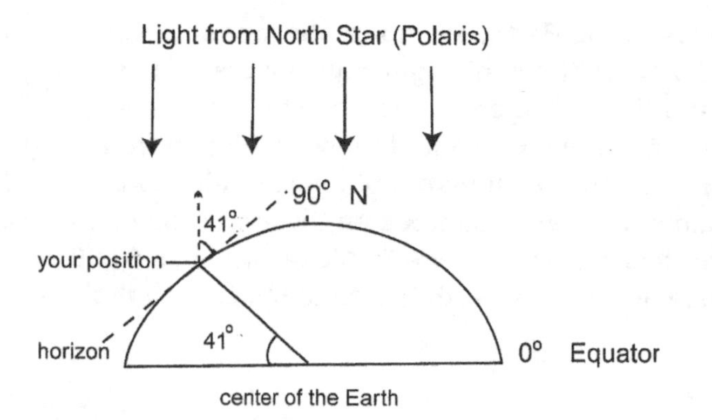

Fig. 1.8 Illustration of the use of the sextant. The angle measured between the North Star (Polaris) and the horizon is a direct measure of latitude in the Northern Hemisphere. The North Star is not visible south of the Equator, so other celestial markers must be used.

Determining position in an east-west reference frame, or *longitude*, was a long-standing problem. Early sailors relied on celestial tables or "dead-reckoning" (an educated guess based on apparent direction and speed, neither of which could be measured very accurately). We can determine longitude (position, in degrees, minutes, and seconds, east or west of the **Prime Meridian**, which is in Greenwich, England) with a very accurate clock or **chronometer** that keeps track of the exact time at a known location. John Harrison solved the 'longitude problem' with his intricate and amazingly accurate sea-worthy clocks, 4 in total, built between 1728 and 1760. Captain James Cook (1772-79) made the first accurate maps of Earth's surface (Pacific Ocean) utilizing this new invention. We still use the time in Greenwich, England at 0° longitude as our reference point, referred to as GMT (**Greenwich Mean Time**) or UT (**Universal Time**).

By having the ship's chronometer set for Greenwich time (GMT), you can calculate the time difference between your actual location and the chronometer. The time at your actual location can be obtained by using the sextant to measure the height of the sun above the horizon. This is easiest to do at high noon when the sun is highest in the sky. Knowing that the Earth makes one complete rotation every day (360°/24hr or 15°/hr) you can calculate your longitude from the time difference between your location and Greenwich, which is on the Prime Meridian (0° longitude). For example, your time is 5 hours earlier than the time at Greenwich (Prime Meridian = 0°) so your longitude is (5 hours x 15°/hr) = 75°W longitude. Remember, the Earth turns toward the east (e.g., the sun rises in New York before it rises in Chicago), so that it is earlier west of the Prime Meridian (west longitude) and later towards the east (east longitude).

The Earth turns through 360° in 24 hours. Therefore, each hour the Earth rotates through 360°/24 = 15°. In other words, a one-hour time difference represents 15° of longitude. It is later east of your position, and earlier to the west (Fig 1.9).

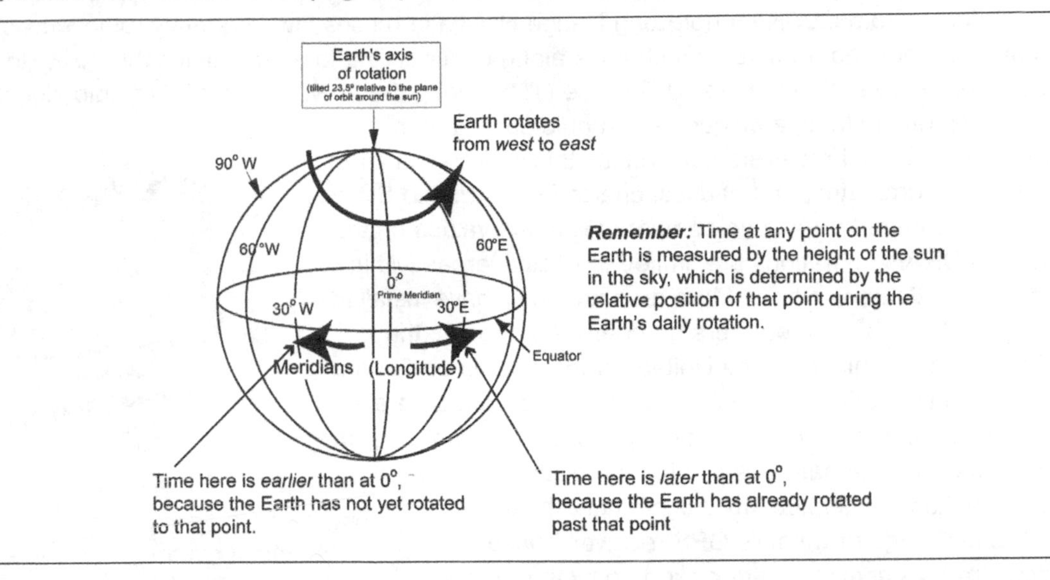

Fig. 1.9 The rotation of the Earth through 15°/hour causes differences in time that can be used to calculate location east or west of the Prime Meridian.

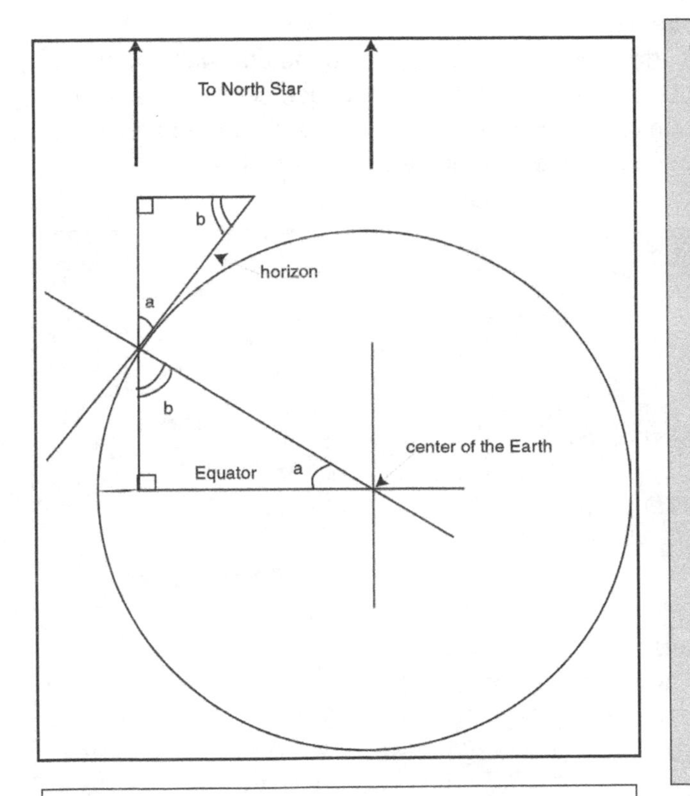

Fig. 1.10 The sextant measurement gives the angles for a right triangle that is similar to one that has an apex at the center of the Earth.

The Power of Trigonometry

Mathematics is a powerful tool for much scientific study, and the science of navigation is based heavily on the principles of trigonometry. Trigonometry was developed by the Babylonians and Egyptians during the "Dawn of Civilization" and was refined and extended by the ancient Greeks. The word itself means "measuring three angles" and the mathematics is based upon solving problems related to triangles, specifically right triangles. Figure 1.10 redraws the measurements of latitude with the sextant shown in fig. 1.7 so that you can see that the problem is one of determining the angles in two right triangles. The two angles a, which represent the angle measured with the sextant and the angle your position makes with the center of the Earth, are the same. With trigonometry, we can solve many problems easily that deal with angular relationships. An interesting review of trigonometry and its applications can be found on the NASA web site: http://www-istp.gsfc.nasa.gov/stargaze/Strig1.htm.

Investigation 1.3 provides some practice in using a sextant.

1.6 Navigation Today

Navigation became considerably easier in the latter part of the 20th century with the development of radio- and radar-based navigation systems. LORAN (for Long Range Navigation) uses low-frequency radio waves (in the 90 to 110 kHz band) transmitted from various stations along the coastline to enable ships the ability to triangulate their position. In essence, by noting the time difference (TD) among the arrival times of the radio signals from three different LORAN transmitters, a unique geographic position can be fixed. Many modern LORAN receivers can display this information as latitude and longitude coordinates, and nautical charts for the United States are marked with TD numbers that can be compared with the values on the receiver (Fig. 1.11). LORAN operations are limited to coastal areas within about 2,000 km of LORAN transmitters. More recently, ships have installed Global Positioning Systems (GPS) receivers on board. As a result, the operation of LORAN-C transmitters in the United States ceased on February 8, 2010. GPS uses the time differences in signals received from several orbiting satellites to fix a position anywhere on the globe and is not limited to coastal waters. There are 24 satellites circling the globe in six different orbital planes at an altitude of 20,200 km. Accordingly, there are normally several within range of a ship's GPS receiver. These satellites broadcast radio signals that are picked up by the receiver and by comparing the time that the signal was sent with the time it was received, the distance to the satellites can be calculated. When three or more satellites are in range, the position of the ship can be fixed precisely by triangulation (Fig. 1.12). Today, even most small receivers can accurately locate themselves on the Earth's surface with an accuracy of 10 meters, well within the limits necessary for marine navigation. GPS Units display the results in latitude and longitude coordinates, and they can also display the boat's location directly on navigation charts. However, navigators still need to know how to sail by the stars, since electronic equipment can fail from time to time, but the heavens never lie!

A typical marine GPS unit showing the map display (Copyright © 2010 Garmin Ltd or its Subsidiaries. All Rights Reserved).

SUMMARY OF NAVIGATION TECHNIQUES

- **Celestial Navigation** — **Accuracy: 2 – 10 km**
  Uses position of sun and stars
  a. North Star at night or height of the sun at local noon gives latitude
  b. Local noon compared to Greenwich (GMT or UT) used to calculate longitude
- **Radio Navigation Systems** — **50 m – 15 km**
  Land-based signals: Omega, Loran
  a. Radio beacons send signals from land-based stations
  b. Time differences from three different beacons are compared
  c. Position can be located by triangulation (trigonometry)
- **Satellite Navigation** — **0.1 – 200 meters**
  Global Positioning System (GPS)
  a. 24 satellites: *21 primary, 3 orbiting "spares"*
  10,900 miles up, each orbits twice/day
  b. At least four satellites above horizon for every point on Earth
  c. Determines position using triangulation (trigonometry)

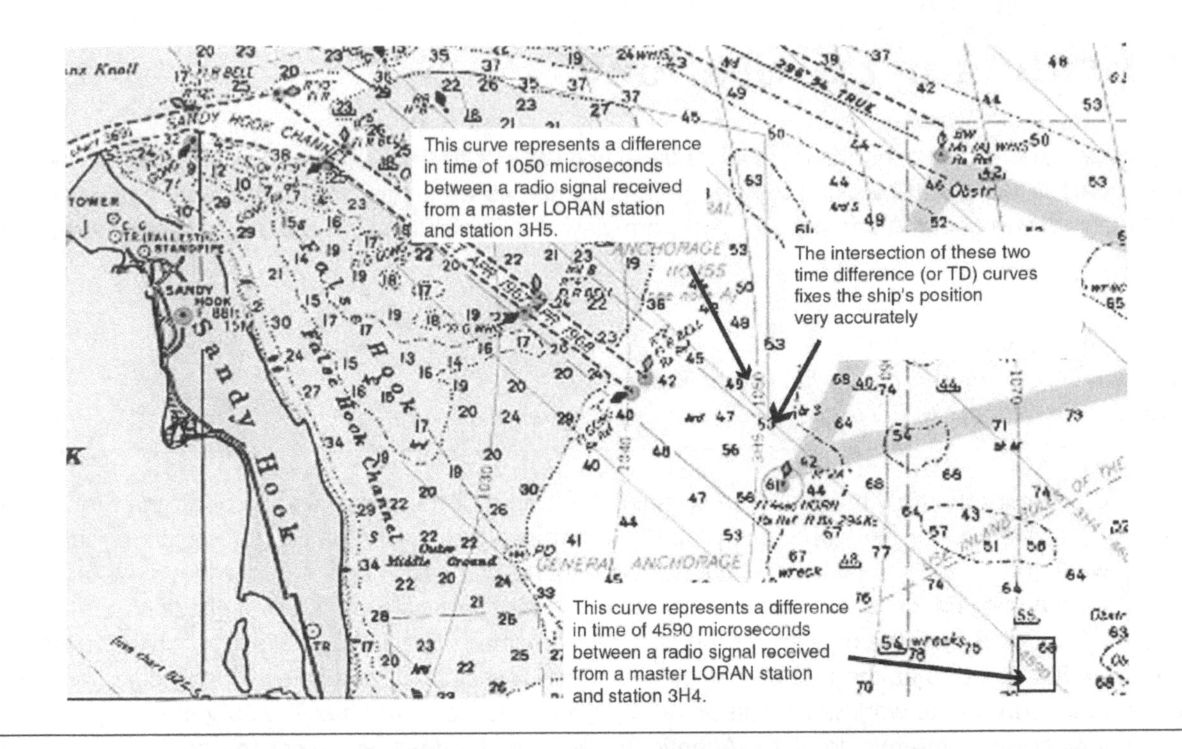

Fig. 1.11 Example of LORAN navigation. The ship's LORAN display reads "3H4-4590" and "3H5-1050." The intersection of these curves on the nautical chart gives the ship's position.

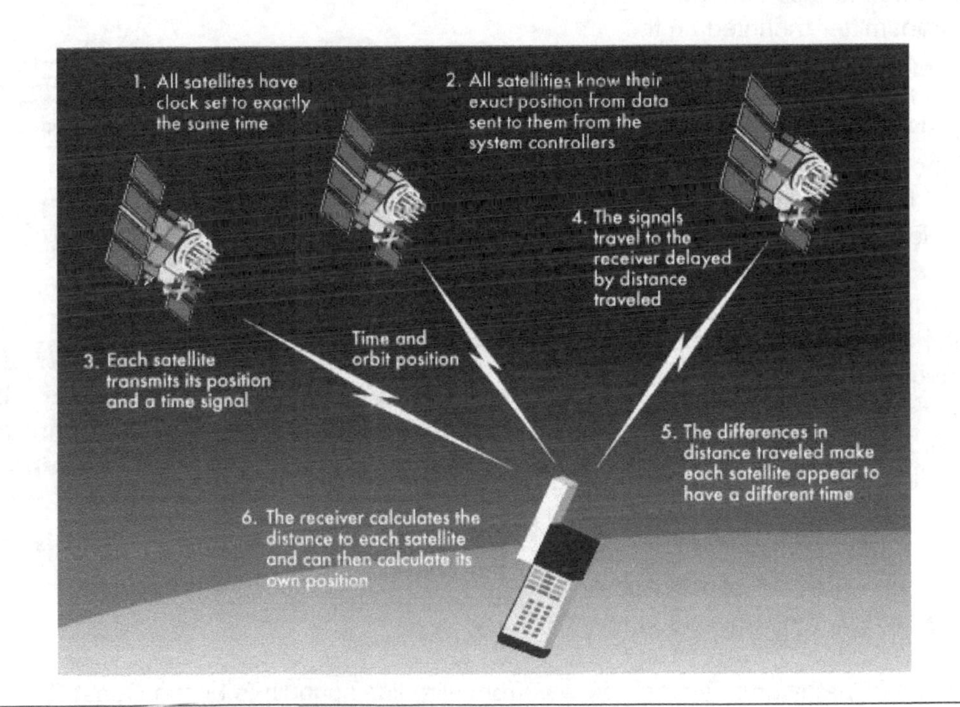

Fig. 1.12 How the Global Positioning System works. The receiver computes a latitude and longitude based upon the position of the satellites and the difference in the time of the signal from each satellite (Courtesy of The Aerospace Corporation).

Investigation 1.4 explores navigation techniques in greater detail.

1.7 Exploring the Seafloor

Exploring the surface of the ocean is relatively easy, since we can travel by ship to any location on the sea-covered part of the Earth by using the navigation techniques we just explored. But what lies beneath us? The water mass of the ocean hides a great deal from view. Our curiosity about the unknown has led to several questions:

- *What is the ocean floor like? Is it all flat?*
- *How can we obtain data about the ocean depths?*
- *Do differences in depth tell us anything about how the seafloor formed?*

Prior to the 20th century the only means of determining the depth of the ocean was through the method known as **sounding.** This was a long and laborious procedure that involved lowering a weighted rope or cable from the ship and waiting for it to "go slack" as it touched bottom. As you can imagine, this was a slow process that yielded only sparse information about the ocean bottom. On most ordinary sailing vessels, lines of 1000 feet failed to reach the bottom, so the mystery of the seafloor remained. The HMS *Challenger*, which sailed around the world from 1872 to 1876 as the first true scientific research vessel, carried miles of sounding line and took 492 sounding measurements worldwide. This voyage proved that the ocean has a wide variation in depth, with relatively shallow areas in the middle of the Atlantic Ocean, and the deepest part of the ocean, the Marianas Trench, in the North Pacific.

Echo sounding came into use during the 1920's. A sound transmitter mounted on the hull of a ship emits high frequency sound waves (many sound waves per second). The sound waves travel through the water and are reflected off the seafloor because of the different density of the seafloor sediments or rock compared to that of water. These returned "echoes" are detected by a listening device called a **hydrophone**, which may also be mounted on the hull of the ship. Ships can generate a continuous two dimensional profile of the seafloor as they travel across the ocean surface (Fig. 1.13). Numerous closely-spaced echo sounder profiles (ship-tracks) can be used to construct a **bathymetric map** of the seafloor. **Bathymetry** refers to the depth of the seafloor below the ocean surface, just like **topography** is the height of the land surface above sea level.

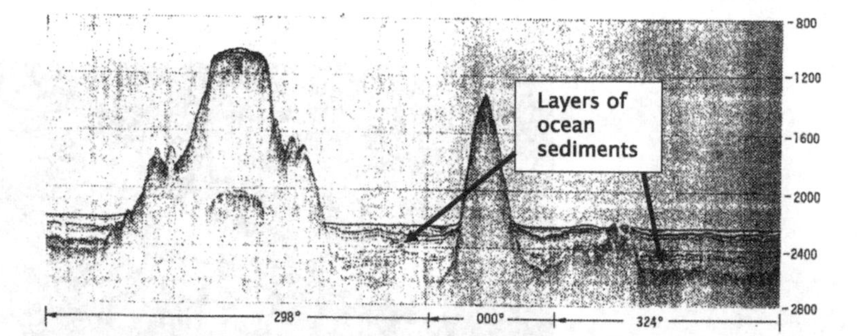

Fig. 1.13 A continuous profile of part of the Pacific Ocean recorded on an echo sounder with additional seismic reflection that penetrates through the sea floor showing the sedimentary layering. Water depth (in meters) is at the right-hand side of the chart, and the ship's track (compass heading) is on the horizontal axis.

One of the first maps of bathymetry ever made was from wire-line soundings by the Coast Survey Steamer *Blake* in the Gulf of Mexico during 1874-1875. The *Blake* voyages were contemporaneous with those of the British research vessel, HMS *Challenger*. The *Blake* was engaged in pioneering use of new technology for mapping the ocean floor. You can see a copy of this map at the National Oceanic and Atmospheric Administration's *Ocean Explorer* web site: http://oceanexplorer.noaa.gov/history/breakthru/media/12_gulfbathy.html. Modern bathymetric maps show the same information, even though soundings can be done much more quickly. **Contour lines**, sometimes also called **isobaths**, connect points that are at equal depths below sea level. The lines provide a way of visualizing three dimensions on a flat piece of paper (Fig. 1.14).

Further refinement of the sounding techniques led to the development of **seismic reflection profiling.** In this system, the ship uses a low-frequency sound source such as air gun that transmits loud "pops" through the water (Fig. 1.15). These sounds can more easily penetrate through the sea floor and show the thickness of buried sediments (Fig. 1.13). These analyses help with determining the origin and evolution of the ocean crust, as we shall see in Part 2 of this book.

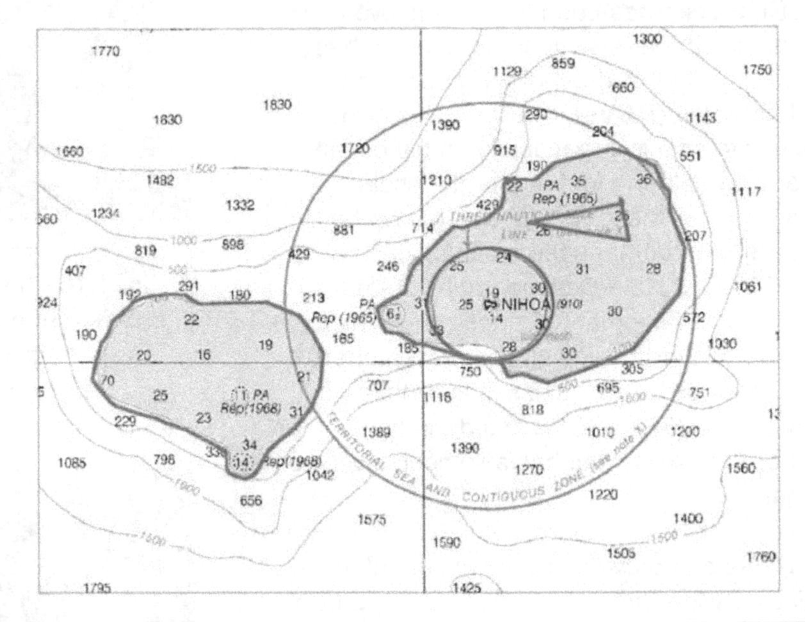

Fig. 1.14 This bathymetric chart shows a small area of the sea floor near Hawaii (the small island of Nihoa), that is currently undergoing a detailed investigation by the RV Kilo Moana (http://oceanexplorer.noaa.gov/explorations/02hawaii/logs/oct24/media/nihoachart.html). The numbers represent depths in fathoms (1 fathom = 6 feet), and the numbered isobaths show how the seafloor bathymetry deepens away from the small islands.

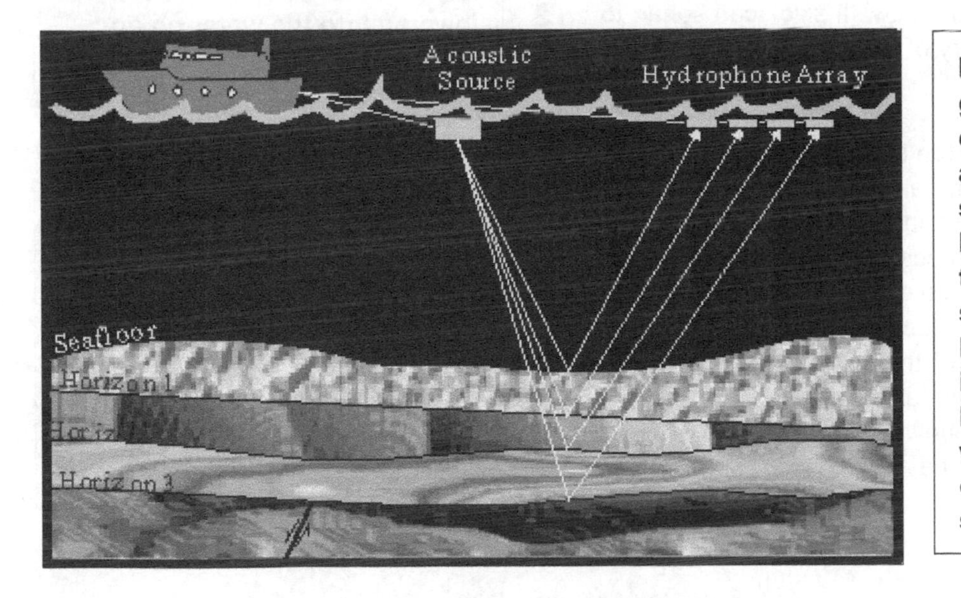

Fig. 1.15 A typical array for gathering seismic reflection data. The sounds from the acoustic source penetrate the sea floor and are reflected by layers and structures in the subsurface. The reflected sounds are picked up by the hydrophones and processes into the display seen in Fig. 1.12. See also http://woodshole.er.usgs.gov/operations/sfmapping/seismic.htm.

Investigation 1.5 examines the basic principles of echo sounding.

■1.8 Advances in Seafloor Research

Echo sounding and seismic reflection provide some of the primary information about the nature of the ocean floor. In recent years, our knowledge of the face of the deep has been further improved by technological advances on several levels. Direct exploration has been expanded via the deployment of deep-diving **submersibles** and **remotely-operated vehicles (ROVs)**. Submersibles give researchers the opportunity to dive to great depths in the ocean and observe first-hand and sample the features of the ocean bottom. Many different designs of these submersibles have been implemented over the years, with perhaps the most famous being the ***Alvin***, operated out of Woods Hole Oceanographic Institution (Fig. 1.16). More recently, the development of the ROVs., which are sophisticated robotic exploration craft, allows ocean researchers to explore the sea floor for longer periods of times in less hazardous circumstances. The ROV ***Jason*** (Fig. 1.17) is noted for the exploration of the wreck of the *Titanic*, but has also been involved in many scientific expeditions.

Fig. 1.16 The research submersible *Alvin* (left) with the tender ship *Atlantis II.*

Fig. 1.17 The ROV *Jason* is lowered into the water on an undersea mission.

Both submersibles and ROVs can provide visual data about the seafloor, but more detail over wider areas has been gathered by side-scan sonar and Earth-orbiting satellites. **Side-scan sonar** is an advanced echo-sounding technique that sweeps the seafloor with sound waves over a swath up to 100 m wide. With overlapping images and digital technology, we can now produce very detailed images of the seafloor (Fig. 1.18). Although depth information cannot be obtained directly, detailed bathymetric maps can be produced by merging the information with the data from echo sounders. Because the ocean is so vast, only a relatively small portion of the seafloor has been mapped with side-scan sonar; to this day, we still know the bathymetry of the seafloor only as an approximation in many places.

Satellites can also be used to measure the height of the sea surface very precisely. The elevation of the sea surface is actually a very subdued image of the relief of the underlying ocean floor. This occurs because the bathymetric highs and lows of the seafloor exert small but measurable gravitational influences on the level of the water in the ocean (Fig. 1.19). Together with all the other measurement techniques, we now have an excellent idea of the composite features of the ocean floor.

For further information on these technologies:
Submersibles and ROVs:
http://www.whoi.edu/page.do?pid=8124
(Woods Hole Oceanographic Institution)
http://oceanexplorer.noaa.gov/technology/subs/subs.html
(National Oceanic and Atmospheric Administration)

Side-scan sonar:
http://chartmaker.ncd.noaa.gov/HSD/wrecks.html
(National Oceanic and Atmospheric Administration)

Satellite measurements:
http://topex-www.jpl.nasa.gov/
NASA Jet Propulsion Laboratory

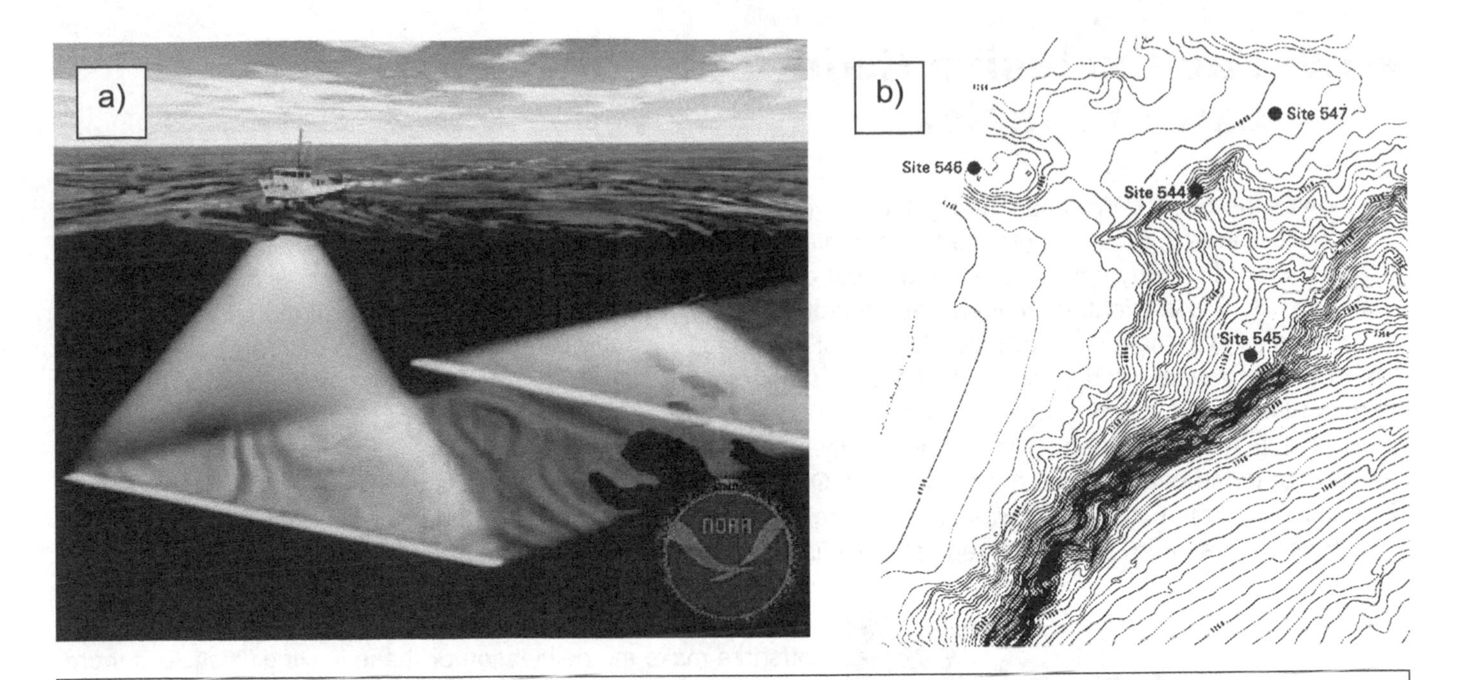

Fig 1.18 a) An Illustration of side-scan sonar in operation. The device can be mounted either on the hull of a ship or, more commonly, on a separate towed vehicle. Overlapping swaths enable the viewing of the sea floor in three dimensions, and a bathymetric map can be easily produced (Courtesy of NOAA). B) A detailed bathymetric map off the coast of northwest Africa synthesized from side-scan sonar data for the Deep-Sea Drilling Project. The contour interval is 50 meters.

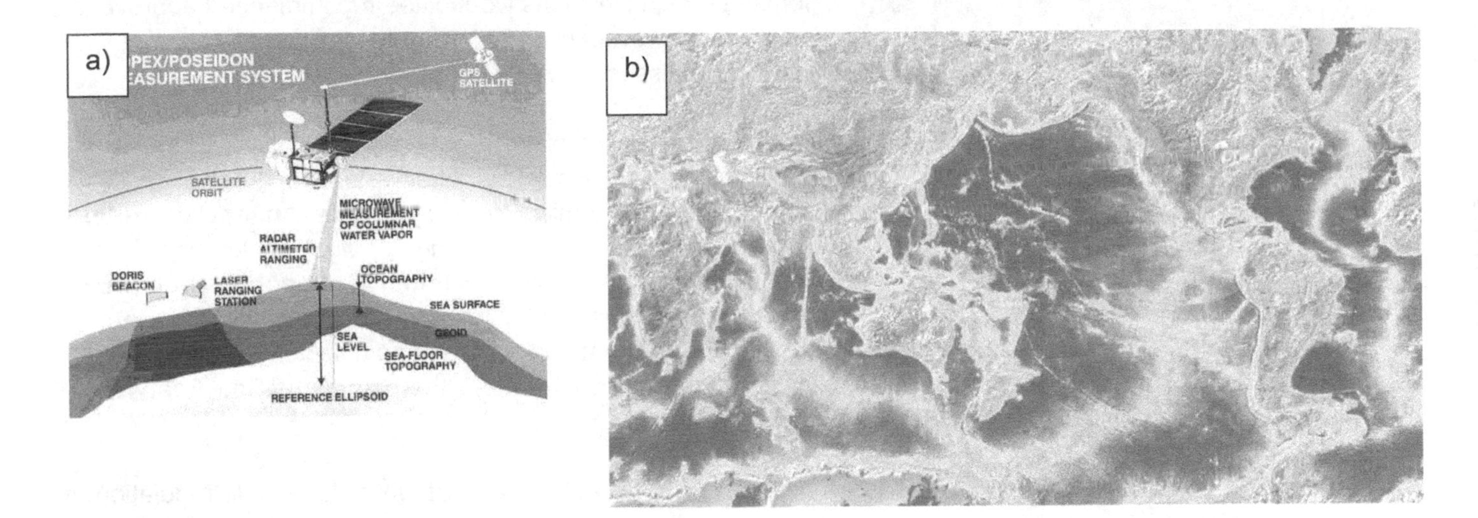

Fig 1.19 An illustration of satellite mapping of sea-floor bathymetry. a) Precise altimeters (using microwaves) can map the relief of the ocean surface with centimeter-scale resolution. Bathymetric highs and lows on the seafloor, and differences in rock density, cause measureable gravitational distortion of the ocean surface (Courtesy of NASA/JPL). b) A composite map of the Earth showing the bathymetry of the ocean floor derived largely from the satellite measurements by the U.S. Navy GEOSAT. Dark shades of gray represent the deepest parts of the ocean; shallow areas are light gray to white. See the full color image on the back cover of this book.

Learn more about bathymetric maps in Investigation 1.6.

■1.9 The Exclusive Economic Zone (EEZ) and Law of the Sea

Who owns the ocean? Who has the right to harvest fish from the water or to pump oil from beneath the seafloor? These are issues that have confronted communities and civilizations from the beginning of their relationship with the sea. From the early days of seafaring, most countries subscribed to unwritten laws regarding "freedom of the seas." By this convention, nations had control over their coastal waters 3 miles out from the shoreline (the distance of a long "cannon shot"), but the rest of the ocean was unregulated and open to all. This concept of "international waters" worked fine until the 20th century, when technology, human population increases, greater demand for fish as a food source, and the discovery of valuable economic resources offshore made conflicts inevitable. In 1945 President Truman unilaterally proclaimed that rights to the seabed for the United States would extend out to the edge of the continental shelf. Other nations quickly followed with similar claims. In 1947, the first successful offshore oil well was drilled in the Gulf of Mexico, and the 200 nautical mile limit proclaimed by countries such as Peru encompassed valuable fishing grounds.

The open ocean and Antarctica have much in common in trying to establish the twin goals of preservation and fair use among the nations of the world.

The irregular nature of coastlines and the existence of islands offshore make the delineation of these limits difficult, and there are often conflicting or overlapping claims. In order to codify the ownership of the ocean, the United Nations convened three Law of the Sea Conferences. The most recent one ended in 1982, and went into force in 1994 after 60 nations ratified it. President Clinton signed an amended version after extended negotiations on seabed mining to satisfy U.S. concerns, and in 2004 the Senate Foreign Relations Committee recommended approval of the treaty. However, as of 2011, the full Senate still has not yet taken up the issue.

The major provisions of this treaty are that nations with coastlines have a 12-mile territorial water limit. In addition, there is a further 12 miles in which nations can regulate certain illegal activities such as smuggling or illegal immigration. Coastal nations also have an **exclusive economic zone (EEZ)** that extends 200 nautical miles from the shoreline (Fig 1.20). However, beyond this limit the open ocean is still regarded as international waters, and disputes over the protection and exploitation of resources will remain. To help deflect such issues, the Law of the Sea Treaty establishes an International Seabed Authority to monitor this area.

As you can see from the list of major provisions (Table 1.1), the Law of the Sea attempts to provide regulation of many commercial activities and to ensure fair use and protection of marine resources. This is obviously not an easy task, especially the attempt to have marine resources shared with nations that do not have a coastline. The conference has established a framework for implementing these provisions as international law, but a real test of the enforcement and regulatory power of the organization is yet to occur.

Table 1.1 Major provisions of the United Nations Law of the Sea Conference.

- The right to freedom of navigation and overflight in a country's EEZ by other nations, as well as freedom to lay submarine cables and pipelines;
- If there is a surplus of fish or other resources in a coastal EEZ, landlocked nations have the right to claim a share of the surplus. Highly migratory species of fish and marine mammals are accorded special protection;
- Coastal states have sovereign rights over the continental shelf (the national area of the seabed) for exploring and exploiting it; the shelf can extend at least 200 nautical miles from the shore, and more under specified circumstances;
- Coastal states share with the international community part of the revenue derived from exploiting resources from any part of their shelf beyond 200 miles;
- An international Commission on the Limits of the Continental Shelf was established to review claims by states regarding the extent of the continental shelf when the outer boundaries extend beyond 200 miles;
- States bordering enclosed or semi-enclosed seas are expected to cooperate in managing living resources, environmental and research policies and activities;
- Land-locked states have the right of access to and from the sea and enjoy freedom of transit through the territory of transit States;
- States are bound to prevent and control marine pollution and are liable for damage caused by violation of their international obligations to combat such pollution;
- All marine scientific research in the EEZ and on the continental shelf is subject to the consent of the coastal State, but in most cases they are obliged to grant consent to other States when the research is to be conducted for peaceful purposes and fulfils specified criteria;
- States are bound to promote the development and transfer of marine technology "on fair and reasonable terms and conditions", with proper regard for all legitimate interests;
- The convention established an International Seabed Authority to regulate all activities related to the ocean floor beyond the EEZ of maritime nations. This authority has a unique commercial arm, "The Enterprise" that is to pursue deep-sea mining activities on behalf of the international community.
- Disputes can be submitted to the International Tribunal for the Law of the Sea established under the Convention, to the International Court of Justice, or to arbitration. Conciliation is also available and, in certain circumstances, submission to it would be compulsory. The Tribunal has exclusive jurisdiction over deep seabed mining disputes.

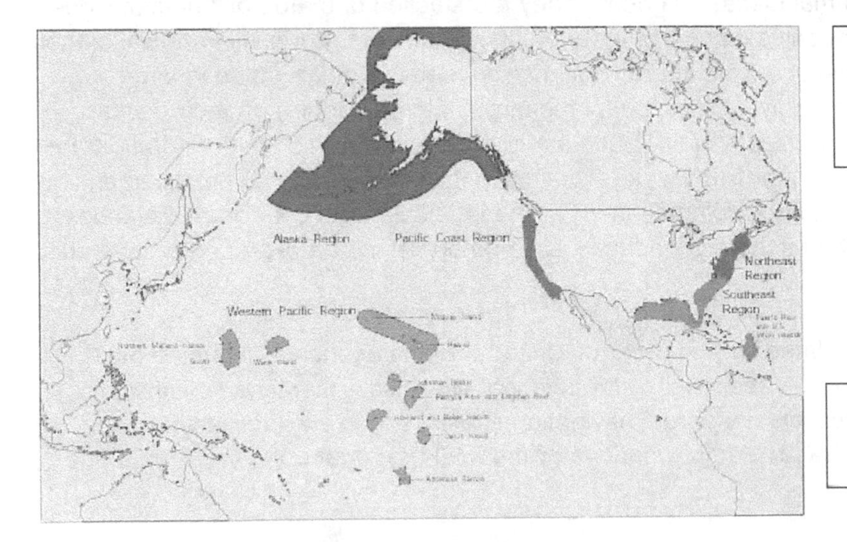

Fig. 1.20 The Exclusive Economic Zone (EEZ) of the United States (shaded areas) subdivided by region.

Investigation 1.7 looks at some possible scenarios for applying the Law of the Sea.

■1.10 International Trade and Shipping

For the world today, the ocean plays a dominant role in economic activity. In fact, the backbone of the global economy is shipping, which accounts for 90% of all international trade by volume. The United Nations Conference on Trade and Development estimates that the operation of merchant ships contributes about US $380 billion to the global economy, which is equivalent to about 5% of total world trade. Maritime transportation of raw materials, food stuffs, and manufactured goods is relatively inexpensive and efficient (Table 1.2).

Table 1.2 The low cost of transporting goods by sea (information from the Round Table for International Shipping Associations www.shippingfacts.com). Tonne = metric ton (1000 kilograms); for reference a U.S. ton = 2000 lbs. (907.2 kg).

Cargo	Unit Size	Retail Price	Shipping Costs
Crude oil from the Middle East to the U.S.	1 gallon	>$2.00	~$0.02
Iron ore from Australia to Europe	1 tonne		~$12.00
TV set	1 unit	~$700.00	~$10.00
DVD/CD player	1 unit	~$200.00	~$1.50
Vacuum cleaner	1 unit	~$150.00	~$1.00
Scotch whisky	1 bottle	~$50.00	~$0.15
Coffee	1 kg	~$15.00	~$0.15
Biscuits/cookies	1 tin	~$3.00	~$0.05
Beer	1 can	~$1.00	~$0.01

In 2005, the world fleet consisted of more than 46,000 ships. Of these, general cargo ships make up 39% of the total, tankers: 25%, bulk carriers: 13%, and container ships constitute 7% of the world fleet, while passenger ships (including ferries and cruise ships) and specialist ships make up 12% and 4%, respectively. These different types of ships are for different types of cargo (Fig. 1.21). **Container ships** transport truck-size containers that are typically 20 or 40 feet long and filled with manufactured goods. They are stacked one atop of another, side-by-side, and end-to-end. The largest container ships can carry up to 10,000 containers. Ports with special cranes load and unload these ships. **Bulk carriers** transport metal ore, coal, rice, wheat and other grains in large cargo holds deep in the ship. These ships are easily recognized by the large hatches (doors) on their decks for access to the cargo holds below. **Tankers** transport liquids such as hydrocarbons (oil, liquified natural gas), chemicals (ammonia, chlorine, styrene monomer), or fresh water. They have flush decks with oil pipelines and vents. Supertankers were designed to transport large volumes of oil from the Middle East over great distances. **Specialist ships** include supply vessels for the offshore oil industry, salvage boats, ice breakers, and research ships.

Shipping is a global industry that is highly regulated by a number of United Nations agencies, including the International Maritime Organization (IMO), which is responsible for safety of life at sea, maritime security, and protection of the marine environment. Construction standards, navigational rules, and crew qualifications are regulated in all ships involved in international trade. Member nations of the IMO are required to implement and enforce these international rules. The safety record of the international shipping industry has been steadily improving, as has its environmental record.

The International Chamber of Shipping (ICS) is the international trade association for merchant ship operators and works closely with the IMO. The ICS developed a "**Code of Practice**", now in its third edition (1999), concerning the environmental impact of shipping. The Code outlines the principles of environmental management, including a review of current international environmental legislation. It covers a wide spectrum of environmental issues ranging from marine pollution (oil, chemical, liquefied gases, dangerous goods, garbage, sewage, ballast water, and anti-fouling paints) to atmospheric pollution (exhaust emissions, cargo vapor emissions, ozone depleting substances, and noise). **Oil spills** have been the largest marine pollutant from transportation activities, with normal ship operations being the largest contributors followed by tanker accidents. The trend from the 1980s and 1990s shows declining frequency and quantity of oil spills as greater concern about environmental impacts have been voiced and regulatory policies enforced, and as improved technologies to respond to and mitigate spills have been developed.

Ship **ballast water** has become an international concern in recent years. Ships take on ballast water in port or in coastal waters in order to stabilize the hull and/or balance the load in the vessel for its ocean crossing. This ballast water may contain a variety of animals, including plankton, nekton, and benthic organisms at various stages of their life cycle, as well as water-borne pathogens. Large ships may carry more than 200,000 cubic meters of water. The ballasts are flushed at or near the port of destination introducing these translocated organisms, including bacteria and viruses, into a 'new' environment. Some of these organisms may flourish at the expense of indigenous species, which might not be able to cope with the introduced, or **invasive species** and pathogens. The problem of invasive species has also had serious consequences in the Great Lakes-St. Lawrence Seaway, which connects the Gulf of St. Lawrence on the Atlantic Ocean with Lake Superior. The IMO has issued guidelines for the handling and treatment of ballast water.

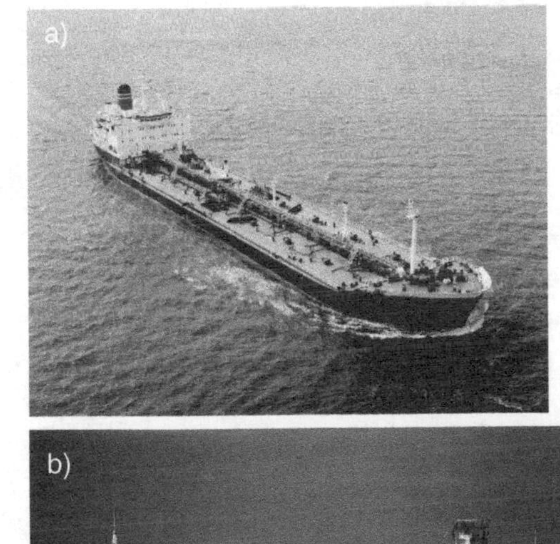

Fig. 1.21 Types of commercial ships involved in international trade. a) Supertankers are the prime means of moving petroleum long distances. b) Container ships carry much of the world's goods across the ocean. c) Bulk carriers can be adapted to transport a wide array of raw materials.

■*Oceanography in Action*

The Longitude Problem

One of the more fascinating episodes in the history of the development of ocean exploration and scientific inquiry is the quest to determine longitude of ships at sea. As we have seen, it is relatively easy to measure one's latitude using the sun and the stars, but knowing where we are in an east-west direction requires a precise knowledge of time, both at our reference location (Longitude = 0° at Greenwich, England) and aboard ship. The earliest explorers rarely bothered with longitude. Their navigation method usually entailed getting on a line of latitude and sailing east (or west) until they reached the landmass on the other side of the ocean basin. When they bumped into their chosen continent, they simply followed the coastline until they arrived at their destination. This crude method worked surprisingly well, but often led to serious problems when storms blew ships off course, or poor winds delayed them enroute. It was impossible to predict when a voyage might end, and onboard supplies frequently ran out because there was no reasonable way to estimate the need for rations or when landfall might occur. In addition, navigating close to a coastline was extraordinarily hazardous in bad weather. Arguably the most infamous incident of this nature occurred in 1707 when a fleet of five British warships returning home from a victorious battle with the French near Gibraltar sailed for several days in fog and overcast. The fleet's navigators misjudged their longitude very badly, and four of the five ships ran into the rocks jutting from the Scilly Isles, off the southwestern point of England. Two thousand British sailors perished.

The first marine clock of John Harrison (H1). This instrument weighs 75 pounds and is roughly four feet on each side. It was used successfully to determine longitude on a cruise between London and Lisbon in 1736.

Because incidents such as this affected all seafaring nations, there was a rush to develop an accurate way of determining longitude, and handsome prizes were established by various governments to encourage innovation. Most of the earliest techniques involved some sort of astronomical event whose timing was known beforehand, such as eclipses of the sun or moon. However, these occurred too infrequently to be of much use to sailors needing daily (at least) checks on position. Galileo Galilei worked out an ingenious method that involved telescopic observations of the moons of Jupiter and their appearance from behind that distant planet. This turned out to be a reliable method when observations could be made over a long period of time from a fixed point on land. At sea, in a rolling ship, using a telescope to watch the moons was practically impossible. Moreover, Jupiter isn't always visible from the Earth depending upon its relative position in its orbit. No one claimed any of the prizes with these methods.

The British Parliament issued its own handsome prize in 1714 with the passage of the Longitude Act. In addition to large number of proposals to determine longitude that could only be characterized as bizarre, a number of clockmakers realized that if they could develop a reliable timepiece, the problem could be easily solved. Yet again, clocks and watches in the eighteenth century were not exactly precise; they often ran slow by as much as 15 minutes per day. To win the maximum prize, longitude had to be fixed within an accuracy of half a degree; this corresponded to a timekeeping error of no more than 3 seconds in a 24 hour period. What's more, this accuracy had to be maintained on board a rolling, pitching sailing ship. Since most clocks of the day used a pendulum to keep time, this was indeed a steep challenge. But one among them, John Harrison, rose to the challenge. He developed a series of marine clocks, known as **chronometers**, which used a variety of springs and rods in place of the pendulum to help maintain accuracy. The first test of Harrison's device came on a voyage to Lisbon, Portugal 1n 1736, and it passed with flying colors. However, to receive the prize, it must make a journey to the West Indies and back. Over the years, Harrison worked on various refinements of his chronometer, finally developing one that resembled an oversized pocket watch in 1757 that was dubbed "H-4." After many delays, some caused by political machinations over the longitude prize, H-4 finally made it to the West Indies in January, 1762 after a three-month voyage. It returned to London in March having lost only two minutes of time in the entire journey.

Although the longitude problem appeared now to be solved, John Harrison did not immediately receive the prize. The Board of Longitude, which evaluated the claims to the prize, was dominated by astronomers who were not pleased that a long-standing problem was being solved by a watchmaker, and many were hoping that a competing method that used measurements of the moon's position could be made to work. Since the moon moves relatively rapidly through the sky, its position with respect to various stars can be used as an indicator of time. Although this was still a difficult measurement to make, it was becoming more accurate as mathematical tables were published that gave the necessary data about the position of the moon in the sky. So the Harrison timepieces sailed across the Atlantic once again in 1764, repeating their measurement of longitude within the boundaries specified by the act. The Board of Longitude grudgingly handed over half of the prize money to Harrison, with strict provisions on what he must do to collect the remainder.

One of the tireless promoters of the lunar method was one Neville Maskelyne, who became the Astronomer Royal at the Greenwich (England) Observatory and the chief judge of success in measuring longitude. As a result, Harrison's clocks, and duplicates made by other watchmakers, were subjected to more rigorous testing, including sailing with Captain James Cook in his explorations of the South Pacific during 1772–1775. Once again, the clocks did their job, and ultimately became the method of choice to easily determine longitude in an accurate manner. However, Harrison died without ever collecting the remainder of his prize, although the British Parliament awarded him additional funds in recognition of his achievements. The efforts by the Astronomer Royal to promote the lunar method led ultimately to the worldwide recognition as Greenwich as the Prime Meridian and the reference for all our measurements of time. To further educate yourself about this fascinating story of the ocean, science, and human nature, consult the following references:

Longitude, by Dava Sobel. New York Walker and Co., 1995.
This is an extraordinarily readable and engaging narrative of the tale centered on Harrison's clocks and the longitude prize.

The Board of Longitude, http://www.kellnielsen.dk/bol.htm
Provides additional information about the lunar distance method for determining ones east-west position on Earth.

■*Oceanography in Action*

Shackleton's Boat Journey

One of the most incredible stories of skill overcoming unbelievable adversity involves a spectacular success in using celestial navigation. In November 1915, Ernest Shackleton's expedition to cross the Antarctic continent was in a desperate situation. His ship, the *Endurance*, had just sunk in the Weddell Sea off the Antarctic coast, crushed by the ice in which it had been trapped for 281 days. There was no radio, satellite communication, or other means by which to alert the outside world of their predicament. The ship's party, after spending time camped on sea ice, made their way in three small lifeboats to Elephant Island, a deserted little speck in the Southern Ocean. Realizing that rescue from this barren, rocky point would be almost impossible, the crew rebuilt one of the small boats, the *James Caird*, to undertake a much longer and hazardous journey. Shackleton and five of his crew, including Frank Worsley, the *Endurance* captain, set sail in this 20-foot-long boat for the South Georgia Islands where they hoped to find a whaling station and organize a rescue for the rest of the crew. This trip required a journey across 800 miles of the Southern Ocean during the Antarctic autumn, one of the most hostile areas of the ocean on Earth.

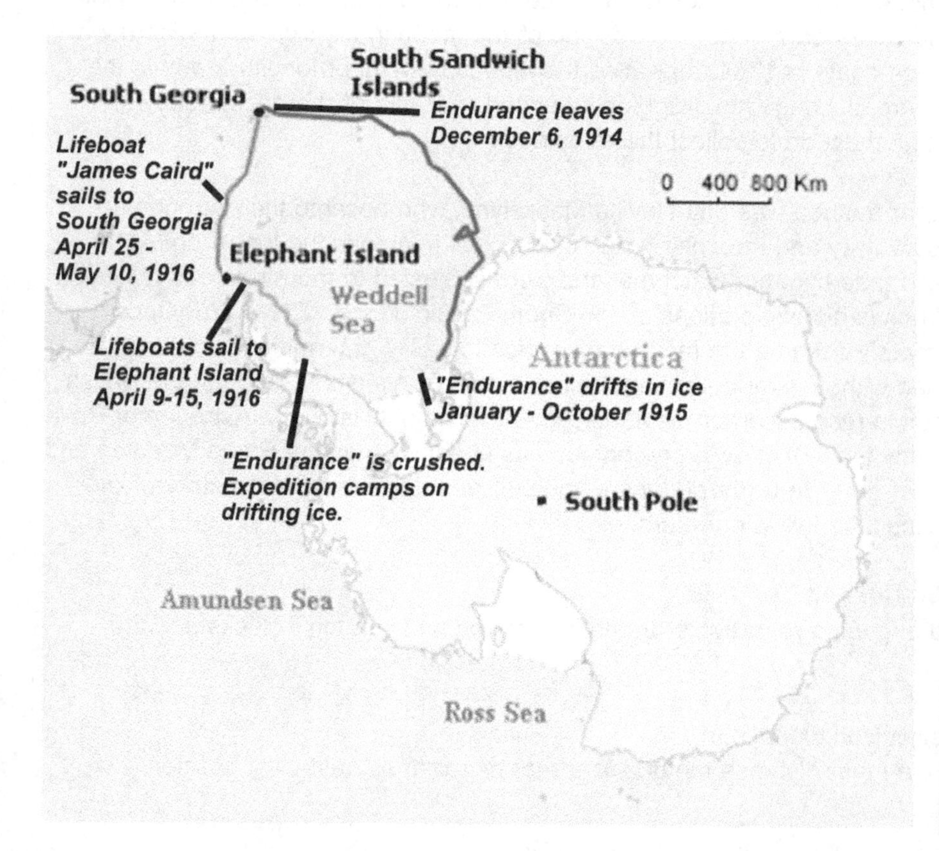

Map of the course of Shackleton's Antarctic Expedition. The journey from Elephant Island to South Georgia remains one of the most remarkable feats on navigation in history.

The small craft left Elephant Island on April 23, 1916, with provisions calculated to sustain its crew for up to a month. The list of instruments on board is alarmingly thin: sextant, binoculars, prismatic compass, sea anchor, charts, and an aneroid barometer. In the words of Shackleton himself, "The tale of the next sixteen days is one of supreme strife amid heaving waters. The sub-Antarctic Ocean lived up to its evil winter reputation." They battled extreme cold, heavy seas, unbelievably uncomfortable conditions and an Antarctic cyclone during the first six days of sailing by compass only. On the sixth day, they were finally able to use the sextant to determine their latitude and longitude, noting that they had made 380 miles during this time. A few days later, they were engulfed in another howling gale, and the *James Caird* was nearly swamped by a monstrous wave. The glass on the compass, their principal navigation tool, was broken and held together by a strip of adhesive tape from their medical supplies. Nevertheless, on day 12 their sextant sightings revealed that they were not more than 100 miles from South Georgia Island and the end to their privations.

But these last days turned out to be anything but easy. Their fresh water supply was dwindling, and raging thirst had become a constant companion. On day 14, land was sighted. Despite the unspeakably bad conditions these men had endured for the last two weeks and the barest of navigational aids, they were able to sail these uncharted and hostile waters powered only by the wind and currents, and arrive precisely where they wanted to be. Much of the credit has to be given to Frank Worsley, whose sextant readings and seamanship kept them on course. But these navigational skills could not spare them two more hellish days at sea; just when salvation seemed imminent a horrendous storm blew up and prevented them from securing a landing spot. They were tossed and battered by waves and winds, on the verge of the ultimate catastrophe as the storm threatened to drive the boat into the rocky shore. They were totally out of drinking water, had not had any change in clothing for nearly a year, soaked to the bone with cold brine and tired beyond belief. Just when the situation appeared totally hopeless, the storm ended, and they were able to steer the boat to a safe harbor on the shore.

Sir Ernest Shackleton (1874–1922). An original contemporary photograph by Nadar.

Troubles over? Not for this crew: they landed on the western coast of the island, but the inhabited whaling station was on the eastern shore, separated by an uncharted mountain range over 4500 feet high. In one last superhuman feat, the three fittest members of the little band (Shackleton, Worsley and Crean) climbed this range with their meager equipment in an all-night march, arriving the following afternoon at the whaling station. This heroic journey has a final happy ending: the rest of the *Endurance* crew who were left at Elephant Island was ultimately rescued in August 1916. Not one man lost his life during this entire ill-fated expedition, an almost miraculous result that was made possible by the excellent navigational skills of Worsley and Shackleton. For further information on this incredible journey, see the following references:

The Endurance: Shackleton's Legendary Antarctic Expedition by Caroline Alexander. New York: Knopf, 1998. Beautifully illustrated with photographs taken by official photographer Frank Hurley, this book offers a fresh and lively retelling of this fascinating survival story.

Shackleton's Boat Journey by F. A. Worsley. New York: Norton, 1998.
A chronicle of what must be the most amazing small-boat navigating success in history, written by the navigator himself, Captain Frank Worsley.

The American Museum of Natural History in New York had an exhibition about the Shackelton expedition, which can be found at their webs site. *http://www.amnh.org/exhibitions/shackleton/*

Table 1.3 Latitude and longitude for major cities and significant places around the world.

	Place	Latitude	Longitude		Place	Latitude	Longitude
	Europe				**North America**		
1	Greenwich	51° 30' N	00° 00'	**23**	Chicago	41° 53' N	87° 38' W
2	Paris	48° 50' N	02° 20' E	**24**	New York	40° 45' N	74° 00' W
3	Rome	41° 54' N	12° 29 E	**25**	Los Angeles	34° 04' N	118° 15' W
4	Madrid	40° 25' N	03° 45' W	**26**	Calgary	51° 00' N	114° 10' W
5	Athens	37° 58' N	23° 46' E	**27**	Gander	48° 58' N	54° 35' W
6	Oslo	59° 55' N	10° 45' E	**28**	Mexico City	19° 20' N	99° 10' W
7	Reykjavik	64° 10' N	21° 57' W	**29**	Havana	23° 08' N	82° 22' W
8	Moscow	55° 45' N	37° 35' E	**30**	Managua	12° 06' N	86° 20' W
	Asia				**South America**		
9	Ankara	39° 57' N	32° 54' E	**31**	Rio de Janeiro	23° 00' S	43° 12' W
10	Jerusalem	31° 47' N	35° 10' E	**32**	Lima	12° 00' S	77° 00' W
11	Cairo	30° 01' N	31° 14' E	**33**	Santiago	33° 24' S	70° 40' W
12	Shanghai	31° 15' N	121° 26' E	**34**	Buenos Aires	34° 30' S	58° 20' W
13	Tokyo	35° 45' N	139° 45' E	**35**	Caracas	10° 30' N	66° 55' W
14	Baghdad	33° 20' N	44° 30' E	**36**	Quito	00° 15' S	78° 35' W
15	Bombay	18° 55' N	72° 50' E		**Africa**		
16	Bangkok	13° 45' N	100° 35' E	**37**	Nairobi	01° 17' S	36° 50' E
	Australia & Oceania			**38**	Timbuktu	16° 49' N	02° 59' W
17	Sydney	33° 53' S	151° 10' E	**39**	Cairo	30° 03' N	31° 15' E
18	Perth	31° 57' S	115° 52' E	**40**	Johannesburg	26° 10' S	28° 20' E
19	Auckland	36° 52' S	174° 46' E	**41**	Luanda	08° 50' S	13° 15' E
20	Fiji	17° 20' S	179° 00' E		**Antarctica**		
21	Tahiti	17° 40' S	149° 39' W	**42**	McMurdo	77° 00' S	170° 00' E
22	Midway	28° 12' N	177° 24' W	**43**	South Pole	90° 00' S	------------

Name ______________________________

First three letters of last name

Investigation 1.1 The Earth and the Ocean

The ocean is arguably the centerpiece that distinguishes Earth from all the other worlds in the Solar System. With this in mind, take a few minutes to produce a "concept map" that will illustrate your perception of the importance of the ocean for our planet. A concept map is a visual representation that will allow you to construct your own version of the meaning and interrelationships of scientific ideas and principles. It is best done in a **cooperative-learning** format so that you can discuss your reasoning as the map is developed. Expert thinking is often characterized by grouping and linking knowledge in complex ways to arrive at a synthesis or a conclusion. A concept map can help you progress in this direction, and provide some structure to complex and intersecting processes. The figure below illustrates one idea of how a concept map can look, although these can vary quite a bit according to the topic and the vision of the author. To see some examples of concept maps for various topics, go to http://www.graphic.org/concept.html. To quote some of the brief directions from that site:

"A concept map consists of nodes or cells that contain a concept, item or question and links. The links are labeled and denote direction with an arrow symbol. The labeled links explain the relationship between the nodes. The arrow describes the direction of the relationship and reads like a sentence."

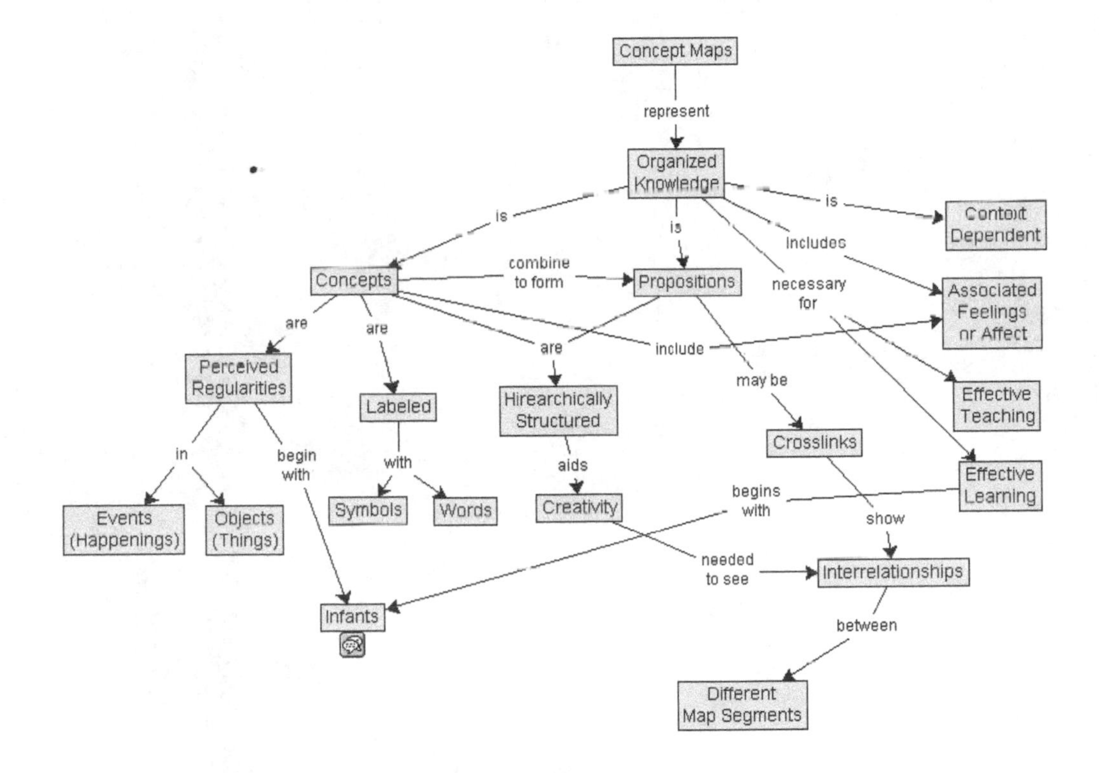

Example of a concept map (http://en.wikipedia.org/wiki/Concept_map).

Use the other side of this paper for your concept map.

Draw your concept map here.

Name ______________________

First three letters of last name

Investigation 1.2 Latitude and Longitude

1). Suppose that you are in a boat that has ventured out into the middle of the Pacific Ocean far from any coastline. How could you possibly determine where you were to be able to direct the rescue team to your location? List your ideas, and discuss these with other members of your class.

2). If you look at Table 1.3 on page 26 you will notice that Paris (in France) and Timbuktu (in the African country of Mali), are almost at the same longitude. Let's assume they are. What is the distance between the two in a north-south direction (along that line of longitude)? Give your answer in both nautical miles and kilometers.

3). On the representation of the globe shown below, label the lines of latitude and longitude according to their values in degrees (°). Be sure to specify whether the numbers are in the Northern (N), Southern (S), Eastern (E), or Western (W) Hemisphere. Now select **two** locations from **each** of the seven continents listed in Table 1.1 and plot these on the globe. Round off the location on the globes to the nearest degree and label the city each point represents.

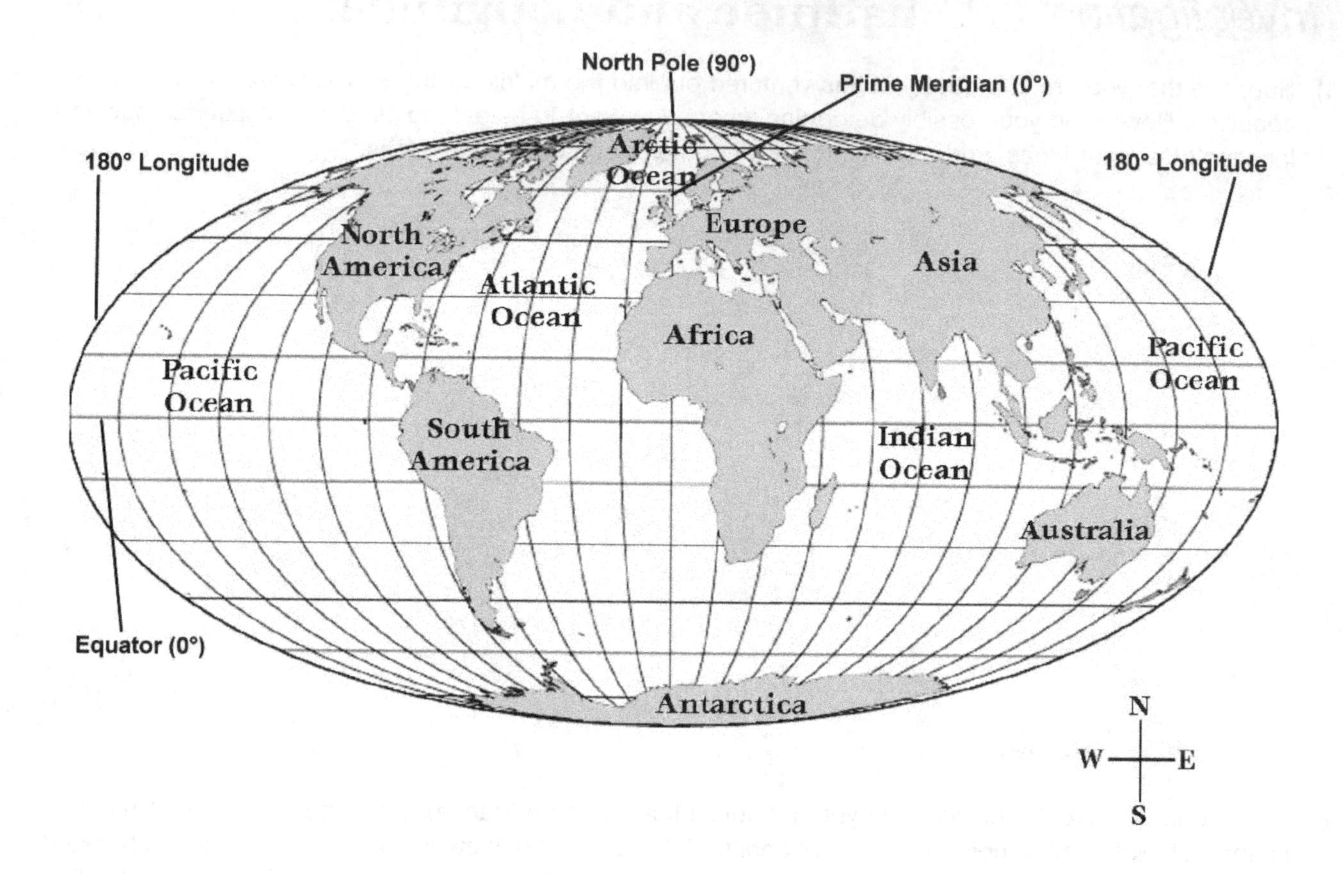

Name ______________________________

First three letters of last name

Investigation 1.3 Using a Sextant

You can construct your own sextant from some simple materials. You will need to have the following items:

- Protractor
- Drinking straw
- String
- Large paper clip or washer
- Tape

Attach the straw across the middle of the protractor using a piece of tape. One end of the straw should project beyond the 90° mark on the protractor and the other end should pass over the center of the straight edge (see the illustration). Affix the string to paper clip or washer and pass the other end of the string through the hole along the straight edge. Now when you sight through the straw, the string will allow you to determine the angle of an object that is above (or below) you.

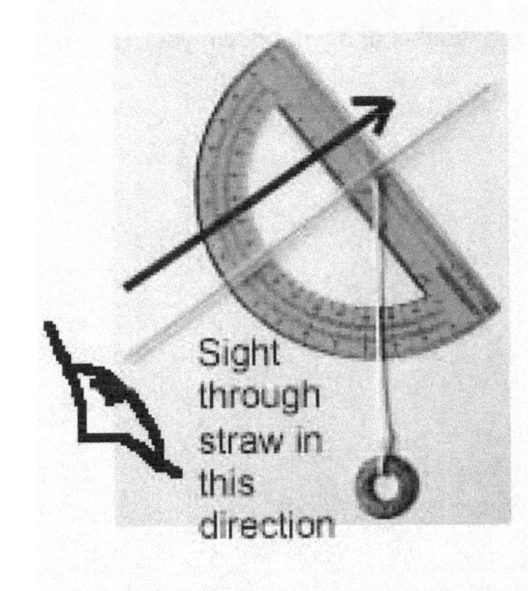

1). Hold the sextant in front of you so that the string hangs right over the middle of the curved part (that is, the string will be parallel to the straw). The flat part is now horizontal, but what angle does the string read?

Explain what angle you are now measuring.

2). Your instructor will project a light spot on the wall to simulate the "North Star." Use your protractor-sextant to measure the angle of this "star" above the horizon. What result do you get and how does this compare to latitude?

3). Do students at the back of the room have the same measurement as those at the front of the room? Compare your answers with others to find out!

First Row ________________

Front Half of Room__________

Back Half of Room__________

Last Row_________________

4). How does location in the room simulate the situation on the surface of the Earth? Which part of the room simulates being closer to the North Pole?

The Equator?

Discuss this and write down your answers.

Extra: When the weather is clear at night, use your sextant to sight the real North Star and determine your actual latitude!

Name ______________________________

First three letters of last name

Investigation 1.4 Navigation

Now we have chance to relate our study of latitude and longitude to actually locating ourselves on the surface of the Earth by using celestial navigation techniques. Remember that in order to find the longitude of a place, we need to know the time difference between the place and the time at 0° longitude. You should review the information in **section 1.5** to help you answer the following questions.

1). Write a formula that will allow you to calculate the time difference between a location and Greenwich Mean Time (GMT) if you already know the longitude.

2). Using the information in Table 1.3 (p. 26), calculate the time difference to the nearest minute between Greenwich, England, and the following locations:

a. New York, New York

b. Los Angeles, California

c. Nairobi, Kenya

d. Paris, France

e. Tokyo, Japan

3). The chronometer on your ship is set for Greenwich Mean Time (GMT or Universal Time, UT). When the sun is at the highest point in the sky, it tells you it is high noon at your present location; your chronometer reads 5 pm UT. What is your longitude?

4). You measure an angle of 21° between the North Star and the horizon with your sextant. Your local time is 12:00 pm (noon) and your ship's chronometer tells you that it is 10:30 pm in Greenwich (UT). What is your latitude and longitude? Name the geographic location where you are (hint: look on a map). Draw a diagram to illustrate how you determined the latitude.

5). You are navigating your entry into Edgartown Harbor on Martha's Vineyard in Massachusetts. As you sail, your LORAN-C receiver shows the following sequence of information:

Time	9960W	9960X	9960Y
1000 hrs	14050	25280	43909
1015	14064	25290	43905
1030	14080	25300	43901

Plot these locations on the navigation chart below. Are you on a proper heading to take you into Edgartown?

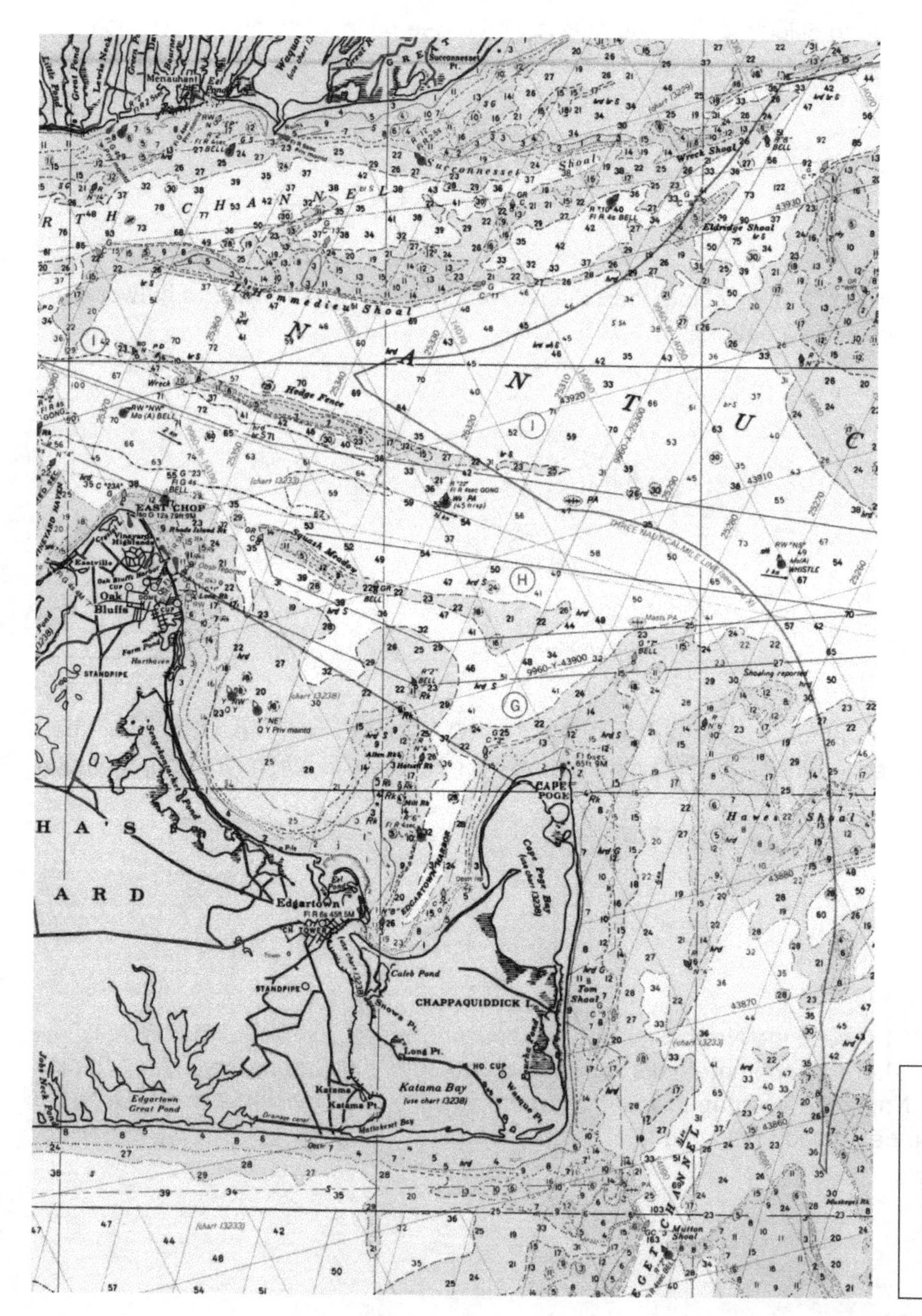

Part of NOAA navigation chart 13237 "Nantucket Sound and Approaches." Soundings are in feet. See larger color image on inside front cover of the book.

Name ___________________________

First three letters of last name

Investigation 1.7 **Law of the Sea**

1). On the map below, draw the 200-mile limit for the Exclusive Economic Zone (EEZ) around the coasts of Canada and the United States. Devise a method to resolve overlapping areas.

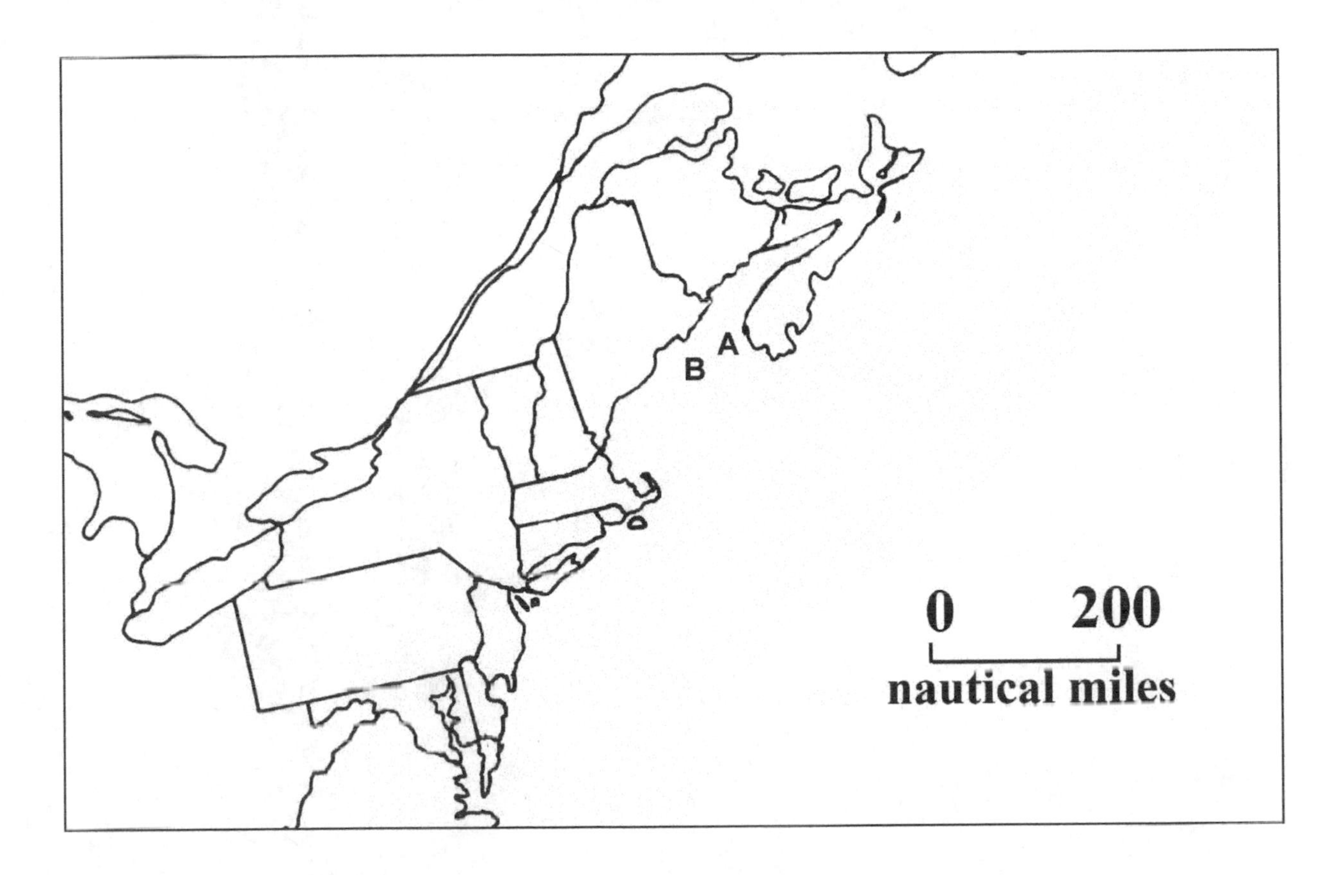

2). The Canadians drill a successful oil well at location "A." In the process of developing the oil field, they drill horizontally at depth to tap into the reservoir extension at "B." The United States objects, claiming that this oil is in its EEZ. How would you settle this dispute?

3). The Law of the Sea Treaty has allowed Canada to fish for 180,000 metric tonnes of cod from its offshore region each year. As the year draws to a close, the Canadians have only collected 150,000 tonnes. The United States sends its fishing fleet into the Canadian EEZ to collect 30,000 tonnes of cod. Is this allowed under the Treaty? Is it good policy?

PART 2

Geology and the Ocean

When we hear the wor[illegible] oceanography," most of us immediately think of dolphins, coral reefs and the fascinating world [illegible]arine life. Yet this is only a part of the science of the oceans; equally important – and just as[illegible]scinating – are the processes that have formed the ocean floor and maintain it in a dynami[illegible]tate today. The Earth and the rest of the solar system came into existence some 4,560 million yea[illegible] ago, as documented by the analysis of radioactive isotopes in rocks and meteorites. The oldest [illegible]ks on the ocean floor are only about 200 million years old. What kind of mechanism exists for r[illegible]cling the materials that make up the sea floor on such a large scale? In addition, volcanoes and [illegible]rthquakes are common occurrences in many parts of the ocean, although they don't occur everyw[illegible]re. How can we explain the patterns that we see? Investigating such problems through probi[illegible] the Earth's interior and examining the sediments on the sea floor is the domain of geological oc[illegible]nography. This chapter explores the main ideas that our studies of the ocean floor have genera[illegible].

In this chapter you will learn:

- Basic concepts of geologic time
- The structure of the Earth's interior and how it is determined
- The differences between continents and ocean basins
- The theory of plate tectonics and sea-floor spreading
- The significance of sediments on the ocean floor
- The relevance of ocean geology to our way of life

2.1 History of the Earth

The Earth and our entire Solar system formed around 4.56 billion years ago (or Giga-annums, Ga) and during its earliest history (until 4 Ga) our planet was an uninhabited and inhospitable place. Meteorites and other objects pounded the surface while the decay of unstable radioactive isotopes within the interior also kept the Earth very hot. During this time the Earth began to separate into concentric spheres of differing density, and when the planet finally cooled these became 1) an iron-nickel core, 2) a dense silicate mantle, 3) a less dense silicate crust, and 4) a gaseous atmosphere. (Fig. 2.1) The oldest preserved crustal rocks are about 4 billion years old. Water was an abundant ingredient in the materials that formed the Earth. During the initial heating of the planet, extensive volcanic activity released gases from the Earth's interior that produced an early atmosphere rich in water vapor (H_2O), carbon dioxide (CO_2) and nitrogen (N2). As Earth's surface cooled further, the water vapor condensed into a liquid, causing torrential rains that ultimately collected in the low spots of the planet and formed the ocean. Some of Earth's surface water may have also come from continued bombardment of the young Earth by comets, which are composed of ice and rock.

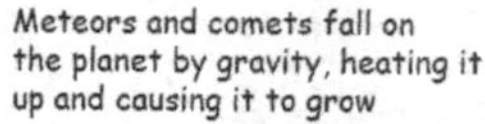
Meteors and comets fall on the planet by gravity, heating it up and causing it to grow

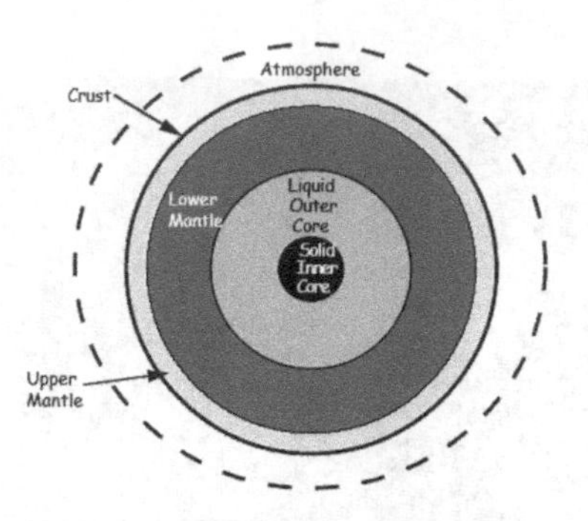

Heating causes growing planet to differentiate into layers with differing density and composition

Fig. 2.1 The Earth and other inner planets formed when objects in the early solar system assembled into larger bodies that grew by attracting more and more objects. As the Earth reached its present size, it developed layers with the denser materials migrating to the center to form the core.

Gases emitted by volcanoes today contain mostly carbon dioxide (CO_2), water (H_2O), and hydrogen chloride (HCl). These gases originate from the Earth's mantle and give geologists a glimpse of what the earliest composition of the atmosphere was probably like. HCl dissolves easily in water to form a strong acid (hydrochloric acid). Carbon dioxide also reacts with water to form carbonic acid (H_2CO_3), a weak acid. Water condensing in the atmosphere in the presence of these gases would reach the Earth with a very low pH, an extreme form of acid rain. Acid rain accelerates the process of **chemical weathering** (i.e., breaking down and dissolving) of exposed crustal rocks. The rain produced during the early history of the Earth was much more acidic than at present, and therefore the rate of chemical weathering of exposed rocks was much greater. The high rate of chemical weathering produced large amounts of dissolved ions from the dissolution of rocks. Some elements or substances occur in the atmosphere, ocean, and sediments in far greater amounts than can be accounted for by the chemical weathering of crustal rocks. These substances are called **excess volatiles** and they originated from the mantle by way of volcanism (e.g., CO_2, H_2O, Cl, N, S). Notice what's in this list of "excess volatiles": **carbon** (the building block of life), **water**, and **chlorine** (chloride Cl^- is the most common solute in seawater making up 55.1% by weight of the dissolved ions in seawater) The dissolved ions together with the excess volatiles are the salts in seawater. The world ocean became salty in its earliest days because of extensive volcanism and the very high rate of chemical weathering early in Earth's history. Notice what's not

Here's a summary of the principal reactions that gave rise to the salts in the ocean:

$HCl \Rightarrow H^+ + Cl^-$
Hydrochloric acid

$CO_2 + H_2O \Rightarrow H_2CO_3 \Rightarrow H^+ + HCO_3^-$
in atmosphere — *carbonic acid (a weak acid)*

H^+ + water + rocks ⇒ dissolved ions ("salts")

Oxygen is a by-product of **photosynthesis** according to the following generalized formula:

$CO_2 + H_2O$ + inorganic nutrients + solar radiation $\Rightarrow$ organic compounds + O_2

nitrates, phosphates *energy source* *carbohydrates, proteins, fats* *free oxygen*

included: **oxygen** (O_2), which is necessary for life as we know it to exist on Earth. In other words, the Earth's earliest atmosphere lacked free oxygen; it was **anoxic**.

The earliest forms of life were probably bacteria that could exist without oxygen (anaerobic bacteria). They manufactured their own food using energy from *chemical oxidation* in a process called **chemosynthesis**. **Cyanobacteria** ("blue-green algae") are found as fossils in rocks by ~3500 Ma. Cyanobacteria are **photosynthetic autotrophs**, organisms that manufacture organic compounds (carbohydrates, proteins, lipids) using energy from *sunlight*.

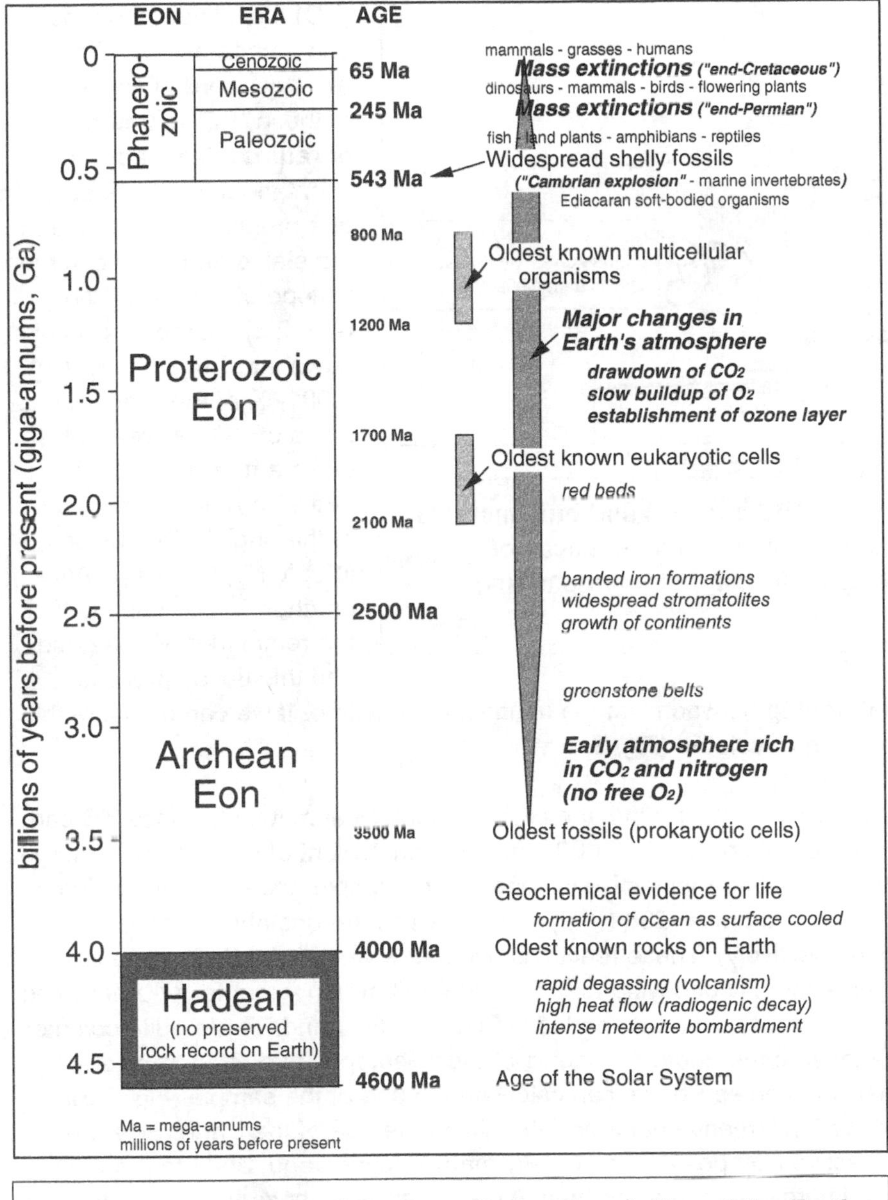

Fig. 2.2 A chronology of the formation and evolution of the Earth.

Extensive mats of cyanobacteria became widespread in shallow marine waters during the early part of the Proterozoic Eon (i.e., after 2.5 Ga; Figure 2.2). These organisms were responsible for altering Earth's atmosphere and making it possible for the evolution of multicellular life. The evolution of our present oxygen-rich atmosphere took many hundreds of millions of years, and involved the gradual build-up of free O_2, draw-down of CO_2, and development of the ozone layer which protects life from harmful ultraviolet solar radiation. Single-celled **eukaryotic protists** (microorganisms with a nucleus and organelles such as mitochondria and chloroplasts) evolved by way of bacterial **symbioses** early in the Proterozoic Eon, while true multicellular animals did not appear until late in the Proterozoic. The rapid development of **invertebrate animals** with shelly hard parts began some 543 million years ago (534 Ma or mega-annums). This "**Cambrian explosion**" marks the beginning of the Phanerozoic Eon and was triggered in part by a critical threshold in atmospheric oxygen concentration. The great diversification of animal and plant life since 543 Ma has also included catastrophic extinction events called "mass extinctions".

■2.2 Radiometric Dating and Geologic Time

How can we possibly know that the Earth is 4560 million years old, or that the "Cambrian explosion" of life on Earth occurred some 543 million years ago? These are unimaginably long times! The answer lies in the "atomic clock," which is the predictable and constant rate of decay of **radioactive isotopes** into more stable elements. Isotopes of the individual elements each contain the same number of protons in the nucleus of the atom, but they have different numbers of neutrons. For example, there are three isotopes of the element carbon and each of these isotopes has six protons, which makes carbon unique among the other 92 naturally occurring elements. Carbon-12 (or ^{12}C) is the most common and has 6 neutrons in its nucleus along with its characteristic 6 protons. Carbon-13 (^{13}C) has seven neutrons, and carbon-14 (^{14}C) has eight neutrons. The last of these, ^{14}C, is **unstable** or **radioactive**, and will spontaneously break down at a predictable rate to form the stable and most common isotope of nitrogen (^{14}N) (Fig. 2.3). Carbon-14 breaks down into ^{14}N at the rate of 0.0012% of the remaining mass of ^{14}C per year, which gives a **half-life** of 5,730 years. In other words, half of the original ^{14}C will be left after 5,730 years. After another 5,730 years, half of the remainder will be gone, and this decay process continues to produce a **logarithmic relationship** between isotope abundance and time. If we can measure the amount of ^{14}C in sample, then the age can be calculated (Fig. 2.4).

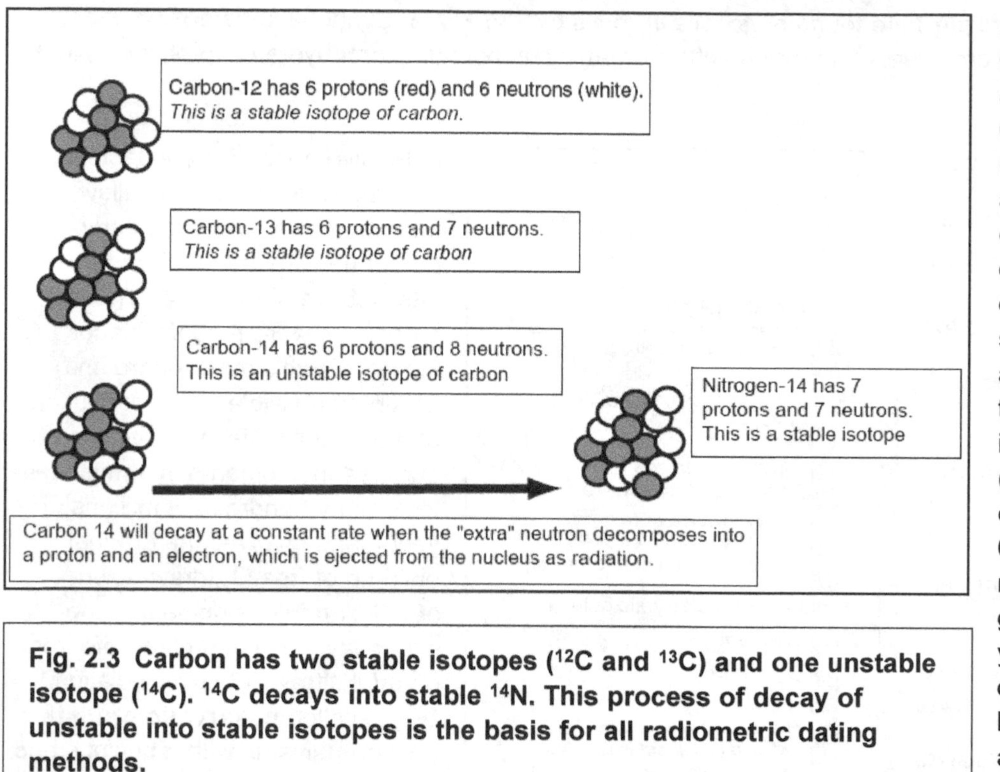

Fig. 2.3 Carbon has two stable isotopes (^{12}C and ^{13}C) and one unstable isotope (^{14}C). ^{14}C decays into stable ^{14}N. This process of decay of unstable into stable isotopes is the basis for all radiometric dating methods.

The rapid decay of ^{14}C makes it unsuitable for determining the age of many geological materials, since ^{14}C can no longer be detected in organic materials older than about 50,000 years, the equivalent of 9 half-lives. However, rocks and minerals contain several other long-lasting radioactive isotopes. For example, the element uranium has two major isotopes: uranium-235 (^{235}U) and uranium-238 (^{238}U), both of which are unstable and decay into stable isotopes of lead (^{207}Pb and ^{206}Pb, respectively). These reactions occur at a very slow rate leading to extremely long half-lives (703.8 million years for ^{235}U decaying to ^{207}Pb and 4468 million years for ^{238}U decaying to ^{206}Pb, so that the ratio of Pb/U will change slowly over long periods of time. Both U and Pb are quite common in rocks and minerals, so that if we can measure the relative amounts of these isotopes in a rock or mineral specimen, and we know the rate at which U becomes Pb, we can calculate the age of the sample (Fig. 2.5). The ratio of Pb/U in meteorites provided the fundamental data for determining the age of the Earth. Scientists have determined the decay rates of radioactive isotopes experimentally many decades ago, and the precision of these decay rates has been tested and improved upon since then. All radioactive isotopes have a unique rate and mode (pathway) of decay that is unaffected by pressure and oxidation state because radioactive decay is a process of the nucleus only, not the orbiting electrons. The co-occurrence of more than one isotope in a mineral or rock sample provides a further test and confirmation of the radiometric dating method and its experimentally determined decay rates.

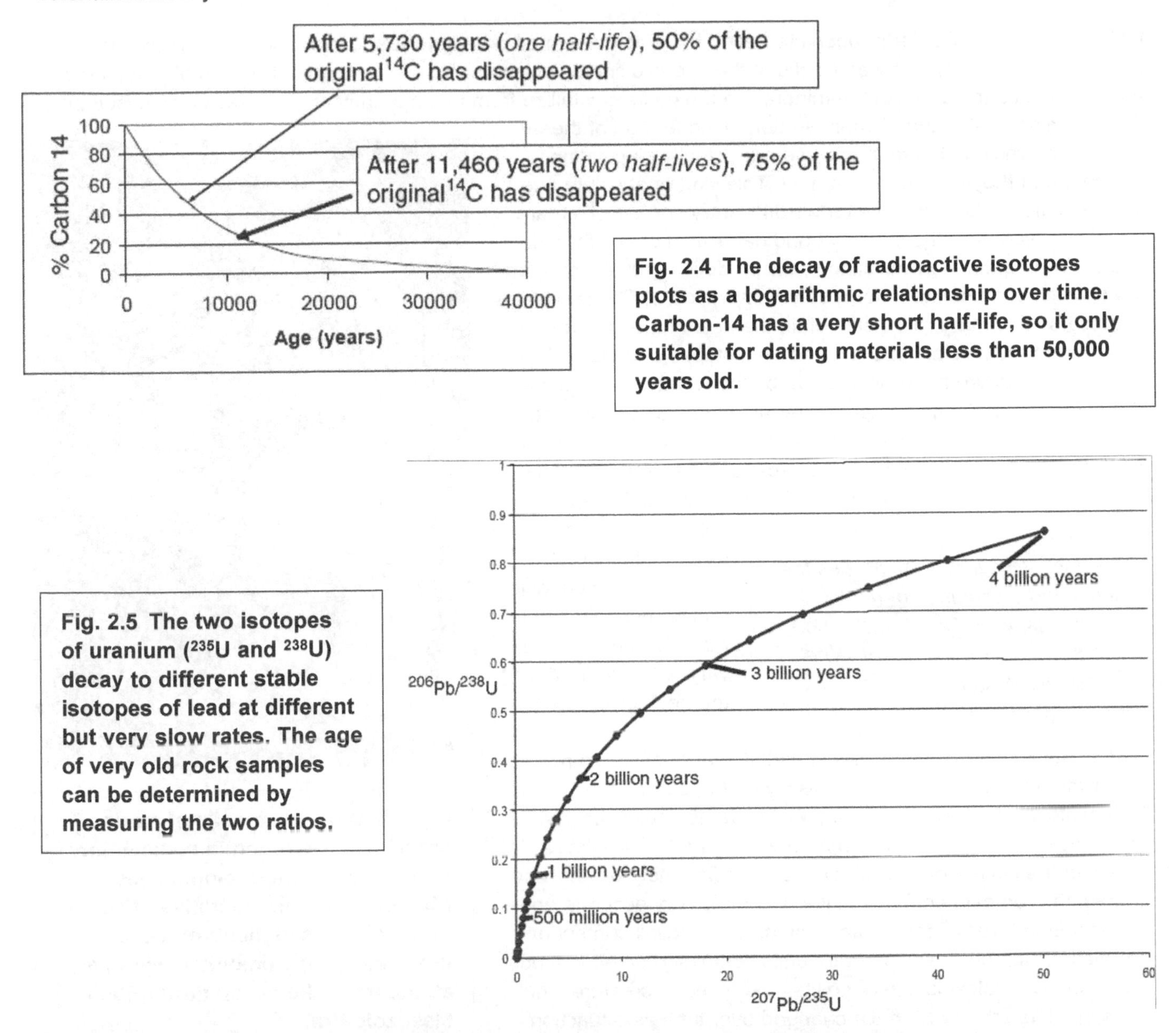

Fig. 2.4 The decay of radioactive isotopes plots as a logarithmic relationship over time. Carbon-14 has a very short half-life, so it only suitable for dating materials less than 50,000 years old.

Fig. 2.5 The two isotopes of uranium (^{235}U and ^{238}U) decay to different stable isotopes of lead at different but very slow rates. The age of very old rock samples can be determined by measuring the two ratios.

Follow Up: Probability and the Decay of Radioactive Isotopes

Your instructor will ask the entire class to stand, and each of you will flip a coin. All those who flip "heads" can sit down, and the class will write down the number who remains standing. After 1 minute, all those still standing will flip a coin, and those with "heads" will sit down, and the class will again write down the number who remain standing. Repeat this process until everyone has sat down (or only one remains standing). Plot the numbers that you write down and examine the resulting graph. Now discuss how this experiment is related to the decay of radioactive isotopes.

Investigation 2.1 examines the method for determining the age of a sample from radioactive isotopes.

■2.3 Correlation of Rock Units

Not all rocks are suitable for absolute dating by radiometric methods. **Igneous rocks**, such as granite (rocks of the continental crust) or basalt (rocks of the oceanic crust), which are formed by the cooling of molten magma, are the best candidates. As the minerals in the rocks crystallize from magma, they lock the radioactive isotopes into the mineral structure. When we determine an age of these rocks using radiometric methods, we are actually pinpointing the date that they cooled from a melt. This kind of absolute age determination is less suitable for **sedimentary rocks**, which are largely derived from the transport and deposition of weathered rocks. Weathering of preexisting rocks produces gravel, sand, and mud, which accumulate to form sedimentary rocks. The fragments in these sedimentary rocks still retain the age information of their parent rocks, since the radioactive isotopes and their decay products are not broken down by the weathering process. Consequently, radiometric ages determined on most sedimentary rocks are too old. However, one of the best ways to determine the age of sedimentary rocks is to date **volcanic ash fall deposits** within the layers of sand and mud. The minerals contained in volcanic ash can be dated radiometrically. Such volcanic deposits represent an instant in Earth history and are very valuable for dating the geological record.

Sections 2.14 and 2.15 discuss the origin and distribution of marine sediments, which are transformed into sedimentary rocks by the heat and pressure of burial.

Fig. 2.6 Different fossils of marine organisms are found in sedimentary rocks of different geologic ages. a) trilobites are representative of some of the oldest sedimentary rocks (Paleozoic); b) ammonites were very abundant in the ocean during the Mesozoic Era.

Sediments accumulate in layers in sedimentary basins. Burial under the weight of more and more layers transforms the sediments into lithified mudstone, shale, sandstone, limestone, and conglomerate. These sedimentary basins tell geologists a lot about the history of our planet. Many sedimentary basins also contain the remnants of ancient life (**fossils**). Very accurate ages of sedimentary rocks can be determined using fossil content and correlation with other sedimentary units containing dated igneous rocks such as volcanic ash deposits. The types of creatures that have inhabited the Earth have changed over time as a function of biological evolution, and their remains have been preserved as fossils. Different kinds of fossils have therefore become diagnostic of different geological periods and the identification of these fossils is an important tool for determining the relative ages of sedimentary rocks. For example, **trilobites** were common in the ocean during the Cambrian to Devonian Periods and **ammonites** were common during the relatively younger Devonian through Cretaceous Periods (Fig. 2.6). When we find rocks containing such marine fossils occurring together with igneous rocks that can be dated radiometrically, then we can determine the time frame when these sedimentary rocks were formed (Fig. 2.7). Rocks containing similar fossil assemblages at more distant locations can then be correlated with the dated sequence. In this way, geologists have been able to build a time scale and reconstruct the environmental changes of the Earth throughout its long history.

The same principles can be applied to the sediments and sedimentary rocks that comprise the ocean floor. These are usually studied by means of drill cores that are widely spaced – often hundreds of kilometers apart--so that techniques for age determination and correlation become especially important for reconstructing past events and environments. Volcanic ash deposits occur in some ocean cores, but age determination and correlation frequently relies upon the fossil assemblages, in this case made up of **microfossils** such as **foraminifera**, which are very abundant in the marine environment (Fig. 2.8).

We will learn more about the organisms which produce these microfossils in Chapter 5, especially in section 5.4.

Fossil Ammonites Type 1

Volcanic rocks dated by radiometric methods at 125 Ma

This interval of sedimentary rocks must be between 125 and 132 Ma

Fossil Ammonites Type 2

Location A

Volcanic rocks dated by radiometric methods at 132 Ma

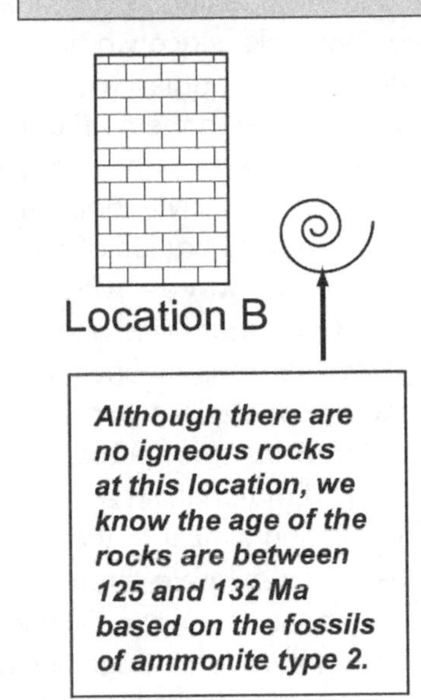

Although there are no igneous rocks at this location, we know the age of the rocks are between 125 and 132 Ma based on the fossils of ammonite type 2.

Fig. 2.7 Determining the age of sedimentary rocks by using radiometric dating of volcanic rocks and correlating by using fossils. Note that there are two different species of ammonite present in the rocks at Location A that allows the dating of the rocks at Location B.

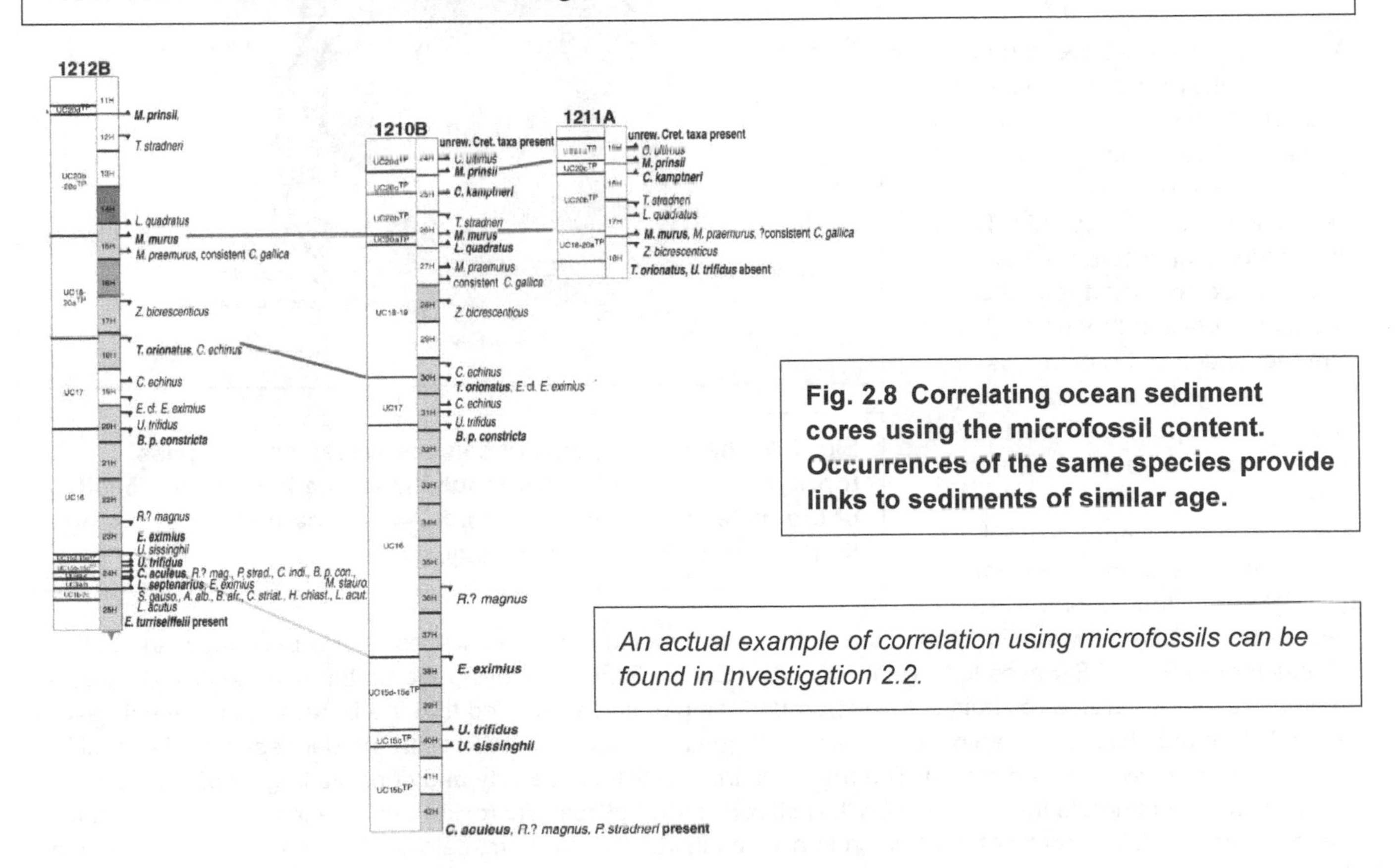

Fig. 2.8 Correlating ocean sediment cores using the microfossil content. Occurrences of the same species provide links to sediments of similar age.

An actual example of correlation using microfossils can be found in Investigation 2.2.

■2.4 Earthquakes and Seismic Waves: Earth Structure Revealed

We noted in the opening section that the solid part of the Earth is layered into the core, mantle, and crust. How could we know this, since we have never seen the Earth's interior? Much of this information comes from studying earthquakes. In the human experience earthquakes are associated with disaster and suffering on a large scale and they are the often the stuff of news headlines. However, from the geological standpoint, they are the natural consequence of the dynamic movements of the Earth's crust and upper mantle. Earthquakes are commonly caused by volcanic activity or by slip along a fault zone that suddenly releases energy locked-up by frictional forces between solid bodies of rock. The energy released by an earthquake radiates from its point of origin, or **focus**, as **seismic waves**, which travel through the Earth. The point on the Earth's surface directly above the focus is the **epicenter**. This energy is transmitted in multiple forms. **Rayleigh waves** transmit energy along the surface similar to water waves and are primarily responsible for the damage produced near the epicenter. Primary or pressure waves, **P-waves**, migrate through solid and liquid materials in an alternating push-pull, or compression-relaxation, motion similar to that of sound waves. Secondary or shear waves, **S-waves**, migrate through solid materials in a transverse motion analogous to a wave initiated by whipping a rope or a rug. S-waves cannot travel through liquids. P-waves propagate nearly twice as fast as S-waves. By comparing the difference in arrival times of the P- and S-waves at numerous locations around the Earth, it is possible to pinpoint the focus and epicenter of an earthquake.

Think of density as the amount of clothes (mass) contained in a suitcase (volume); compare, for example, the weight of a suitcase containing a few articles of clothing (less dense) to the same suitcase stuffed with clothes (more dense).

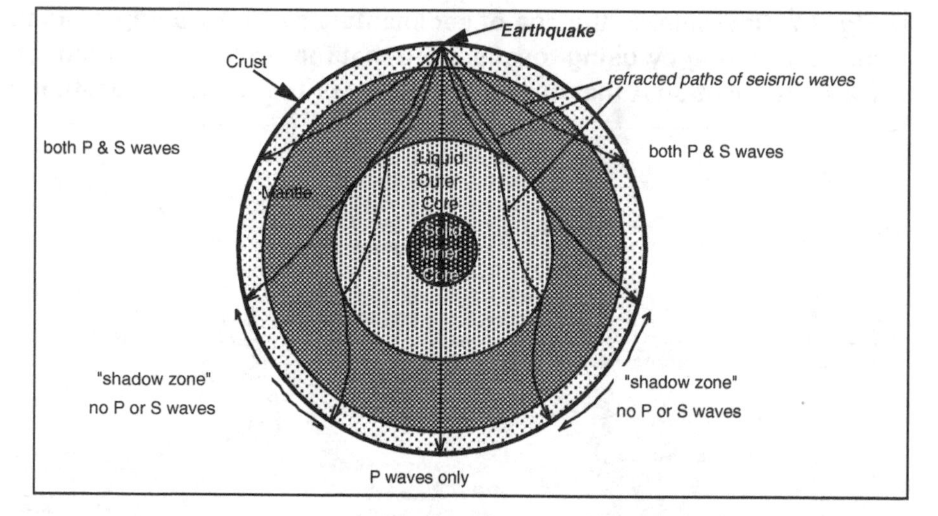

Fig. 2.9 The curved paths of seismic waves as they pass through the Earth's interior results from the increasing density of the material at greater depth. S –waves cannot travel through liquids, regardless of the density.

As P- and S-waves travel through the Earth, they encounter materials of differing composition and density. **Density** is the amount of mass per unit volume, measured in grams per cubic centimeter (g/cm^3). These differences cause some of the energy to be **reflected** from the boundary between the materials. The remainder of the energy is **refracted** (bent) due to the change in physical properties (Fig. 2.9). Both P- and S-waves travel faster through denser rocks. Seismic refraction is analogous to the bending of light when viewing a spoon in a clear glass of water; the spoon appears bent at the surface between the air and the water. This bending of seismic waves results in changes in the time it takes for the P- and S-waves to travel through the Earth's interior. Studying the patterns in the arrival times of seismic waves at multiple recording stations around the globe has revealed that the Earth's interior must have a layered structure. These concentric layers are arranged according to density, with the densest materials making up the core (metallic iron and nickel). The mantle is intermediate in density and consists largely of iron and magnesium-rich minerals that contain very low silicon (called **ultramafic** rocks), and the least dense materials make up the crust. The rocks of oceanic crust are rich in iron, magnesium, calcium and have more silicon than the mantle, whereas the rocks of the continental crust are rich in aluminum, potassium, sodium, and contain the most silicon. The oceanic crust is almost entirely the rock **basalt**, whereas the composition of the continental crust resembles **granite**.

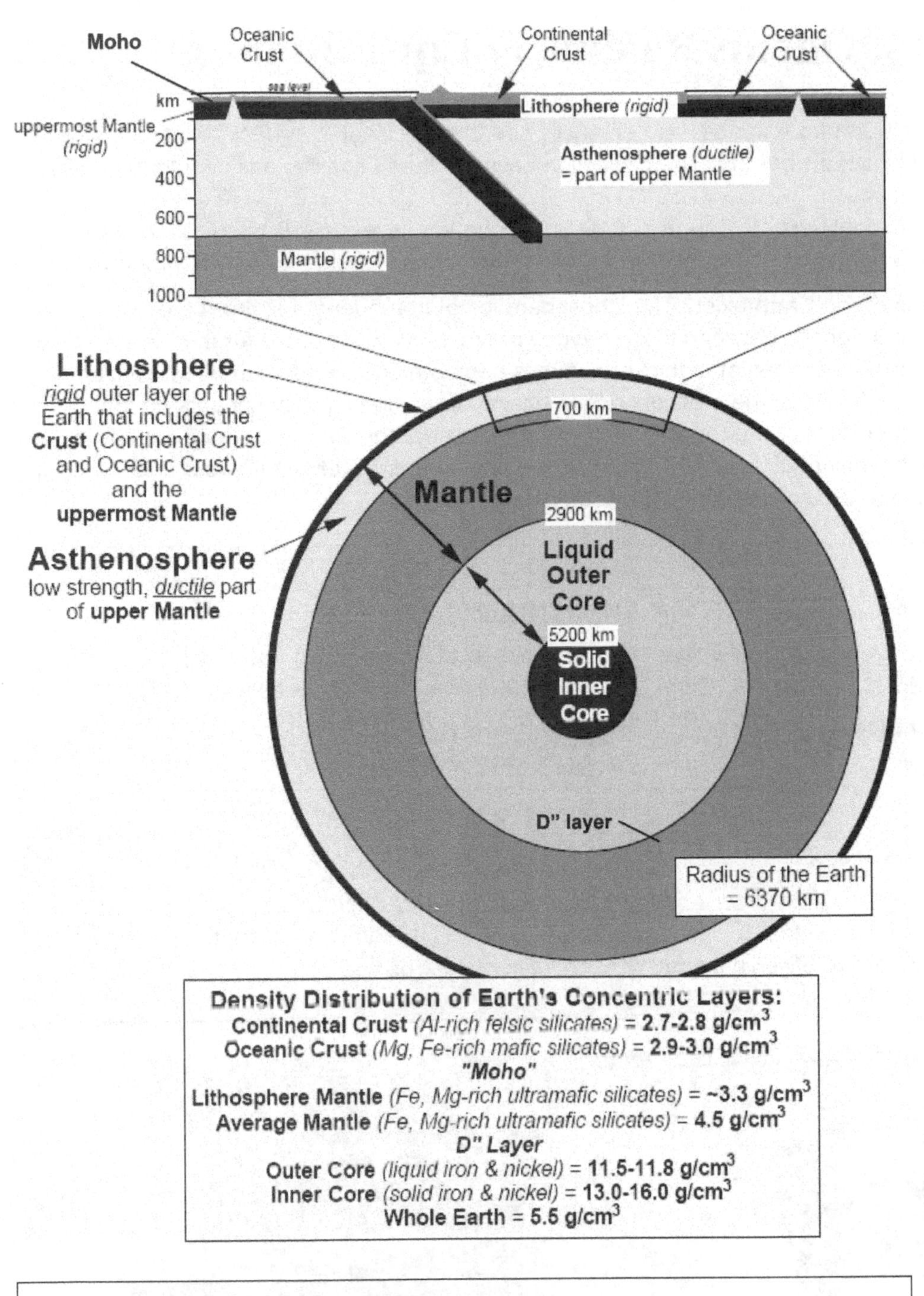

Fig. 2.10 Interior cross-section of Earth showing the various layers of different density. The upper diagram is a close up of the outer part of the Earth illustrating the relationship of the continents and ocean basins to the underlying mantle.

There are several steps of greater seismic velocity with increasing depth within the Earth. Prominent among these are the marked increases of seismic velocity at the crust/mantle and mantle/core boundaries (Fig. 2.10). Such changes in velocity are attributed to changes in the composition or physical properties of the rocks due to changing conditions of temperature, pressure, and volatile content (such as water) with depth. The increase in seismic velocity at the crust/mantle boundary is known as the **Mohorovicic Discontinuity**, or **Moho**, which marks the transition to rocks of different composition and greater density. A zone of lower seismic velocity in the upper mantle corresponds to an interval of easily deformed rocks called the **asthenosphere**. The **D" Layer** (D double prime) marks the transition from mantle rocks rich in silicate minerals to the core composed of iron and nickel. We know that part of the core must be liquid because no S waves are recorded on the side of the Earth opposite an earthquake, and we know that the core must be very dense because P-waves are highly refracted thereby creating a broad **shadow zone** where no P or S waves arrive (Fig. 2.9).

Investigation 2.3 provides a closer look at the differences between continents and ocean basins.

■2.5 Continents, Ocean Basins, & Equilibrium

When we look at pictures of the Earth from space, we can easily see that the Earth's surface has two major divisions: the **continents** and the **ocean basins**. The distinction between these two regions is determined by their relationship to sea level.

- The average height of the continents is 840 m or 0.84 km above sea level (= 2760 ft. or 0.5 mile)
- The average depth of the ocean basins is 3800 m or 3.8 km below sea level (= 12,500 ft. or 2.4 miles)

Why do these two different parts of the Earth exist? The lithosphere is not homogeneous; there are two types of crust. Differences in thickness and density between the two types of crust are responsible for the two prominent levels on the Earth's surface. **Continental crust** is thicker and less dense (more buoyant) than oceanic crust. Therefore, the continents stand higher than the adjacent ocean basins. In addition, the continents have the oldest rocks on the planet, since once they are formed the rocks remain near the Earth's surface. **Oceanic crust** is thinner and denser than continental crust. The oceanic crust is comparatively young and undergoes a continuous recycling in response to the convection in the asthenosphere.

Oceanic Crust	Continental Crust
thin, more dense • composed of dark-colored *mafic* rocks like **basalt** (rich in Fe, Mg, Ca & Na) (Fig. 2.11) • avg. density: **2.9-3.0 g/cm³** • thickness: **4-10 km**	**thick, less dense** • composed of light-colored *felsic* rocks like **granite** (rich in Si, O, Al & K) (Fig. 2.11) • avg. density: **2.7-2.8 g/cm³** • thickness: **25-40 km**
forms ocean basins	"buoyant" continents stand high
Rocks undergo continuous recycling into the mantle	Rocks remain near the Earth's surface once formed
ocean basins <200 million years old *(i.e., the present ocean basins are relatively **young** features)*	continents >3500 million years old *(i.e., the continents are **old**)*

Fig. 2.11 a. Basalt makes up ocean crust. It is dark and fine-grained, so that individual mineral grains are hard to see without a microscope. b. Granite is typical of igneous rocks comprising continental crust. Granite contains numerous light-colored minerals.

The ductile asthenosphere supports the rigid lithosphere. The rigid lithospheric blocks will "float" on the asthenosphere in a way that will compensate for their thickness and density. Oceanic crust (more dense) will sink lower into the asthenosphere than the lower-density continental crust such that equilibrium is established. This is **isostasy or isostatic equilibrium.**

> *The **density** of a material is a physical property that is very important for various parts of the science of oceanography. The density is the mass of a substance per unit volume. The most common expression of density is in the units of grams per cubic centimeter (g/cm^3). Water has a density near 1 g/cm^3. For larger masses such as those involved with the mass of the Earth, the units of kilograms per cubic meter (kg/m^3) are useful: 1 g/cm^3 = 1000 kg/m^3. In general, it is easier to convert among various units in the metric system, although density can also be expressed in more cumbersome English units such as pounds per cubic inch. A handy converter among many ways to measure density is available online at http://www.unitconversion.org/unit_converter/density.html.*

The asthenosphere and lithosphere can accommodate changes in the redistribution of load that occur in the crust by bending and flexing. For example, mass added to the crust by the growth of an ice sheet, a volcano, an island arc, or a mountain range, will depress the crust. Later, the crust will **rebound** if the load is reduced or removed due to the retreat of the ice sheet or erosion of the mountains. In other words, the crust and lithosphere maintain isostatic equilibrium with the underlying asthenosphere. In a similar fashion, an ice cube floating in a glass of water will maintain its relative proportions exposed above and below the level of the water as the ice melts and the cube shrinks in size.

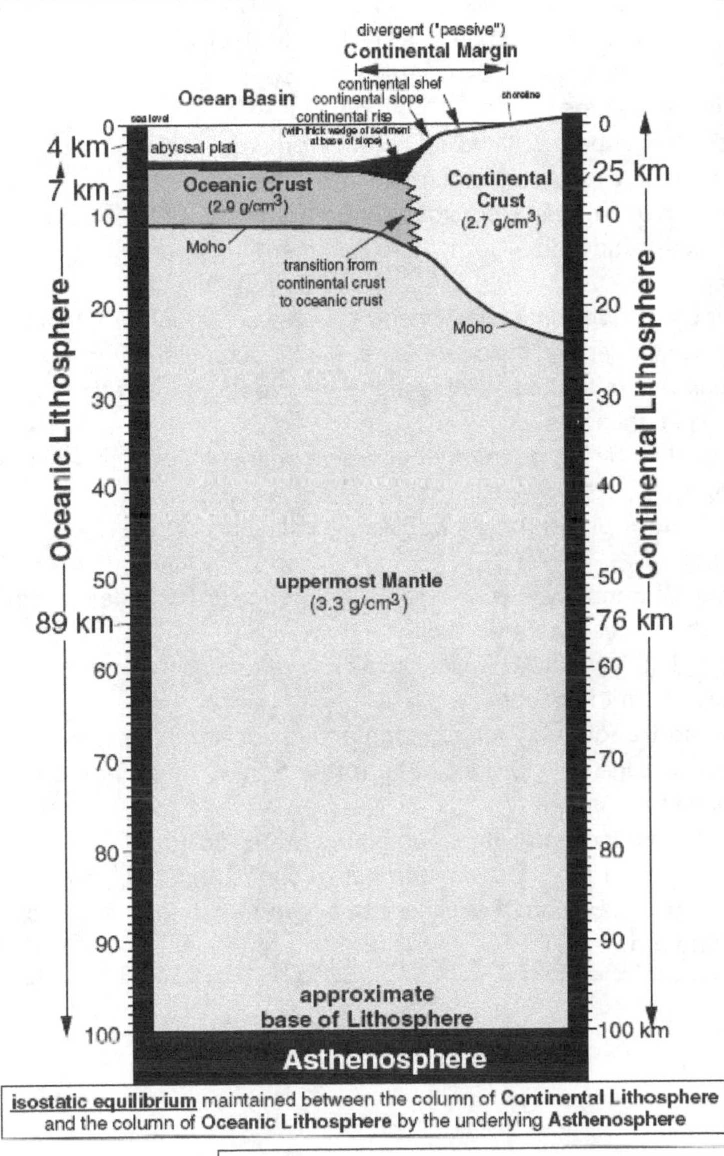

isostatic equilibrium maintained between the column of **Continental Lithosphere** and the column of **Oceanic Lithosphere** by the underlying **Asthenosphere**

> *The profile through the lithosphere (Fig. 2.12) shows one type of **continental margin** that is found at various coastlines including the Eastern coast of North America. The ocean crust and continental crust are part of a single lithospheric plate that includes the rigid part of the upper mantle. The two types of crust are connected at this type of continental margin, called "passive." In spite of the differences in density and thickness between the two types of crust, the mass of material at the base of the lithosphere is the same. This equilibrium keeps the oceanic crust below sea level creating the distinctive basins that contain all the sea water on the Earth.*

Fig. 2.12 Isostatic equilibrium occurs when the mass of material per unit area at the base of the lithosphere is the same at various points. The mass per unit area at each location can be obtained by multiplying the density (in kg/m^3) of the segment of the lithosphere by its thickness (in meters). In the illustration, the mass of water in the ocean is 4 km (4,000 meters) x 1000 kg/m^3 (1 g/cm^3) = 4 x 10^6 kg/m^2. Adding this to the mass of oceanic crust and upper mantle calculated in the same manner will give the total mass of oceanic lithosphere at point "A."

Investigation 2.4 explores the concept of isostasy in further detail.

■2.6 Features of the Ocean Floor

The continents and ocean basins are the most obvious physical features of the Earth's surface. However, just as the continents have high mountains, low hills and flat plains occurring in specific areas, so does the ocean floor. The physical features of the seafloor can be divided into two major provinces: continental margins, which are near the coastlines of the world, and ocean basins farther out to sea.

The ocean floor features discussed here were largely discovered through echo sounding, as presented in section 1.5. Only a very small portion of the sea bottom has been mapped in detail.

Continental Margins are the transition from continental crust to oceanic crust. They are the regions of relatively shallow water near the coastlines that represent the "step" from thick, buoyant continental crust to thinner, denser oceanic crust. **Passive continental margins** are found in the middle of the Earth's tectonic plates and are not associated with plate boundaries. The coastlines around the Atlantic Ocean are all passive margins. **Active continental margins,** on the other hand, are near the boundaries between two (or more) colliding plates and they are characterized by earthquakes and volcanic activity (Fig. 2.13). The Pacific Ocean is surrounded by active continental margins.

Features of the Continental Margins

1. **Continental shelf**
    - offshore extension of the continent (underlain by continental crust). Passive continental margins usually have a much wider continental shelf.
    - relatively shallow, gentle seaward slope (typically <1°)
    - shelf-slope break: 120-200 m water depth
2. **Continental slope**
    - variable slope (gentle to steep escarpments)
    - underlain by thinned continental crust
    - dissected by numerous **submarine canyons** (deep erosional gullies, conduits for downslope sediment transport to the deep-sea)
3. **Continental rise** *(only found along passive continental margins)*
    - characterized by **deep-sea fans**, thick accumulation of sediment at the base of the slope, derived from the erosion of the continents
    - underlain by the boundary between continental and oceanic crust
4. **Accretionary prism** *(only found along active continental margins)*
    - zone at trench where sediments are squeezed and deformed as the plates converge
    - high fluid flow and chemical recycling (affects chemical mass balance of the ocean)
5. **Deep-sea trench** *(only found along active continental margins)*
    - narrow zone of very deepwater (often > 6000 m) adjacent to continent
    - marks the location where two plates are colliding
6. **Fore-arc basin** *(only found along active continental margins)*
    - thick accumulation of sediment between trench and volcanic island arc

Ocean Basins

The ocean basins are underlain almost entirely by **oceanic crust** composed of basalt. Although the surface of the ocean hides the **bathymetry** (the depth below sea level) of the sea floor, the ocean basins possess a wide variety of high mountains and deep valleys. As we shall see, these are not distributed randomly, but are related to the fundamental processes of plate tectonics that have shaped the ocean floor over the past hundreds of millions of years.

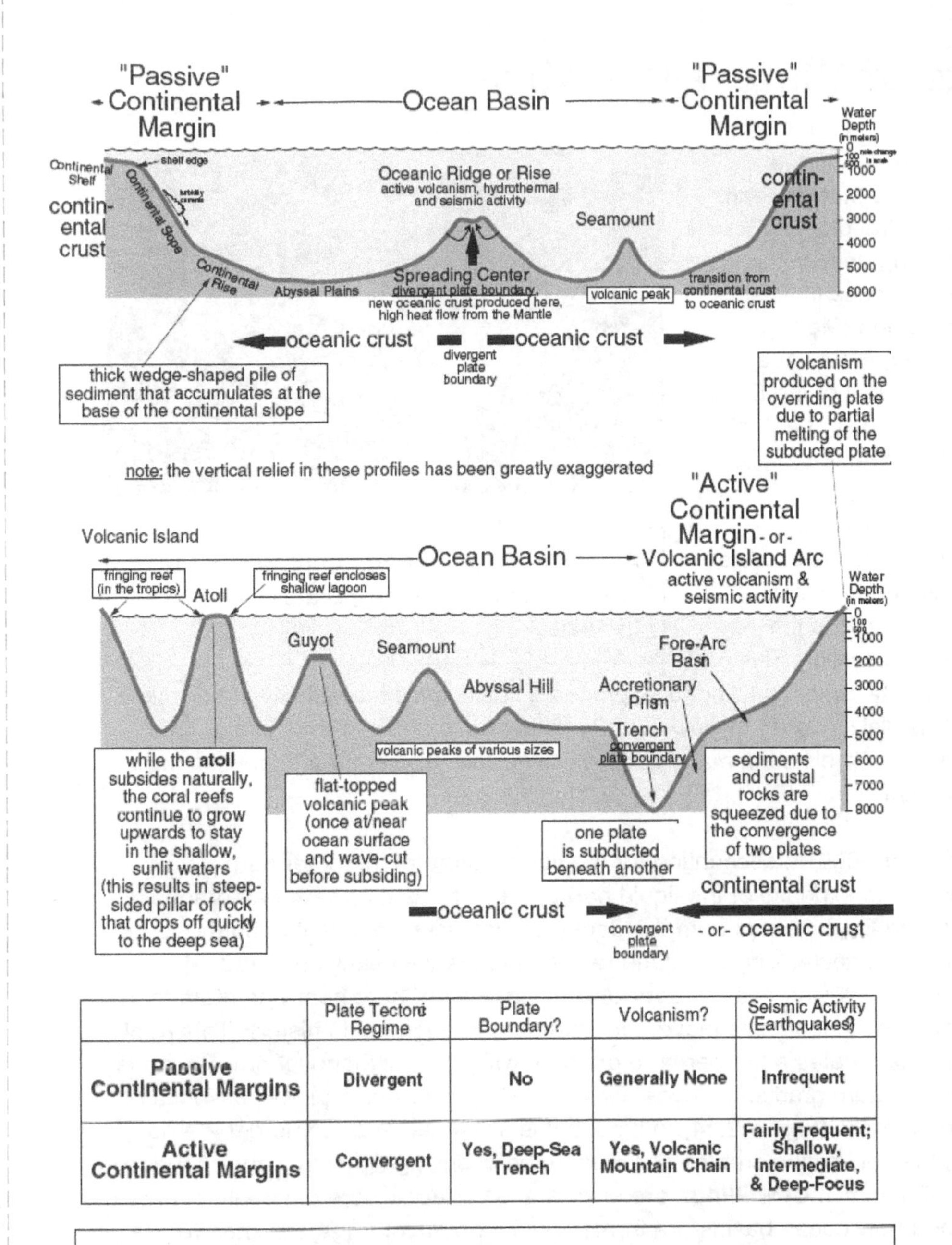

	Plate Tectonic Regime	Plate Boundary?	Volcanism?	Seismic Activity (Earthquakes)
Passive Continental Margins	**Divergent**	**No**	**Generally None**	**Infrequent**
Active Continental Margins	**Convergent**	**Yes, Deep-Sea Trench**	**Yes, Volcanic Mountain Chain**	**Fairly Frequent; Shallow, Intermediate, & Deep-Focus**

Fig. 2.13 Profiles across typical ocean basins illustrating passive (above) and active (below) continental margins.

Investigation 2.5 examines the distribution of seafloor features throughout the world ocean.

Features of the Ocean Basins

1. **Abyssal plains**
   - covers a large area of the sea floor; virtually flat (except where interrupted by volcanoes).
   - 4000-6000 m water depth.
2. **Volcanic islands**
   - active, dormant, or recently extinct volcanoes above sea level. Mauna Kea on the big island of Hawaii is the tallest mountain on our planet, rising 10,099 m or 33,132 ft. above the Pacific ocean floor. In contrast, Mt. Everest in the Himalaya Mountains is only 8,848 m (29, 028 feet) above sea level.
   - **atolls** are steep-sided rings of coral reefs enclosing a lagoon perched on top of an extinct volcano.
   - **guyots** are flat-topped volcanoes that were formerly atolls at sea level at which time they were flattened by wave erosion. They eventually subsided below sea level when their volcanic activity ended.
   - **seamounts** are submarine volcanic peaks that do not have their tops flattened. They were never above sea level.
   - **abyssal hills** are very small volcanic peaks that are found in deeper parts of the ocean basin.
3. **Deep-Sea Trenches**
   - long, narrow, steep-sided troughs (e.g., Peru-Chile Trench).
   - deepest parts of ocean (>6000 m; Mariana Trench – 11,022 m below sea level).
   - occur where two tectonic plates collide (convergence).
   - seismically active (shallow to very deep earthquakes landward of trench).
   - associated with volcanism landward of trench: either **island arcs** or **volcanic mountain ranges** on land.
4. **Oceanic ridges & rises**
   - active volcanic mountain ranges rising 2-3 km above the adjacent abyssal plains (e.g., Mid-Atlantic Ridge, East Pacific Rise).
   - continuous through ocean basins (extending >65,000 km around Earth).
   - extensive hydrothermal activity and chemical recycling of seawater through oceanic crust (important component of chemical mass balance of the ocean).
   - fault scars cut across and off-set these features (= **transform faults** and **fracture zones**).
   - seismically active (shallow earthquakes).
   - occur where tectonic plates move apart (convergence).

■2.7 Basic Concepts of Plate Tectonics

The features of the sea floor that were examined in the previous sections are not distributed randomly in the ocean, but are arranged in distinct patterns around the globe. These patterns are the result of processes occurring deep within the Earth, in the mantle. Despite the marked increase in seismic wave velocity across the crust/mantle transition (**Moho**), the uppermost mantle behaves like the crust; the crust and uppermost mantle are rigid. This rigid outer shell of the Earth is the **lithosphere**. The base of the lithosphere is at a depth of approximately 100 km, although this depth varies.

A satellite image of Mt. Saint Helens in Washington, which erupted explosively in 1980.

The region of the upper mantle underlying the lithosphere behaves like a ductile substance. In other words, it is capable of flowing like hot plastic or hot asphalt, although it is not liquid. This low strength region of the upper mantle is the **asthenosphere**, as mentioned in the previous section. This part of the mantle is also known as the **low-velocity zone**, attesting to its properties that cause the velocity of seismic waves passing through it to slow down. This distinguishes the low-velocity zone from the rest of the mantle. The base of the asthenosphere is not known very well, although many geophysicists place it where the deepest known earthquakes occur at a depth of about 700 km.

The core of the Earth is very hot (>5000°C or 9000°F) accounting for the liquid nature of the outer core. The solid inner core has been slowly growing at the expense of the liquid part of the core as the Earth has gradually cooled over time. Much of the heat within the Earth comes from the decay of radioactive elements and the concentration of radioactive isotopes has been decreasing over time resulting in the very slow and gradual cooling of the Earth. The Earth has been slowly losing heat by **conduction** (transfer of heat from one atom to another) and **convection** (differential heat loss that causes movement of mass) throughout its history. This **heat flow** deep within the Earth's core and mantle creates a temperature gradient within the asthenosphere. Because of its weaker physical properties, this temperature gradients drives convection in the asthenosphere; essentially a conveyor-like flow of hot, easily deformed rocks (Figure 2.14). Although it is still a matter of some debate how deep into the mantle convection occurs, the convection creates stresses in the overlying rigid lithosphere due to the upward, lateral, and downward flow of material. **Upwellings** are sites at the surface where old continents are rifted apart, oceanic crust is produced, and new ocean basins are formed, while **downwellings** are sites where old oceanic crust is recycled back into the mantle, volcanic islands and volcanic mountain ranges are formed, and where continents collide. Because of these deep-seated stresses, the outer shell of the Earth is broken into numerous rigid **lithospheric plates** (also called tectonic plates), which move slowly around the globe at rates of about 2 to 20 cm/year.

The rigid plates interact with each other in one of three ways:

1. *they move apart (**divergence**)*
2. *they collide (**convergence**) and*
3. *they slide past one another **(transform or strike-slip motion)***

All of these observations have been brought together to form the theory of **plate tectonics**, which divides the lithosphere into seven major rigid plates and several minor ones that move about on the Earth's surface. These plates are separated by zones of convergence, divergence, or transform motion, and their movement is driven by the convective motion of the asthenosphere. The margins of lithospheric plates are characterized by zones of extensive volcanism, earthquakes, and mountain building.

*Plate tectonics grew out of the concepts of **continental drift** and **sea-floor spreading**. **Continental drift** was a hypothesis championed by Alfred Wegener early in the 20th century to explain, among other geological evidence, the jigsaw puzzle fit of the continents such as South America and Africa. Wegener proposed that the continents were once a single large landmass, which he called **Pangaea**. According to Wegener's hypothesis, Pangaea split up into the present continents, which then drifted over the denser rocks of the ocean basins. We now know that the continents move with the ocean crust as large lithospheric plates. **Sea-floor spreading** was a hypothesis proposed by Harry Hess in 1960. Hess proposed that ocean crust is produced at mid-ocean ridges and then moves symmetrically away from the ridge as new material is added in the central rift valley. In this view, the continents are pushed away from the mid-ocean ridges and toward the deep-sea trenches where oceanic crust is returned to the mantle and partially melted as part of the asthenosphere's conveyor-like motion. Paleomagnetic studies of ocean crust during the early 1960's (F. Vine, D.H. Matthews, and L.W. Morley) largely demonstrated the validity of the seafloor spreading hypothesis.*

Fig. 2.14 Detailed cross-section of the upper part of the Earth showing the crust, upper mantle and two of the three types of plate boundaries: convergent, where trenches and subduction zones are found; divergent, which occur at spreading centers (oceanic ridges).

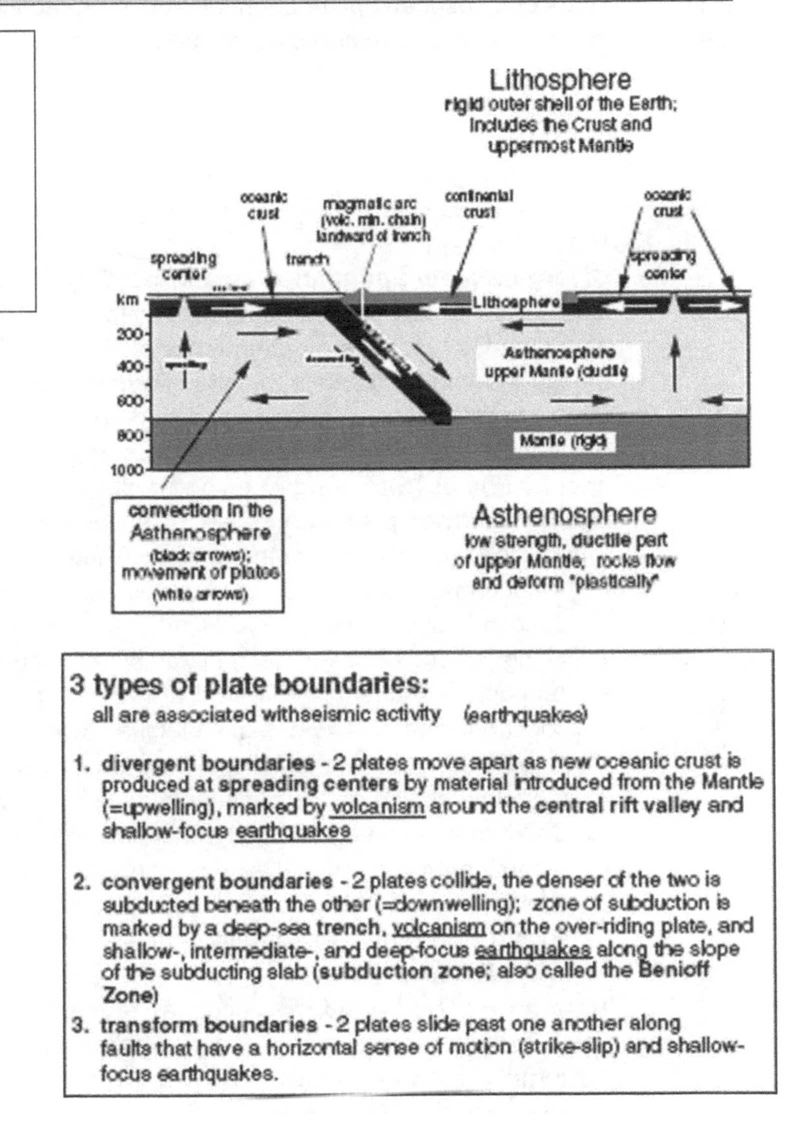

Food for Thought

Alfred Wegener believed that the continents moved into their present positions based upon the way the coastlines of some of them fit together. See if you can reconstruct the supercontinent of Pangaea by moving the continents around at the following web location: http://www.discoverourearth.org/student/tectonics/continental_drift.html

The Continents 225 Million Years Ago

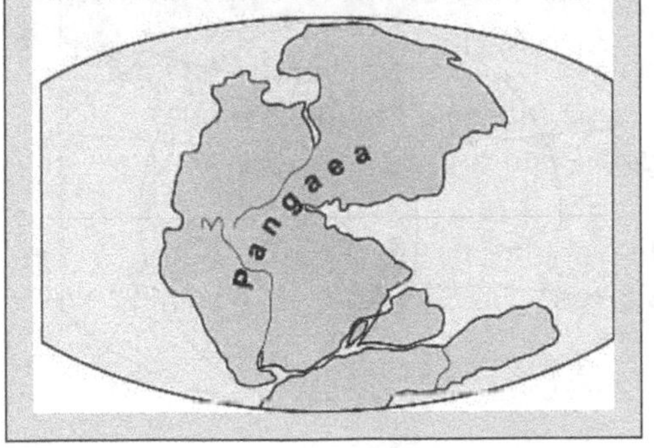

Investigation 2.6 provides additional information concerning several important bathymetric features of continental margins.

■2.8 Plate Boundaries, Earthquakes, & Volcanism

Remember that the asthenosphere, although it is made of silicates, flows like a plastic substance (ductile) under the conditions in the upper mantle. Refer to section 2.4.

As we have seen, the bathymetric features of the sea floor are not arranged randomly; there are definite patterns in the distribution of deep-sea trenches, oceanic ridges, and volcanic islands. Many of these features are related to the processes of plate tectonics, which continuously move large pieces of the lithosphere over the surface of the Earth. High heat flow in the asthenosphere causes convective motion. Material rises towards the surface in some places (upwelling) and sinks back into the mantle in others (downwelling). Lithospheric plates are rafted by the ductile flow in the asthenosphere at rates of 2 to 20 cm/yr.
Seismic activity is associated with all three types of lithospheric plate boundaries (convergent, divergent and transform), while volcanism characterizes divergent (**spreading centers**) and many convergent plate boundaries. The different kinds of lithospheric plate boundaries can be recognized by the patterns in earthquakes and volcanism, and the bathymetric features associated with them.

1. *Earthquakes*
   a. **Divergent plate boundaries** are indicated by the presence of oceanic ridges. At these ridges, new ocean crust is being produced, and two plates are moving away from each other. This process produces an abundance of shallow-focus earthquakes. The island of Iceland in the North Atlantic Ocean is the site of a divergent plate boundary.
   b. **Convergent plate boundaries** are marked by deep-sea trenches, which are the surface expression of **subduction zones**, places where the lithosphere of one plate descends below another (Fig. 2.15). Earthquakes occur all along the contact between the descending slab and the overlying plate, giving rise to shallow-, intermediate-, and deep-focus earthquakes that outline the geometry of the contact. There are three types of convergence:
      - An ocean-ocean collision is where two plates of oceanic crust come together. One slab descends under another producing a trench and an **island arc** on the plate that is not being subducted. Japan is an example of such an island arc.
      - An ocean-continent collision occurs when a plate with ocean crust encounters one with continental crust. The oceanic plate is always subducted in this case, and the subduction is marked by a trench offshore. This is an active continental margin that creates **volcanic** mountain chains on the continental plate. The western coast of South America (Peru and Chile) is an example of this type of collision.
      - A continent-continent collision is where two plates of continental crust collide. Continental crust is never subducted, so the two colliding plates build up massive mountain ranges, such as the Himalaya Mountains in Asia, where the Indian Plate has moved northward in to the Eurasian Plate.
   c. **Transform plate boundaries** occur as **faults** that separate two plates sliding past each other. Transform faults often produce shallow-focus earthquakes. The San Andreas Fault in California is the world's most famous transform fault.

2. ***Volcanism***
   a. **Divergent plate boundaries** are the sites of extensive volcanic activity. Often called **spreading centers**, the oceanic ridges produce new oceanic crust as magma rises from the asthenosphere.
   b. **Convergent plate boundaries** produce significant volcanic activity on the landward side of trenches (Fig. 2.15). The plate that is being subducted is partially melted, which results in the generation of **magma** and volcanism on the overriding plate. As stated above, these can take two forms:
      - island arcs, such as Japan or the Aleutian Islands south of Alaska that are formed by (ocean-ocean collisions).
      - volcanic mountain chains like the Andes in South America that are formed by ocean-continent collisions.

The movement of lithospheric plates may be caused by:

1. Gravitational sliding of the crust off the spreading center (ridge) as new oceanic crust cools and contracts. The oceanic crust becomes denser as it moves away from hot its volcanic source. This is often called the **"ridge push"** mechanism.
2. Pulling of the ocean crust by the plate. descending down a subduction zone. The dense, older oceanic crust descends back into the mantle and exerts a continuous stress on the basalt still on the ocean floor. This is known as the **"slab pull"** mechanism.
3. **Convective motion** in asthenosphere. The ductile material of the asthenosphere flows laterally and drags the rigid lithosphere along for the ride.

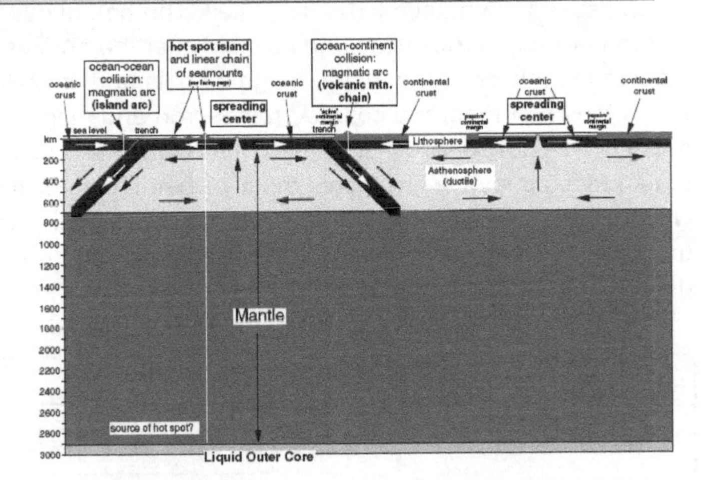

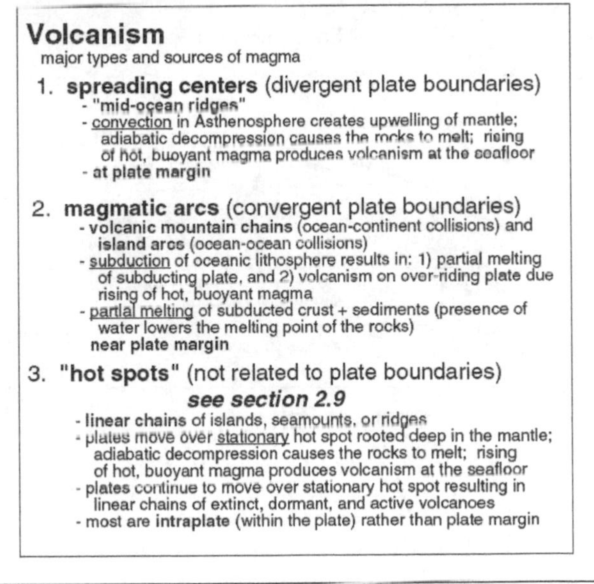

Fig 2.15 Overview of the relationship between earthquakes, volcanoes, and the different types of plate boundaries.

Investigation 2.7 looks at the reasons behind the worldwide distribution of earthquakes and volcanoes.

Follow-Up

The process of convection in the mantle, which drives plate tectonics, is a subject of great research interest. Many people are trying to develop computer models of the Earth's mantle, and this produces animations of astounding complexity. For a look at some of these, go to:
http://www.gps.caltech.edu/~gurnis/Movies/movies-more.html
On the simplest level, convection in the mantle can be modeled as either a one-layer or two-layer system. The differences between these models, and the relationships to plate tectonic features are illustrated at
http://www.edumedia-sciences.com/a399_l2-mantle-convection.html

■2.9 Divergent Plate Boundaries

Divergent plate boundaries are identified by oceanic ridges or spreading centers where new oceanic crust is created as two plates move apart. The spreading centers are a continuous chain of undersea volcanic mountains that extends from the Arctic Ocean, through the Atlantic, Indian, and Pacific Ocean for some 65,000 km. The **Mid-Atlantic Ridge** and the **East Pacific Rise** are parts of this continuous active volcanic mountain range on the seafloor. The spreading centers are situated over sites of **upwelling** in the asthenosphere. The confining pressure is reduced as mantle material flows upward towards the surface, which causes the mantle to partially melt. The hot, buoyant magma or molten rock rises and collects near the surface in magma chambers. Some of the magma cools and crystallizes within the crust to form a coarse-grained iron and magnesium-rich rock called **gabbro**. Another portion of the magma is extruded at the surface as lava, which cools rapidly when it comes in contact with the cold seawater to form the fine-grained, **basalt**, which has the same chemical and mineral composition as gabbro and is the major component of ocean crust.

Oceanic ridges are composed of basalt that formed from molten magma that erupted on the sea floor. The extrusion of hot magma into cold sea water results in the structures called pillow basalt, which is shown in this undersea photograph.

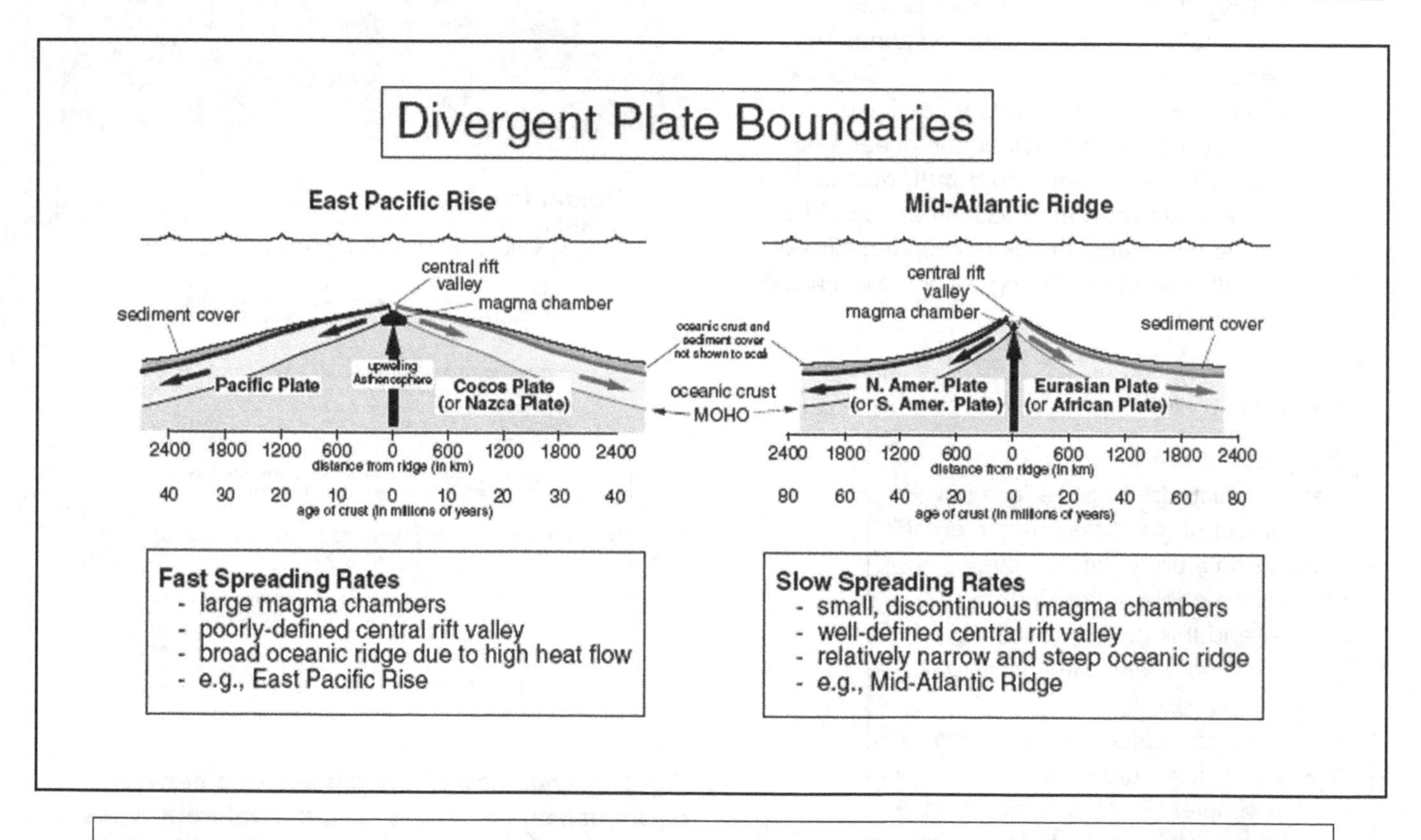

Fig. 2.16 The rate of spreading at oceanic ridges affects the bathymetric profile of the ridges.

High heat flow from the mantle causes the spreading centers to stand high above the adjacent abyssal plains. The shape of the ridge profile is related to the rate of seafloor spreading. Parts of the global ridge system with high rates of upwelling from the asthenosphere produce relatively large magma chambers while other parts are characterized by much smaller magma chambers. The East Pacific Rise is creating new ocean crust at an average rate of about 5-10 cm/year for each flank of the ridge (=half-spreading rate) while the Mid-Atlantic Ridge has a half-spreading rate of about 1-3 cm/year (Fig. 2.16). The full spreading rates for the East Pacific Rise and Mid-Atlantic Ridge are 10-20 cm/yr and 2-6 cm/yr, respectively.

As an old continent is split (**rifted**) into two, a new ocean basin, composed of ocean crust (basalt), is created in the growing void between the rifted continental fragments. **Passive continental margins** form at the transition between the thinned, stretched continental crust and the new oceanic crust. The new ocean basin has an active spreading center (divergent plate boundary) approximately equidistant between the two rifted continental margins. The Red Sea (Fig. 2.17) is an example of a young and growing ocean basin, while the Atlantic is an example of an old ocean basin that has been growing for nearly 200 million years (Fig. 2.18).

Fig. 2.17 a) Spreading along the ridge in the Indian Ocean (black arrows) continues up the Persian Gulf and into the Red Sea. b) Satellite image of the Red Sea. This young ocean basin is growing as the ridge in the middle expands at the rate of ~2 cm/yr.

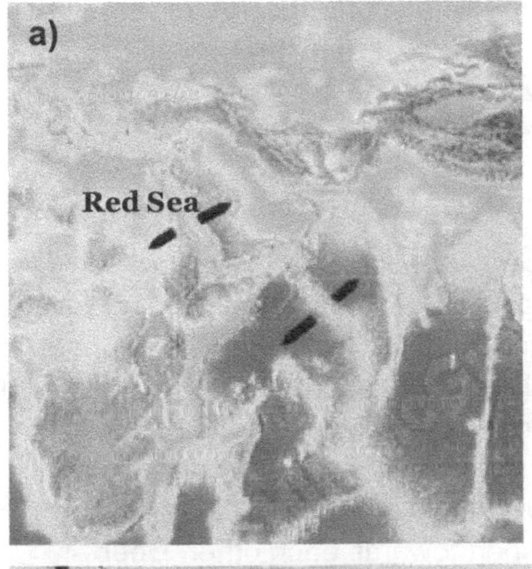

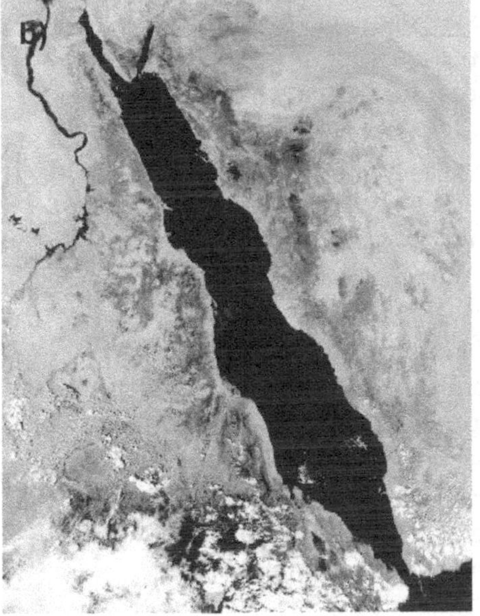

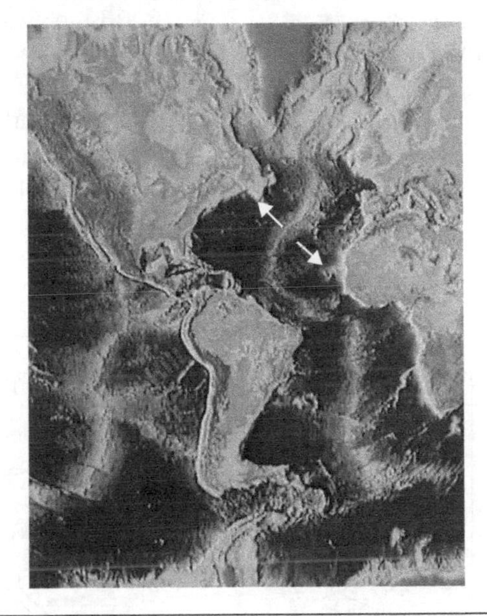

Fig. 2.18 Sea-floor spreading along the Mid-Atlantic Ridge (arrows) has created the Atlantic Ocean over the past 200 million years. The Atlantic continental margin has broad continental shelves and is connected to oceanic crust, typical of a passive continental margin.

Food for Thought

The following web site gives a good animation that illustrates sea-floor spreading and the break-up of the supercontinent Pangaea: http://www.scotese.com/sfsanim.htm
Can you project what the distribution of oceans and continents might be in the future, based on these movements? To see what some researchers have proposed, take a look at http://www.nytimes.com/2007/01/09/science/09geo.html?_r=1&scp=1&sq=Global+Forecast+Fewer+Continents&st=nyt&oref=slogin

Investigation 2.8 looks at the rates of sea-floor spreading in greater detail.

■2.10 Convergent Plate Boundaries

Convergent plate boundaries are where two lithospheric plates are colliding and are associated with very intense levels of seismic activity, volcanism, and mountain building. The seismic activity is a consequence of subduction of oceanic lithosphere beneath oceanic or continental lithosphere, or the collision of two continental plates. Subduction of oceanic crust is associated with so much friction that the process is far from continuous or smooth. Strain builds up where two plates collide; occasionally the strain is released catastrophically and seismic energy is released as a crustal segment lurches forward, causing an earthquake. The pattern of earthquake foci is distinctive in subduction zones, with deeper earthquakes occurring at progressively greater distances away from the trench (Fig. 2.19). This **Benioff Zone** is the region of seismic activity (earthquake foci) created by the friction between the subducting lithospheric plate and the overriding plate that allows geophysicists to study the processes of subduction to depths of nearly 700 km in the mantle. The deep-sea trenches mark plate boundaries where oceanic lithosphere is subducted beneath younger oceanic lithosphere (ocean-ocean collision), or beneath continental lithosphere (ocean-continent collision).

Trenches are the deepest part of the ocean floor and they occur mostly around continental margins, as outlined in section 2.6.

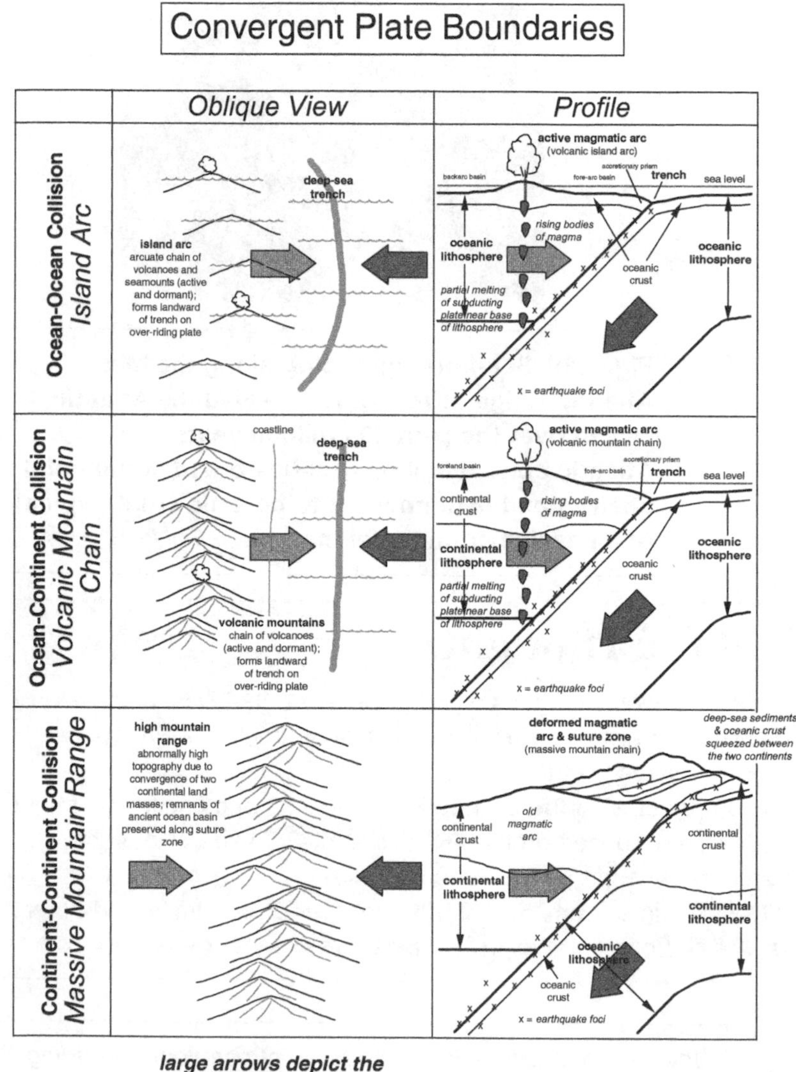

large arrows depict the convergence of two lithospheric plates

Fig. 2.19 Different varieties of convergent boundaries result in uplift and deformation of the Earth's crust.

A continent-continent collision often begins as an ocean-continent collision. Once the thick continental lithosphere collides with another block of continental lithosphere, subduction becomes minimal and massive mountains grow vertically as the two plates are pushed towards each other. Deep-sea sediments and slices of oceanic crust are squeezed and deformed in the **suture zone** which represents all that is left of the ocean basin that once existed between the two continental land masses. The **Himalaya Mountains** and **Tibetan Plateau**, the largest mountains in the world today, are still growing taller as the subcontinent of India drives northward into the continent of Asia (Fig. 2.20a). The old **Appalachian Mountains** are another example of a mountain range produced by a continent-continent collision that occurred in the distant past, ending about 250 million years ago.

The volcanism characteristic of ocean-ocean and ocean-continent collisions is the consequence of subduction of oceanic lithosphere. The partial melting of oceanic crust and deep-sea sediments subducted at the trench is facilitated by the presence of water, which lowers the melting temperature of rocks. The resulting magma is less dense than the parent rock, and since hot rock is less dense than cold rock, the magma rises buoyantly through the lithosphere of the overriding plate. Some of this magma cools slowly within the crust of the overriding plate to form a rock with large crystals such as granite, but some of the magma reaches the surface where it erupts as a volcano. The new accumulation of plutonic and volcanic rock is called an **island arc**. The **Aleutian Islands** and the **Mariana Islands** of the North Pacific, and the **Lesser Antilles** of the Caribbean are all examples of island arcs. (Fig. 2.20b). The volcanoes are not continuously active, but the volcanic chain is approximately the same age all along its length (this is in contrast to the linear chain of volcanoes produced by a stationary hot spot which displays a steady progression of age from older to younger volcanoes towards the single hot spot source). In the case of an ocean-continent collision, a chain of volcanic mountains is produced landward of the trench near the edge of the overriding continent. The **Andes Mountains** of South America and the **Cascade Mountains** of Washington and Oregon (including Mt. Rainer, Mt. St. Helens, Mt. Hood) are excellent examples of such volcanic mountain chains. (Fig. 2.20c).

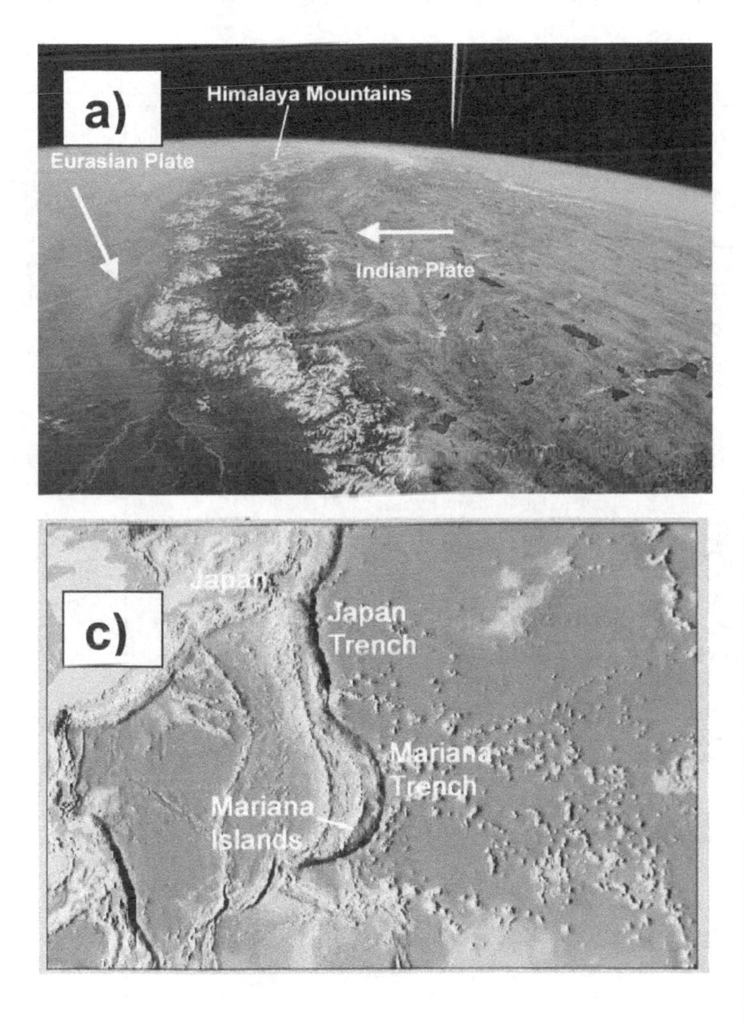

Fig 2.20 Examples of convergent plate boundaries. a) The Himalaya Mountains are being uplifted by the collision of the Indian and Eurasian plates. Arrows show the relative motion of the two plates. b) Island arcs, like the Mariana Islands in the western Pacific Ocean, result from the collision of an oceanic plate with another oceanic plate. c) Mount St. Helens in the Cascade Mountains of Washington is a volcano developed on the North American plate as it collides with the oceanic crust of the Juan de Fuca plate. This photo shows the eruption of May 18, 1980; Mount Rainier is in the background.

Investigation 2.9 examines the characteristics of plate boundaries around the globe.

■2.11 Transform Plate Boundaries

Because the lithosphere is rigid, stresses on the crustal rocks that cover our spherical planet cause the crust to fracture. There are numerous fractures across the spreading centers because not all segments of the volcanic ridge system are active at the same time, which causes differential strain on the brittle oceanic crust. As this strain builds, the crust on either side of the fracture will eventually move. A fault is the general name for a rock fracture along which movement has occurred. **Transform faults** (Fig. 2.21) are the fractures in the ocean crust that are responsible for the offsets observed along the spreading centers. Where the ridge is offset by a transform fault, the sense of motion is opposite on either side of the fault. Transform faults have lateral, or **strike-slip motion**, where two lithospheric plates move past each other making these regions prone to seismic activity. This opposite sense of motion accumulates strain until the rock can no longer accommodate the pressure and the frictional forces snap catastrophically to produce an earthquake. The seismically active **San Andreas Fault System** of southern California (Fig. 2.22) is a transform fault between the East Pacific Rise (Baja California) and the Juan de Fuca Ridge off Oregon and Washington. Strike-slip plate boundaries are characterized by shallow-focus earthquakes. **Fracture zones** (Fig. 2.21) are long, linear zones of highly fractured oceanic crust. They represent continuations of transform faults beyond the zone of active strike-slip displacement. Fracture zones tend to be seismically inactive because the sense of motion on both sides of the fracture is in the same direction.

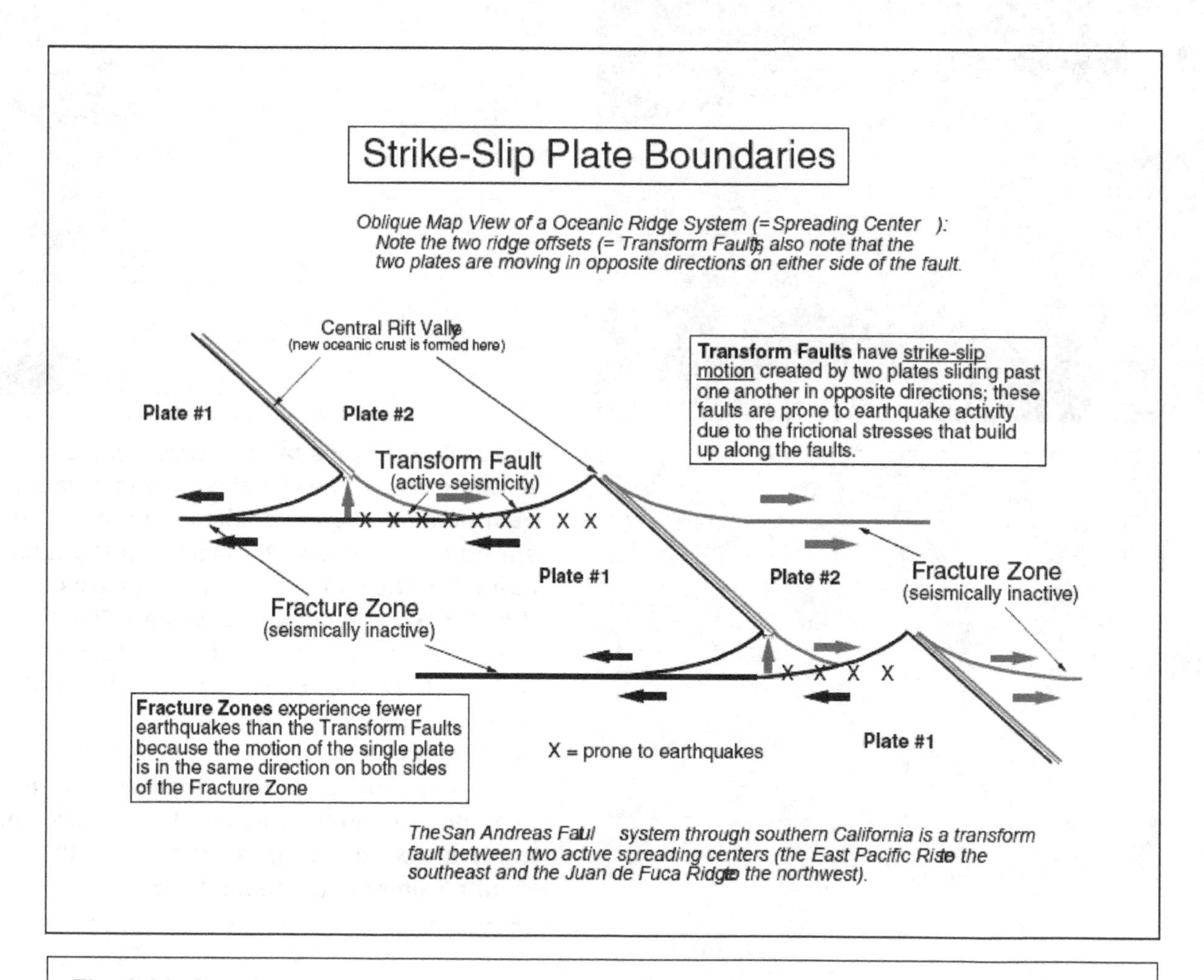

Fig. 2.21 Oceanic ridges can be offset along fracture zones to produce transform or strike-slip plate boundaries.

Fig. 2.22 The San Andreas Fault in California is a transform (strike-slip) boundary between two major lithospheric plates. The Pacific Plate is moving to the northwest relative to the North American Plate.

Transform faults occur because the Earth is a sphere, and the plate motions around the globe are actually rotations around a pole (Fig. 2.23). This causes an interesting situation because the distance the plates move near the pole is less than the distance farther away. In effect, the plates "tear" at various points to accommodate the differential movement, and these tears are the transform faults. The major spreading ridges of the modern ocean – the Mid-Atlantic Ridge and the East Pacific Rise – run almost north-south in their respective ocean basins, so that the poles of rotations for these plates are near the geographic North Pole (Fig. 2.24). Fracture zones and transform faults are parallel to lines of latitude and the greatest amount of movement is near the equator, so that the transform faults are longer in this part of the globe.

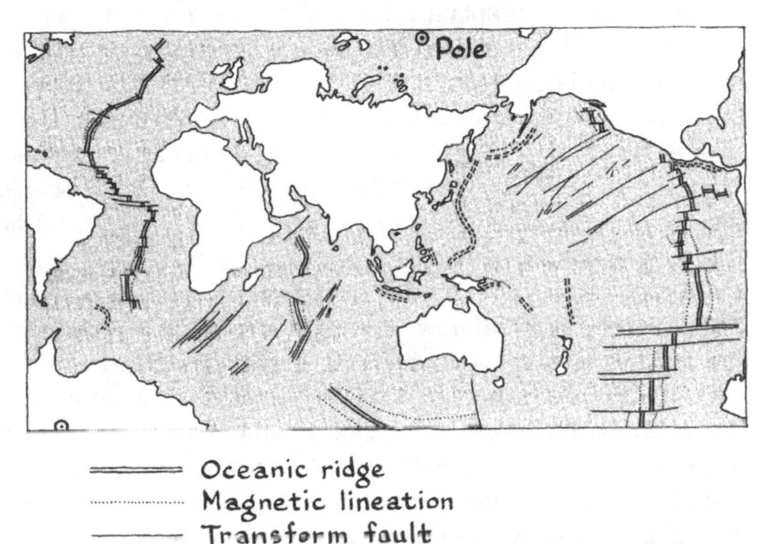

Fig. 2.24 A map of the world drawn around the pole of rotation corresponding to the East Pacific Rise. Notice that the transform faults here are straight lines that give the impression of latitude lines.

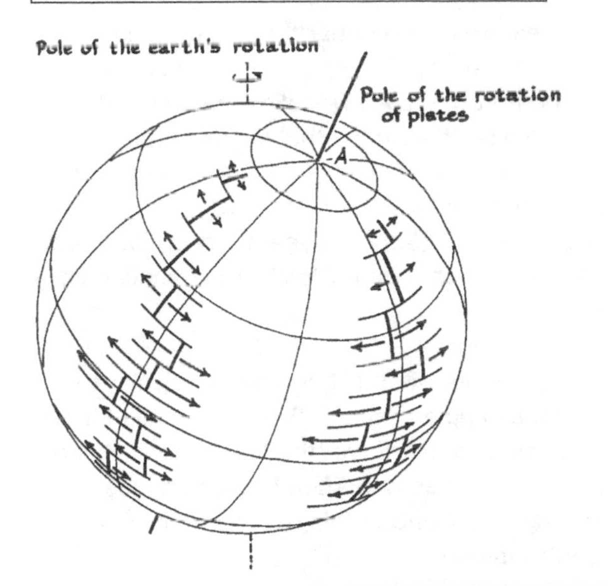

Fig. 2.23 Plate motion on the surface of the Earth can be described as a rotation about an axis. Transform faults become the equivalent of "lines of latitude" with reference to that pole of plate rotation.

Follow-Up

Explanations and diagrams can provide initial insight into how and why transform faults form, but the best way to really understand them is to actually make them! The following web site provides an easy-to-do experiment that is based on the models used by the discoverer of transform faults, J. Tuzo Wilson. http://web.mala.bc.ca/earle/transform-model/

■2.12 Mantle Plumes and Hot Spots

Fig. 2.25 Iceland sits astride the Mid-Atlantic Ridge. The large amount of volcanic activity on this island, as illustrated by the eruption of Eyjaffjallajokull in the spring of 2010, has led some geologists to propose that it is the site of a deep-mantle plume that may be driving sea-floor spreading in this region.

As we have seen, upwelling material from the mantle is found along oceanic ridges, giving rise to divergent plate boundaries. Many researchers think that the driving force behind such upwelling is actually a localized plume or hotspot that arises from deep within the Earth, perhaps at the core-mantle boundary. Along the Mid-Atlantic Ridge, it is believed that one such plume comes up beneath Iceland (Fig. 2.25) giving rise to the enormous amount of volcanic activity in and around this island. However, not all mantle plumes are associated with sea-floor spreading: in some locations on the planet there is extensive volcanic activity that is not associated with any known plate boundary. Two prime examples of this intraplate volcanism are the Yellowstone National Park – Snake River plain in the northwestern United States, and the Hawaiian Islands in the Pacific Ocean. In these cases the lithospheric plate, whether it be continental or oceanic, is moving over a stationary "hot spot" of material that may arise from the core-mantle boundary (Fig. 2.26). This hot jet spawns volcanic activity at the place where it encounters the lithosphere. As the lithospheric plate moves over the hot spot, the volcanic activity eventually ceases at the initial point, but will re-develop at a new place on the plate that now overlies the hot spot. You can think of the process as a conveyor belt (the lithospheric plate) moving over a candle flame (the hot spot) and burn marks will appear on the belt before it moves off of the candle flame. Hawaii, in the middle of the Pacific Ocean, provides the best illustration of how this works (Fig. 2.27). Much of the volcanic activity today occurs on the "big island" of Hawaii, where the active volcanoes of Mauna Loa and Kilauea are located near the southern end of the island. Although volcanoes make up the other islands in the chain, these are all dormant and radiometric dating of the rocks shows that they get progressively older towards the northwest. As we follow the trend of these islands to the northwest, they eventually disappear below sea level but they nevertheless remain as a distinct seamount chain. The Emperor Seamount chain is an extension of the Hawaiian Islands that continues in a more northerly direction. The seamount where the "kink" occurs has been dated radiometrically at 43 million years, and the seamount just south of the Aleutian trench has an age of about 80 million years. Accordingly, the "bend" in the Emperor Seamount Chain-Hawaiian Ridge apparently shows a change in Pacific Plate motion from nearly northward to west northwestward about 43 million years ago.

Seamount chains are present in many places throughout the seafloor, and are often aligned perpendicular to oceanic ridges. The Kelvin Seamount chain in the Atlantic Ocean is an example (Fig. 2.28). Although all of these are old and dormant, they were formed in the past when their position placed them over the Mid-Atlantic Ridge. These patterns have given rise to the idea that plumes are found in some places underneath ocean ridges, and they may constitute the ultimate driving force behind mantle convection. None of this is certain, of course, because of the difficulties in studying processes deep within the Earth's interior.

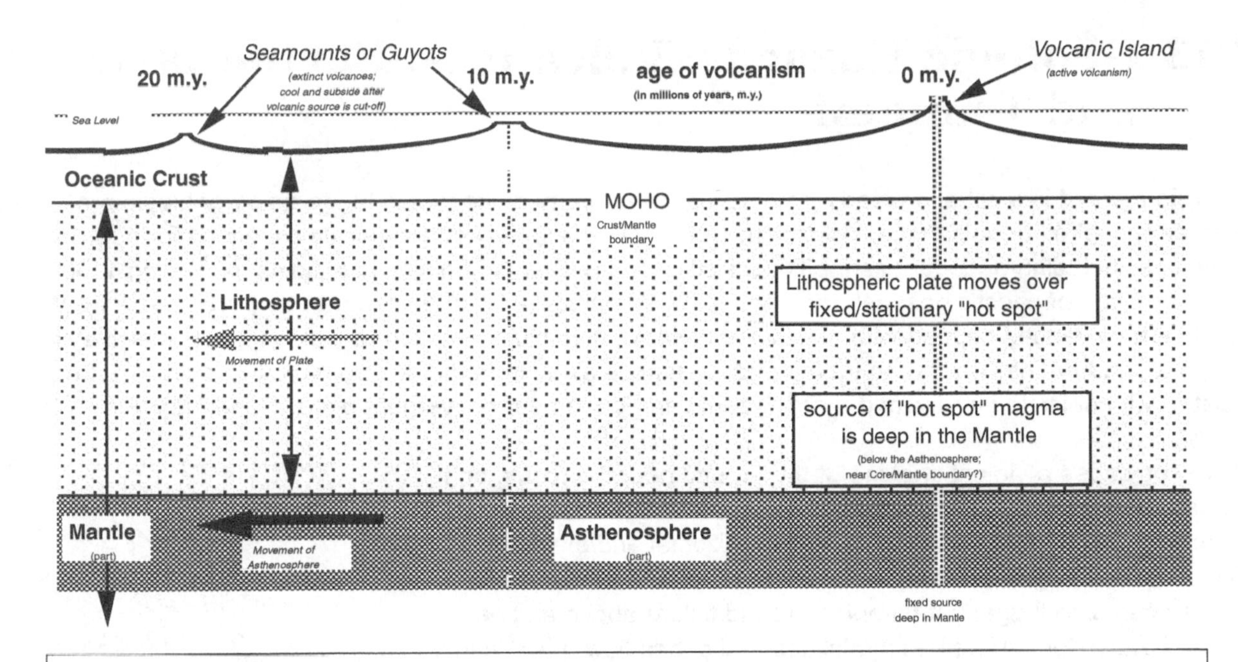

Fig. 2.26 Volcanic Island chains are produced as oceanic crust moves across a fixed "hot spot" or plume of hot material from deep in the mantle. For an animated version of this process, go to http://www.wiley.com/college/strahler/0471480533/animations/ch14_animations/hot_spot.html

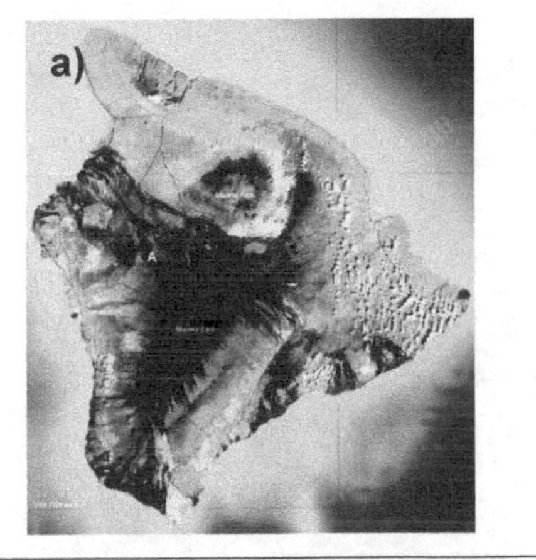

b)

Aleutian Trench

Emperor Seamount Chain

Hawaii

Fig. 2.27 a) The big island of Hawaii contains the active volcanoes of Mauna Loa, Mauna Kea, and Kilauea. b) The Hawaiian Islands are the end of a long chain of seamounts that stretches well into the North Pacific Ocean.

Investigation 2.10 provides a further opportunity to see how hot-spot tracks can provide detailed information about the history of plate motion.

Fig. 2.28 The Kelvin Seamount Chain marks the trace of a hotspot presently located at the Mid-Atlantic Ridge.

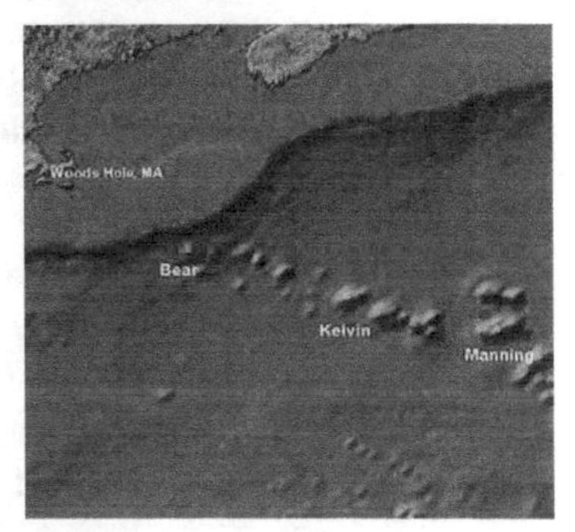

■2.13 Geologic Hazards: Volcanoes, Earthquakes and Tsunami

A **geologic hazard** is a situation leading to the loss of property or life that is triggered by geologic processes, such as earthquakes or volcanoes. Volcanism can produce a variety of dangerous situations for near-by communities, including abundant ash falls consisting of tiny shards of glass, lava flows exceeding 1100°C, or glowing clouds of caustic gas, ash, and hot volcanic rock called a **nuée ardente or pyroclastic flow**. In areas of high volcanoes capped with glacial ice or snow, a volcanic eruption can also trigger massive slurries of ash, mud, and debris, which can travel great distances away from the source. Volcanic activity is frequently associated with seismic activity, and most hazards are found near convergent plate boundaries (Fig. 2.29).

> *Subduction of oceanic crust during plate collision can cause sudden vertical movements of the sea floor. Refer to section 2.9.*

Earthquakes cause a violent shaking of the ground near the focus, and cause saturated soils to lose their cohesive properties in a process called **liquefaction**. Earthquakes can cause rapid horizontal and/or vertical displacement of the ground along preexisting faults and fractures in the rock. They can also trigger catastrophic ground failure above and below sea level. Landslides (as well as mudslides and debris flows) also can be triggered by heavy rainfall events, which rapidly saturate the soil and cause the loss of physical strength against the force of gravity. Communities in tropical regions with high volcanic terrain are particularly vulnerable to both earthquake-induced landslides and heavy rainfall events because the deeply weathered volcanic soils and steep slopes can yield fast-moving and devastating mudslides.

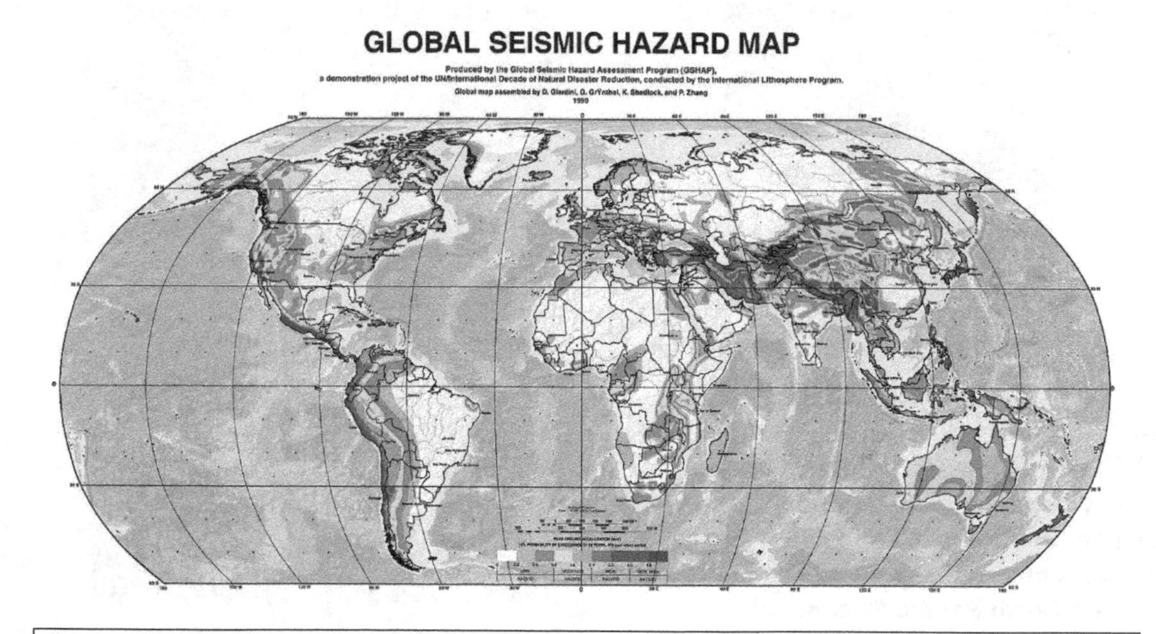

Fig. 2.29 Geological hazards are closely associated with convergent plate boundaries and active continental margins (darker shading represents greater hazards).

Tsunami represent a serious threat to some coastal communities. They have sometimes erroneously been called "tidal waves", but they have nothing to do with tides. These large waves are frequently generated by very strong earthquakes associated with the subduction of oceanic crust (Fig. 2.30). Therefore, communities on Pacific islands and around the rim of the Pacific are particularly at risk, although the disastrous tsunami of December 26, 2004 affected wide areas of the Indian Ocean (see Oceanography in Action). Tsunami may also be generated by undersea landslides along over-steepened slopes of the continental margin. For this reason, the rim of the Atlantic is also vulnerable to these rare events.

Large waves are created as the tsunami moves across the continental shelf. Waves as large as 30 m (98 ft.) are known, but the size depends on the magnitude of the earthquake and configuration of the coastline. Tsunamis are very long wavelength (L) waves (typically L>200 km or L>124 mi) and therefore behave as shallow water waves. In the open ocean, these long, low waves travel nearly as fast as a commercial jetliner (~760 km/hr, ~480 mi/hr), where they pass without notice against the background of wind waves and swell. As they encounter the shallower waters of the continental shelf, the waves slow down significantly and grow in height. Part of the danger with tsunamis comes from the withdrawal of water near the coast, exposing the seafloor and attracting curious on-lookers. The water is drawn into the growing wave that is minutes away from rushing up and over the coast. After the first huge wave, people may think that the danger has passed, only to be followed 5-20 minutes later by a succession of tsunami waves. The **International Tsunami Warning System** monitors earthquake activity around the world and issues warnings about potentially dangerous tsunamis.

The specifics of how ocean waves move are discussed in section 5.1.

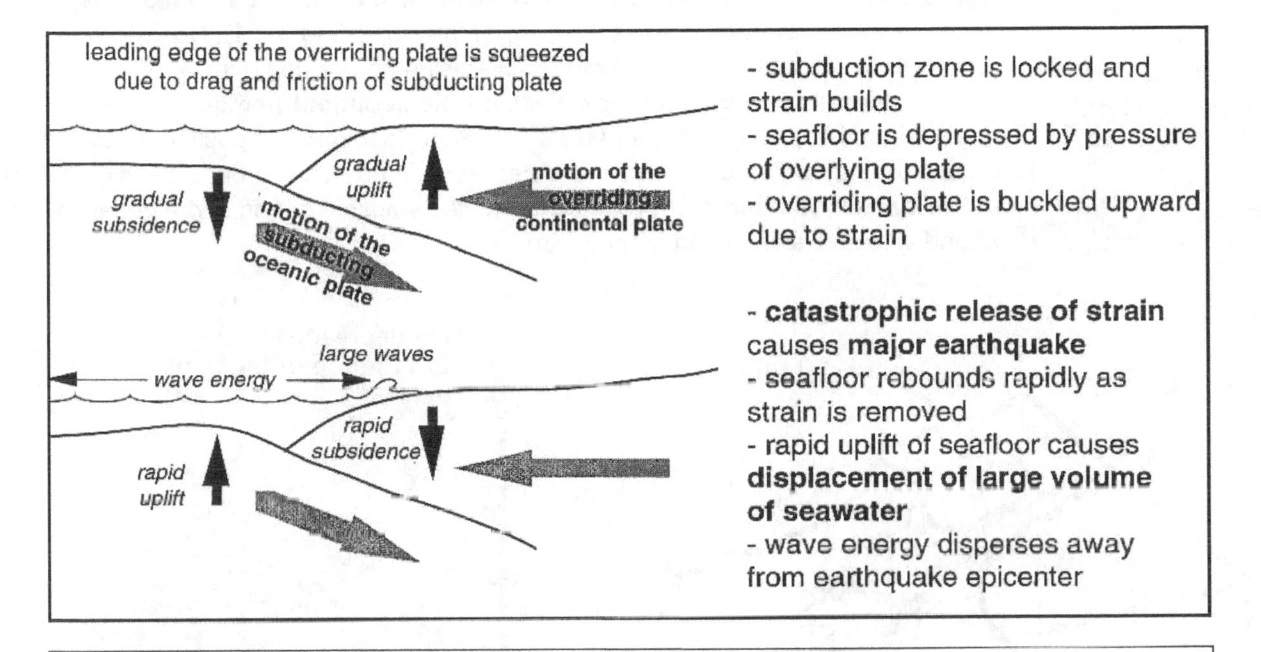

Fig. 2.30 How tsunami are produced by movement of the ocean crust in the vicinity of subduction zones.

Food for Thought

Many areas of the Earth, even those removed from the coast or active continental margin, have some potential for geologic hazards. Do a little exploration of your home town or campus and identify some possibilities that could threaten these locations. For more information about the variety of hazards, take a look at
http://nationalatlas.gov/articles/geology/a_geohazards.html
http://www.usgs.gov/hazards/floods/

■2.14 Types of Marine Sediments

Our analysis of the geology of the ocean up to this point has been concerned with the ocean crust, the basalt that comprises the bulk of the sea floor. However, while the geologic processes of plate tectonics are creating and destroying ocean crust, additional materials, or sediments, are accumulating on top of the crustal rocks. These sediments have a variety of sources and composition. Their distribution in the world ocean is related to a number of factors including proximity to source, transport processes (such as gravity, deep and shallow ocean currents, and wind), and ocean chemistry. Mixtures of sediment types are common.

Terrigenous sediment is composed of sand, silt, or clay-sized particles derived from the physical and chemical weathering of rocks and soil on land. These sediments form an apron of debris around the continents, consisting mostly of sand and mud. Terrigenous sediments accumulate on the continental shelves, slopes, and rises and they can commonly be transported to deeper parts of the seafloor by **turbidity currents**. Such currents are sediment-rich gravity flows initiated by an undersea landslide or earthquake that cause the sediments accumulated on the continental margin to be rapidly transported downslope where they then spread out over the abyssal plain. These accumulations are often marked by large **deep-sea fans**, which constitute the continental rises at the base of the slope (Fig. 2.31). Specific varieties of terrigenous sediment include **red clay** (wind-blown and/or deep current-transported silt and clay deposited on the abyssal plains), **neritic sediment** (terrigenous sediment found on continental shelves), **glacial marine sediment** (sediment deposited by glacial ice or transported out to sea by icebergs and deposited in an apron around the high latitudes), and **volcaniclastic sediment** (eroded or ejected volcanic debris and ash deposited around volcanic islands and seamounts).

See the discussion of the bathymetric features of the sea floor in section 2.6.

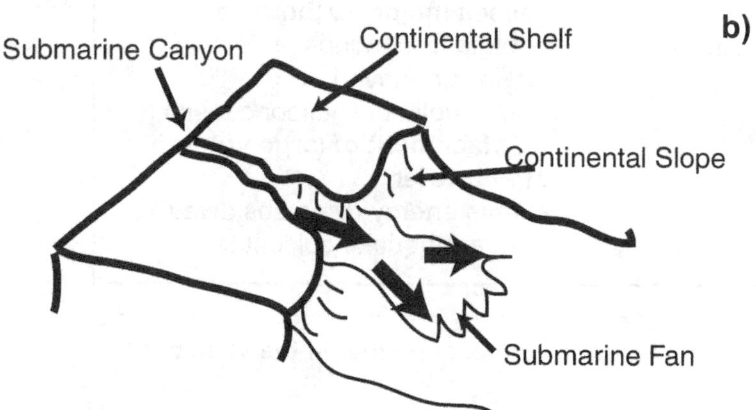

b)

Grains decrease in size toward the top of the deposit

Fig. 2.31 a) Sediment-laden turbidity currents flow down submarine canyons and deposit terrigenous sediments in submarine fans. b) Turbidity current deposits are recognized by coarse material at the base with gradually finer grain sizes deposited above it as the current velocity decreases.

More about the microscopic organisms that form biogenic sediment can be found in section 5.4.

Biogenic sediment is composed of the microscopic shells of marine **plankton**, typically single-celled protists, such as the calcareous coccolithophorids and foraminifera, and siliceous diatoms and radiolarians. Plankton with mineralized shells are particularly important contributors to deep-sea sediments. Plankton with shells of calcium carbonate ($CaCO_3$) produce a type of sediment called **calcareous ooze**, and plankton with shells of **opaline silica** ($SiO_2.H_2O$) produce **siliceous ooze** (Fig 2.32). Plankton are grazed and preyed upon by many types of small and large animals. As a result, their microscopic shells are packaged into **fecal pellets**. Fecal pellets are an important mode of transport of the tiny shells from the surface waters where the plankton live to the seafloor where their empty shells accumulate as sediment. Passive settling through the water column is another mode of deposition. The **Carbonate Compensation Depth** (**CCD**) represents a chemical boundary in the deep ocean (~4000-5000 m water depth). Calcareous ooze does not accumulate on the seafloor at depths greater than the CCD because of intense chemical dissolution caused by low temperature, high pressure, and relatively high concentration of dissolved CO_2.

Authigenic sediment precipitates directly from seawater, and it is most common in areas below the CCD, or in areas of very slow pelagic or terrigenous accumulation rates, or beneath areas of high biological productivity. Manganese nodules are an example of authigenic sediments. These metal-rich accumulations are found in deep areas of the abyssal plain in the Pacific and Indian Oceans. The actual mechanism of their formation is still something of a mystery, but it is believed that the dissolved metals in sea water gradually add to these nodules, causing them to grow over time.

Pelagic sediment refers to those sedimentary particles which settle through the water column, such as shells of plankton and wind-blown silt and clay (biogenic ooze and red clay are pelagic sediments). **Hemipelagic sediment** is typically a mix of terrigenous and pelagic sediments such as terrigenous mud + calcareous ooze, or red clay + siliceous ooze.

The rate at which sediments accumulate in the deep-sea varies considerably. For example, terrigenous sediment accumulates at rates (greater than) >5 cm/kyr (centimeters per thousand years) along many parts of the continental margin. Biogenic ooze typically accumulates at rates of 1-3 cm/kyr, although higher rates can occur in areas of very high biological productivity. Abyssal red clay accumulates at rates (much less than) <<1 cm/kyr, or about the rate at which dust accumulates in your home.

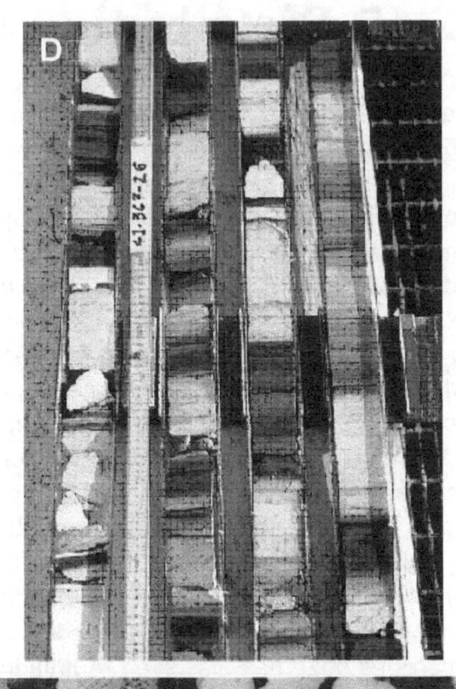

Fig 2.32 a) Sediment core from the deep ocean. Light layers are pelagic (biogenic) sediment; dark layers are hemipelagic (mixed pelagic and terrigenous). b) Photomicrograph of biogenic ooze; a mixture of calcareous and siliceous organisms.

Follow–Up

1). What kinds of materials might you expect to find on the bottom of the sea floor? Do you think that there would be a pattern in their distribution? What could cause this pattern?

2). List the major types of sediments found in the ocean, and give at least one example of each.

3). What kinds of information might be preserved in ocean sediments?

■2.15 Distribution of Marine Sediments

The different types of marine sediments form distinctive patterns on the sea floor (Fig. 2.33). Terrigenous deposits are found closest to the continental margins, owing to the huge amount of debris that is eroded from the land areas of the Earth and carried to the sea by rivers. Pelagic deposits are characteristic of the deep sea, but even here not all types occur equally in all ocean basins. The dominance of biogenic ooze depends on two primary factors: 1) the abundance of the organism that produces the shell in the overlying sea water column, and 2) the ability of the shell to survive the environment of the sea floor. Siliceous pelagic organisms, such as the diatoms, are found in great abundance in polar regions owing to the abundant nutrients that are brought to the surface by upwelling waters. Consequently, the shells of these organisms are very abundant in the pelagic sediments near the Arctic and Antarctic regions. Calcareous pelagic organisms are found in great abundance throughout the surface ocean in temperate and tropical regions. However, the shells of these creatures do not occur in the sediments of the North Pacific Ocean, in spite of their dominance in the overlying water column. In this case, the calcareous shells dissolve before they reach the bottom because the great depths of the northern Pacific Ocean put it below the carbonate compensation depth (CCD). As the calcareous shells settle through the water column, they encounter water that is very cold, enriched in dissolved carbon dioxide (CO_2) and more acidic. The combination of these factors is what makes calcium carbonate unstable in the deep ocean. Consequently this region is dominated by red clay, which we can envision as the "residue" remaining once the calcareous ooze has dissolved. Authigenic deposits are generally more localized. Precipitates of metals are found around deep-sea hydrothermal vents, where hot sea water containing solids dissolved from the ocean crust mixes with normal cold ocean water. Manganese nodules are found largely on the deep abyssal plains of the ocean where the rate of pelagic sedimentation is quite low. The different kinds and distribution of marine sediments is summarized in Fig. 2.34.

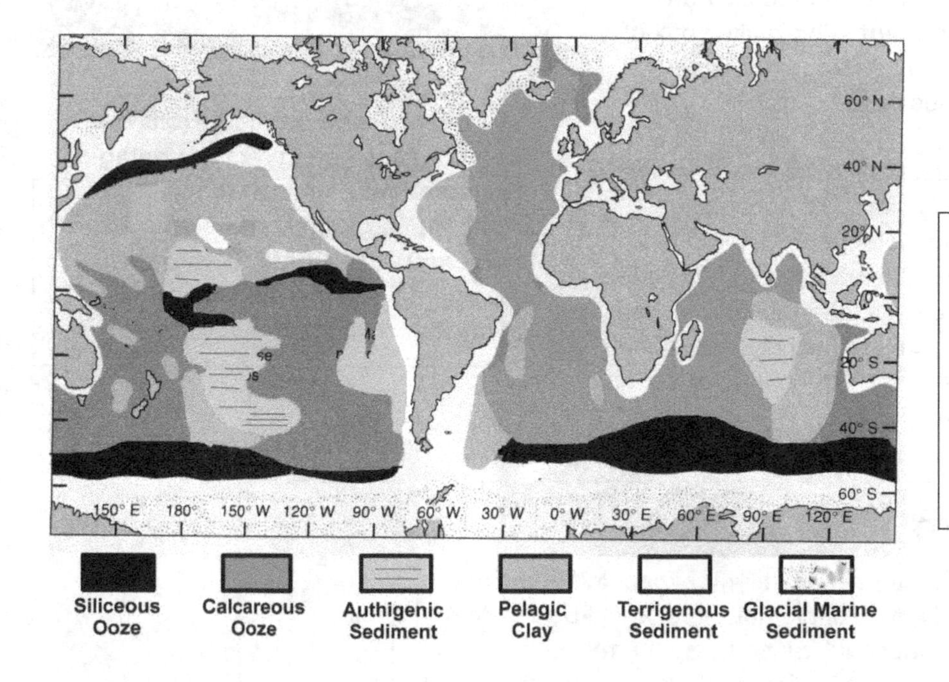

Fig. 2.33 Distribution of different types of sediments on the ocean floor. Terrigenous sediments include neritic deposits. Calcareous and siliceous oozes are subdivided by the dominant shell type found in the sediments.

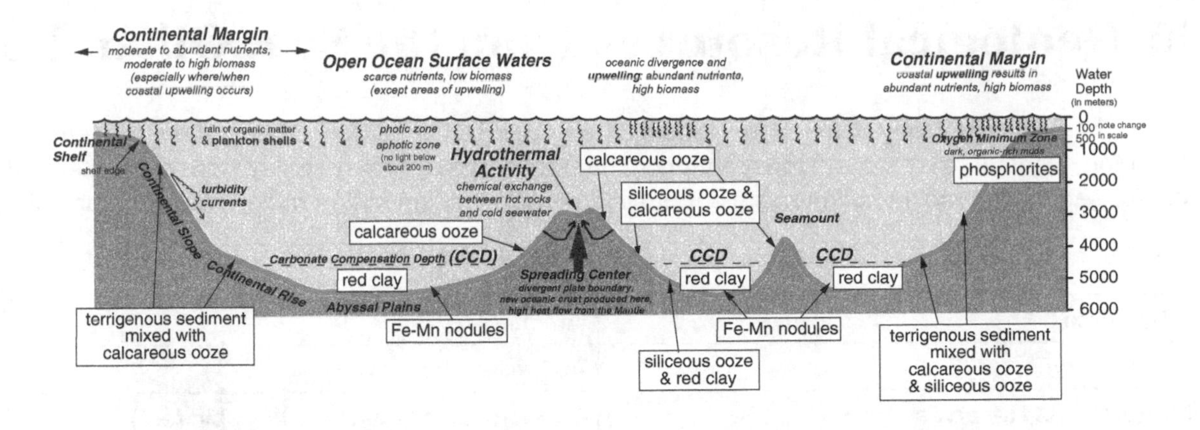

The following represent the major sediment types found on the floor of the deep-sea *(mixtures of sediment types are common)*:

Terrigenous Sediment

- derived from **weathering of rocks** on land
- sand and mud are moved across **continental shelves** by large storms and gravity
- much sediment is funneled into **submarine canyons** at the edge of the continental shelf
- gravity transports sediment down the **continental slopes** via slumps and **turbidity currents**
- terrigenous sediment builds-up as **deep-sea fans** at the base of the continental slope
- the depositional feature at the base of the slope is called the **continental rise**

Terrigenous sediment *accumulates along the continental margins; terrigenous sediment typically masks other sediment types close to the continents because of high sedimentation rates.*

Red Clay

- red or brown clay is derived from **wind-blown dust** which slowly settles to the seafloor, or it is derived from deep **current-transported clays**
- red clay **accumulates at very slow rates** and is diluted by other types of sediment in many areas of the deep-sea

Red clay *accumulates on the abyssal plains, deeper than 4500 meters (below the CCD).*

Biogenic Sediment

1. Calcareous Ooze

- composed of **carbonate** ($CaCO_3$) **shells of plankton**
- dead plankton settle through the water column, or consumed plankton are incorporated into **fecal pellets** which settle to the seafloor
- calcium carbonate dissolves at about 4500 m water depth due to cold temperature, high pressure, and greater CO_2 content of deep waters = **carbonate compensation depth (CCD)**

Calcareous ooze *accumulates on bathymetric highs beyond continental margins, shallower than 4500 meters (above the CCD), such as the spreading centers and flanks of volcanoes that stick up above the abyssal plains.*

2. Siliceous Ooze

- composed of **siliceous** (SiO_2) **shells of plankton**
- **areas of upwelling** provide the nutrients and silica necessary to sustain a large biomass of siliceous plankton

Siliceous ooze *accumulates beneath areas of high biological productivity in the surface ocean, such as the equatorial Pacific and around Antarctica*

Authigenic Sediment

- **ferromanganese nodules** form on the abyssal plains by the slow chemical precipitation of metal oxides directly from seawater (facilitated by biochemical activity of bacteria and other microorganisms, and by the burrowing activity of larger organisms)
- **hydrothermal activity** at the spreading centers is a major source of dissolved metal oxides
- **phosphorite nodules** form on the outer shelf and upper slope where unoxidized organic matter in the **oxygen minimum zone** is biochemically transformed into phosphorite
- some authigenic deposits are **economically valuable**

Authigenic sediment *precipitates directly from seawater under specific (bio)chemical conditions related to source, oxidation-reduction, and/or sedimentation rate.*

Fig. 2.34 Summary of marine sediments and their distribution.

Investigation 2.11 provides additional insight into the worldwide distribution of ocean sediments.

■2.16 Geological Resources from the Sea: Oil and Gas

The ocean is the source of many of the ingredients that are essential for the functioning of our modern civilization. Many coastal nations are dependent upon the ocean as a food source .but both sea water and the sediments (or sedimentary rocks) on the seafloor provide a significant amount of mineral wealth (Table 2.1).

Table 2.1 Estimates of available mineral resources in the ocean.

Resource	Amount
Oil Reserves	400 million barrels
Natural Gas Reserves	2 trillion cubic feet (2 x 10^{12} cubic feet)
Gas hydrates (clathrates)	4 x 10^{20} cubic feet*
Sand and Gravel	800 billion metric tons
Phosphorites	50 billion metric tons
Manganese Nodules	16 billion metric tons

Sources: U.S. Geological Survey and Energy Information Agency.

Oil and natural gas are among the most significant of these resources. Although about one-third of present-day petroleum production is derived from offshore platforms, more than 90% of oil and natural gas has formed in marine environments throughout geological time. Most of the natural gas and petroleum that we use today results from the thermal break-down ("maturation") of organic matter of terrestrial and marine origin. In order to generate and trap mature oil and gas, the right geological conditions are necessary. Three components are required: an organic-rich **source rock**, a porous or fractured rock formation that serves as a **reservoir** for the hydrocarbons, and a **cap rock** that seals the gaseous or low density hydrocarbons in the geological formation and prevents them from escaping to the surface (Fig. 2.35). Although no one knows for sure, it is believed that only a very small percentage of crude oil generated in the source rock is trapped successfully in a reservoir.

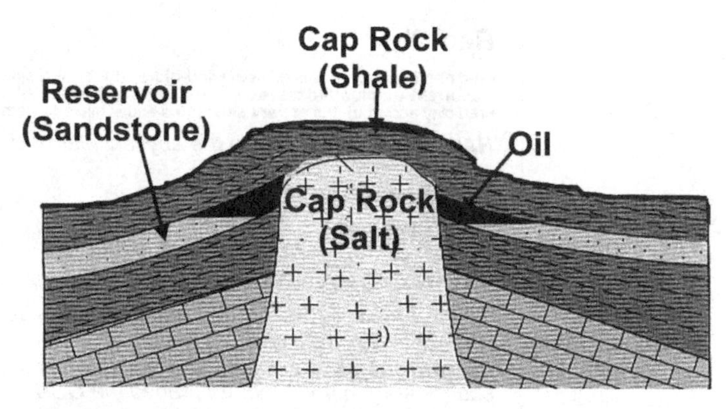

Fig. 2.35 Geometry of a typical subsurface oil reservoir.

You can find out more about the rich biology of coastal areas in section 5.8, and the processes of deep-water sedimentation are outlined in section 2.14.

Marine environments are ideal geological settings for the accumulation of hydrocarbons because continental margins are rich in biological productivity by various types of plankton, particularly photosynthetic protists and cyanobacteria. In addition, terrestrial organic matter is carried to the sea by rivers where it is deposited in estuaries and deltas, or carried out across the continental shelf by storms and redeposited into deeper water by turbidity currents. It is this accumulation of organic-rich sediments on the seafloor of continental margins that provides the raw material for hydrocarbon formation. Fluctuations in global sea level through geologic time have created the alternation of sandy coastal and inner shelf environments, as well as deep-sea fans (future reservoir rocks) during times of falling sea level, and offshore muddy environments (both a potential source rock and cap for underlying rock formations) during times of rising sea level. Burial of these sedimentary layers by additional layers over time can lead to hydrocarbon generation and subsequent migration of oil and gas into potential reservoir rocks (Fig. 2.35). The combination of pressure and heat at depth causes the organic matter to break down into simpler hydrocarbon compounds that are fluids (liquids or gases) at the temperatures of the Earth's surface. Most petroleum geologists agree that temperatures between 60°C and 150°C (140°F to 300°F) are needed for these processes to happen. The results are molecules in a range of sizes that constitute crude oil, with some smaller molecules of propane, ethane, and methane that are part of natural gas. This slow cooking process generally takes millions of years to complete.

The increasing demand for hydrocarbons has forced exploration into deeper and deeper water of the continental margins (Fig. 2.36). Geophysical techniques, including seismic surveys, are used to image deep below the seafloor and reveal the structure of the sedimentary layers that may trap and seal hydrocarbons. A **seismic survey** is done by a ship towing streamers of instruments consisting of seismic sources (typically air guns, which generate sound waves with bubbles of compressed air) and hydrophones to detect the energy that is reflected off the seafloor and underlying layers of sediments and sedimentary rocks. The ship sweeps back and forth across an area of interest in order to "map" the underlying three-dimensional structure. Three-dimensional visualization, based on extensive seismic data collection and high-end computing and graphics software development, is rapidly replacing 2-D seismic reflection data in high risk and expensive offshore exploration plays. Horizontal (or "directional") drilling and many wellheads allow multiple pockets of oil to be tapped from a single offshore drilling platform. Offshore drilling platforms may be free-standing with legs of concrete and steel, or semi-submersible with hollow steel legs that can be extended and filled with seawater for stability and then tethered to the seafloor during drilling and production operations.

Fig. 2.36 An offshore oil platform in the North Sea.

Methane hydrates (also called gas hydrates) are an abundant but still untapped hydrocarbon resource of many continental margins of the world. They are accumulations of methane at relatively shallow burial depths of the lower continental slope and upper continental rise (~1000-2000 m water depth). **Natural gas** is produced by **anaerobic bacteria** living below the sediment-water interface where an abundance of organic matter and lack of oxygen promotes the activity of this type of microbe. The bacteria use organic matter as a food source but produce **methane (CH_4)**, one of the principal components of natural gas, rather than CO_2 as a by-product of their metabolism. Due to the low temperatures and high pressures, the methane becomes trapped in "cages" of frozen water molecules. These ice cages are only stable at the temperatures and pressures of the lower slope and upper rise. The potential economic value of these deposits is still being explored.

Food for Thought

1. Worldwide petroleum reserves are estimated to be about 1,200 billion barrels (1,200 x 10^9). Current worldwide oil production is 84 million barrels/day (84 x 10^6). How long will the supply of oil last at current production rates?
2. What sorts of things could happen that might change the number you calculated for question 1?
3. More exploration and discovery are occurring in very deep water of the continental margins. Would you expect a large amount of oil to be found in the ocean basins themselves? Explain your reasoning!

■2.17 Other Resources from the Sea Floor

Oil and natural gas are not the only valuable materials that are obtained from the ocean floor (Fig. 2.37). **Sand** is a very valuable resource for coastal states. Sand, in the form of barrier islands and spits, dunes, beaches, and offshore sand bars, provides protection from the wrath of the ocean's fury by absorbing and dispersing wave energy associated with large storms, as well as providing a frontline defense against coastal flooding. Sand is supplied to the coast by rivers and erosion of sea cliffs. It is then redistributed along the coast by longshore currents set-up by in-coming ocean swell. However, large storms remove large volumes of sand from the coast, and once that sand reaches water depths exceeding 10 m (~31 ft.), then the sand is lost from the beach and longshore transport system. Sand accumulates on the continental shelf where it can be mined by dredging the seafloor and pumping the sand to a surface barge or directly back to the beach. The process of restoring sand to the beach and longshore transport system is referred to as **beach nourishment.** Both sand and gravel are also valuable as aggregate in the production of cement and asphalt. Geologists and biologists team-up to conduct surveys in state (within 3 miles of the coast) and federal waters (beyond 3 miles) to map the distribution, volume, and quality (e.g., grain size) of potential sand resources on the shelf, and to evaluate the biotic impact that dredging or pumping operations might have on the area. Seismic surveys, a scaled-down version of those used to explore for deeply buried oil and gas, and side-scan sonar are used to generate profiles of the uppermost layers of sediment on the seafloor and map seafloor features. Cores taken in the sediments are then used to ground-truth the seismic profiles and to evaluate the quality of the sand.

The origin of beaches and the natural processes of sand movement are discussed in sections 6.2 and 6.4.

Phosphorite is used to make fertilizers because of their high phosphorous content. It accumulates in the form of nodules, as well as fish bone and teeth concentrated at the seafloor along continental margins characterized by high biological productivity. Although not a major source yet, offshore deposits may prove to be more economically viable as land-based deposits are depleted.

Shell material (calcium carbonate), such as oyster shells, is dredged in some southern states to be used as aggregate for construction materials, and as a source of lime (CaO) to make cement. In tropical regions where deposits of reefs formed during times of higher sea level, reef rock can be mined as building materials and as a source of lime to make cement; in some places, reef rock is mined from offshore. This practice would make the coastline more susceptible to erosion from storms that move in from the ocean such as hurricanes and typhoons.

Other potential mineral resources of the continental shelf are **placer deposits** of gems (e.g., diamonds, rutile, ilmenite, zircon) or metals (e.g., gold, tin, titanium, platinum, chromium, iron). These types of deposits are concentrated by physical processes such as waves or currents on the shelf, or in river beds during times of lower sea level when vast areas of the continental shelves are exposed.

Manganese nodules are metalliferous nodules (up to fist-sized) that are rich in oxides of iron, manganese, and other elements. They accumulate across vast areas of the abyssal plains where sedimentation rates are very slow. The precipitation of metals may be facilitated by bacterial activity. The source of the metals is from hydrothermal vents where active volcanism interacts with cold seawater as observed along the spreading centers where new oceanic crust is produced.

Review the hydrothermal processes at oceanic ridges in section 2.9.

The mining of offshore mineral resources has great economic potential, but in many cases, exploration, evaluation, production, and transportation costs, as well as environmental concerns, may make such ventures prohibitive relative to current onshore mining activities. The economic model is likely to change in the future as land-based resources are consumed.

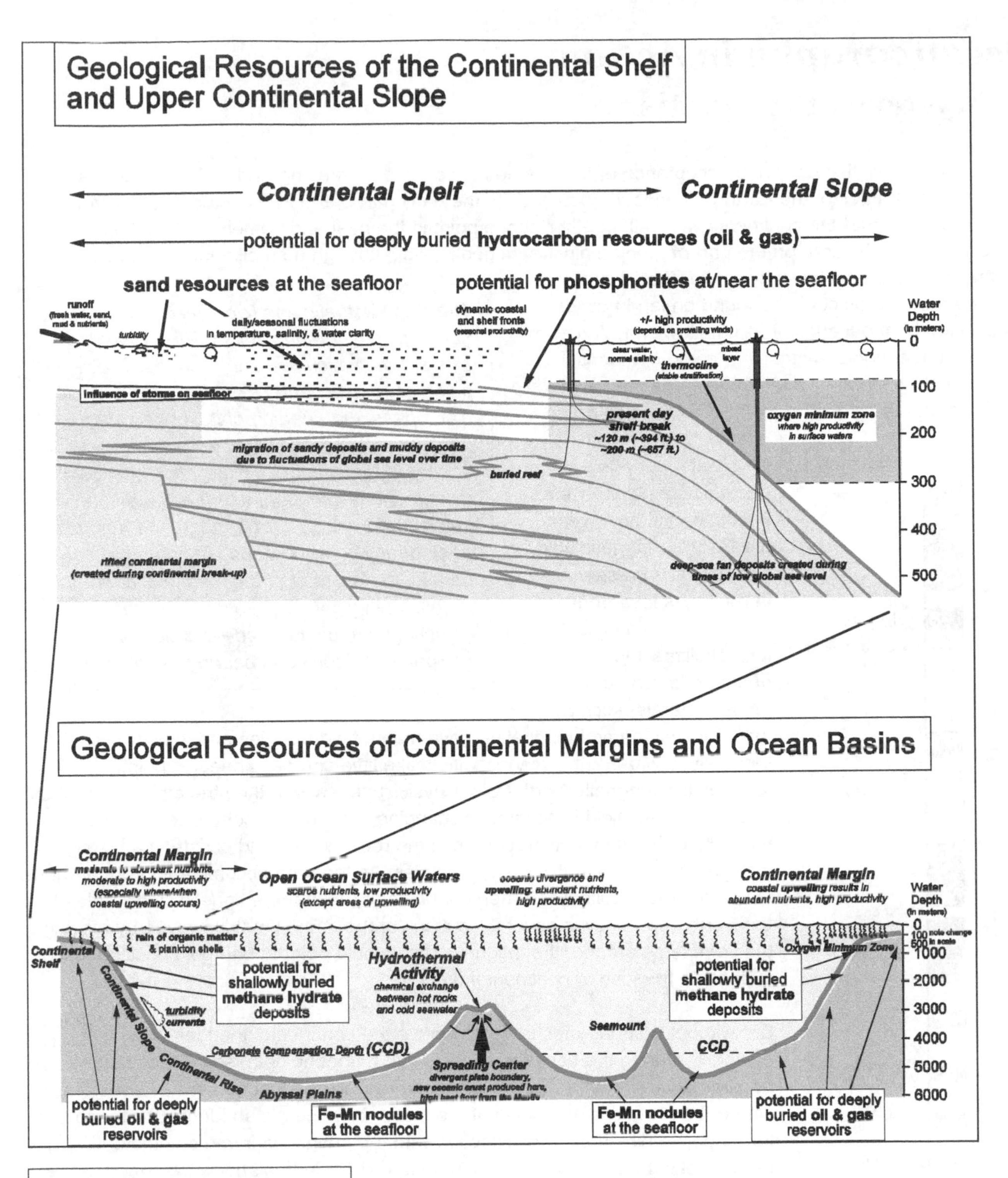

Fig 2.37 The distribution of geological resources in the deep ocean and continental margins.

Follow-Up

Scenario: You are a member of an international committee reviewing commercial applications for seabed mining. One company wants to extract manganese nodules from the sea floor. What questions will you want to ask as you consider this application?

■*Oceanography in Action*

The Mystery of Magnetism

The story behind the discovery and acceptance of the theories of sea-floor spreading and plate tectonics is one of the great dramas of the Earth Sciences. It goes back to the early part of the 20th century when Alfred Wegener proposed that the continents were all together at one point in the past and somehow drifted apart. The idea was greeted with scorn on the part of many mainstream geologists, although a small minority realized that continental drift could explain why similar fossils and rock types of the same ages could be found on landmasses now separated by thousands of miles. However, Wegener, who was a meteorologist by training, could not identify a realistic mechanism that would move huge pieces of the Earth around the globe. In the 1950's, a small group of scientists – mostly physicists, but a few geologists as well—were becoming intrigued with the Earth's magnetic field and how it is preserved in rocks. As lava from volcanic eruptions cools, it crystallizes into a variety of minerals. Some of these minerals, such as the obviously-named magnetite, have magnetic properties and they will align themselves with Earth's magnetic field like little compass needles pointing towards the magnetic North Pole. Physicists knew that the strength and direction of the magnetic field is constantly changing, and they hypothesized that by measuring the magnetic properties in the rocks they could construct a history of the position of the Earth's magnetic poles. As the data accumulated from around the world, the results were often contradictory, with the magnetic North Pole of the Earth apparently in several locations at the same time! However, by moving the continents around, the magnetic data would point to one pole position, giving support to the idea of continental drift.

The Earth actually has two sets of poles. The geographic North and South Poles mark the axis around which the Earth rotates. These poles are permanent. However, when we use a compass, the needle points to magnetic north, which is not in exactly the same location as the geographic pole. Navigation charts will provide the declination, which is the difference between geographic (true) north and magnetic north at any given location. To complicate natters, the position of the magnetic north pole is constantly changing, so that declination adjustments must be made in order for navigation by compass bearing to be accurate.

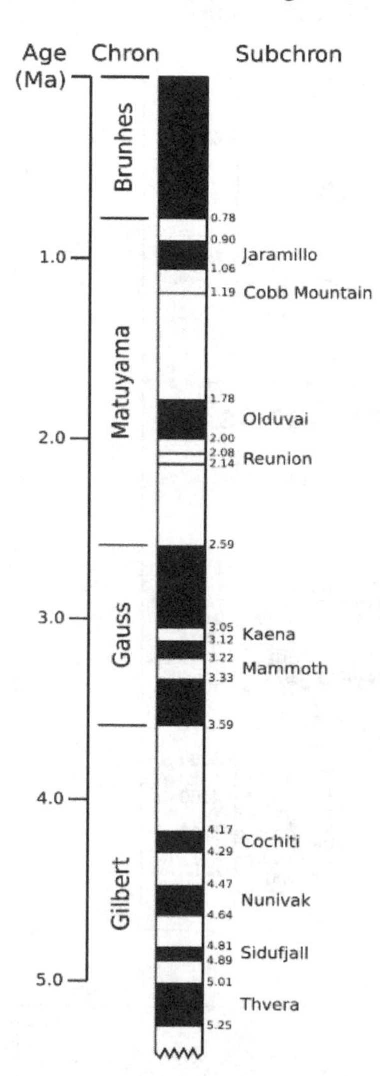

A portion of the geomagnetic time scale. Black areas represent time of "normal" polarity; white areas represent periods of magnetic reversals.

But without a strong mechanism to move the continents, the idea was going nowhere. During the decades of compiling magnetic data, some researchers became aware that the Earth's magnetic field underwent numerous reversals, where the north-seeking poles of the magnetic minerals suddenly pointed in the opposite direction. In conjunction with the advances in radiometric dating of the rocks, these episodes of normal and reversed polarity were added to the geological time scale and became important tie points for correlating rock units around the globe. For example, the last 780,000 years of Earth history has been dominated by "normal" polarity, where North-seeking magnetic minerals point geographic north, although there are eight well-dated short intervals where the North-seeking poles point geographic south. In contrast, the time interval from 2.59 million years ago to 780,000 years ago is dominated by a magnetic field that is reversed from the present-day orientation. How these reversals occur is still not known, and is the subject of much research by geophysicists. The connection to the ocean came when a number of ocean researchers began towing instruments behind their ships that kept track of the intensity of magnetic field in the ocean (magnetometers). When the results of various cruises were pieced together, remarkable patterns of magnetic anomalies on the ocean floor were revealed. These linear arrangements of normal and reversed magnetization of the underlying ocean-floor basalts were both exciting and extraordinarily puzzling. How could such "stripes" on the sea floor possibly be generated? It all began to come together in 1962 when Harry Hess of Princeton University proposed the idea of sea-floor spreading, where molten magma emerged from submarine volcanic areas in oceanic ridges and cooled to form new ocean crust. Although only dimly familiar with Hess' work, Fred Vine and Drummond Mathews of Cambridge University and, independently, Lawrence Morley of the Geological Survey of Canada, recognized that the stripes of magnetization were parallel to ocean ridges, and that these stripes were symmetrical on either side of the ridge. When the geomagnetic time scale was successfully correlated with the timing of normal and reversed polarity on either side of the ocean ridges, the sea-floor spreading hypothesis was confirmed. Molten magma rises from the mantle in the vicinity of the ridges, and as the lava cools into basalt, it acquires the direction of the magnetic field in existence at the time. Further volcanic activity splits the initial basalt, and the new magma cools with the magnetic minerals preserving the orientation of the more recent magnetic field. A reversal will then appear as parallel stripes on either side of the ridge with a similar age. The consistent pattern of increasing age of ocean-floor basalt with increasing distance away from the ridge coupled with the symmetrical pattern of magnetic anomalies that matched the known sequence of reversals from land-based studies was the ultimate proof of sea-floor spreading.

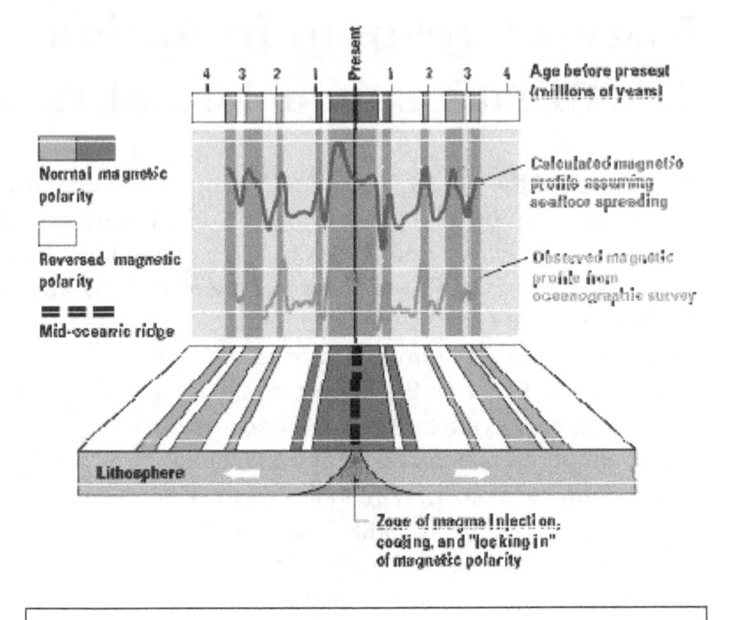

The symmetrical pattern of magnetic anomalies on either side of an oceanic ridge that matched with the geomagnetic time scale confirmed the process of sea-floor spreading.

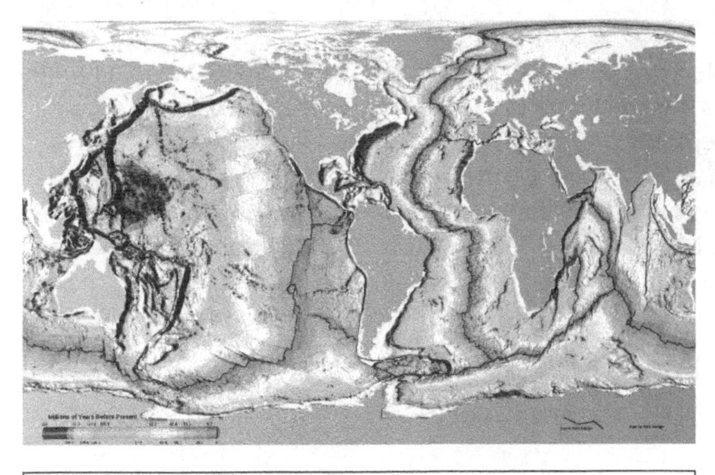

The age of the ocean floor as we now know it, reconstructed from magnetic patterns and radiometric dating of sea-floor basalt. Darkest areas near the continents are the oldest, and moderate grays along ridge axis are youngest. See full color image on inside back cover of the book where yellows and reds = youngest crust, blue = oldest.

Further Reading

Plate Tectonics: An Insider's History of the Modern Theory of the Earth, edited by Naomi Oreskes, Westview Press, 2003.

Essays by some who participated in the development of the ideas, including reflections on magnetism by Fred Vine and Lawrence Morley.

The Road to Jaramillo: Critical Years of the Revolution in Earth Science by William Glen, Stanford University Press, 1982.

A look at the scientific discoveries that led to the confirmation of sea-floor spreading and the sometimes colorful characters who made it happen.

■*Oceanography in Action*

The Great Earthquake and Tsunami of December 26, 2004

The power of the geological forces governing the ocean was revealed catastrophically and tragically in the Indian Ocean on the morning of December 26, 2004. It was a typically beautiful morning in a region that many regard as a paradise, where both locals and a growing tourist population enjoy plenty of sunshine, warm temperatures, and sandy beaches. It was close to 8AM local time when the ground began to shake, the beginning of a gigantic earthquake that lasted 9 minutes. This earthquake, later determined to have a magnitude of 9.0, was the largest on the Earth in over 40 years. The epicenter was off the coast of the island of Sumatra at latitude 3.3°N, longitude 6.0°E, right in the heart of a deep-sea trench, or subduction zone. The earthquake was caused by the release of a buildup of strain that had accumulated over many years by the slow-motion collision of the Indian and Burma plates at a rate of about 6 cm/year. On this morning, a piece of oceanic crust 1200 km long in the Sunda Trench (on the Burma Plate) was thrust upwards by as much as 15 meters. The energy release was incredible. This one earthquake released as much energy as all the other earthquakes that have occurred on the planet during the past 15 years. This is the energy equivalent to a 100 gigaton bomb, or about the same amount of energy consumed in the United States in six months!

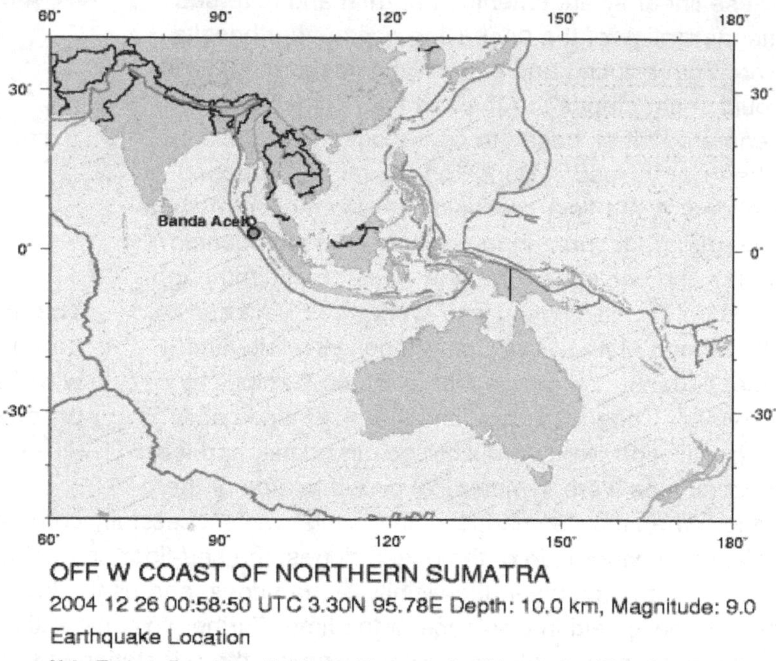

OFF W COAST OF NORTHERN SUMATRA

2004 12 26 00:58:50 UTC 3.30N 95.78E Depth: 10.0 km, Magnitude: 9.0

Earthquake Location

Major Tectonic Boundaries: Subduction Zones -purple, Ridges -red and Transform Faults -green

USGS National Earthquake Information Center

As powerful as this earthquake was, its effect on people living around the coastline of the Indian Ocean proved even more devastating. The motion of the seafloor was transmitted to the overlying water, producing a bulge in the ocean surface that traveled rapidly away from the epicenter. Thirty minutes after the earthquake, this wave appeared as massive tsunami, up to 30 meters high in some localities, smashing onto the shores of the island of Sumatra. This same wave tore apart the coastal regions of Sri Lanka and India some two hours later. About 3½ hours after the earthquake, the low-lying islands of the Maldives were inundated by the water and even the east coast of Africa felt the effects of the large waves after 7 hours had elapsed. In truth, both the earthquake and the tsunami affected the entire globe, since seismic instruments and tide gauges around the world recorded both the shaking and the sea-level fluctuations.

The tsunami breaks on the shores of Phuket in Thailand.

The human tragedy was immense. Current estimates place the death toll at nearly 300,000 making this event one of the worst in recorded history. In addition, as many as 1.5 million people were left homeless by the raging waters. If this event had occurred in the Pacific Ocean, where a tsunami warning system is in place, coastal nations around the "Ring of Fire" would have been alerted, and people in many localities would have had time to evacuate low-lying areas. However, no such network exists in the Indian Ocean, since the historical occurrence of tsunami in this region was negligible. Efforts are now underway to install a tsunami warning system here as well, since the frequent subduction-related earthquakes and explosive volcanic eruptions in the eastern Indian Ocean clearly have the potential to generate significant tsunami.

The devastation caused by the tsunami on the Indonesian island of Sumatra.

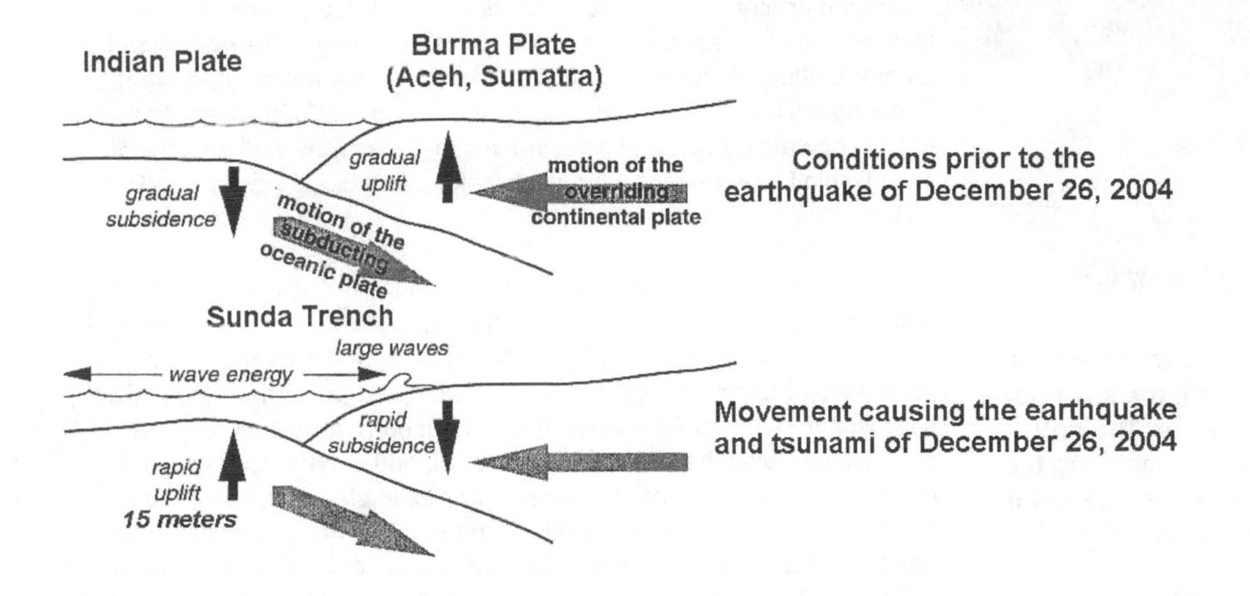

■*Oceanography in Action*

Exploration and Discovery through Scientific Ocean Drilling

Scientific ocean drilling is the longest running geoscience research program in history. Beginning in 1968, the Scripps Institution of Oceanography-based **Deep Sea Drilling Project** (DSDP) initiated the multi-decade mission to study the history of the ocean basins by using the drillship *Glomar Challenger* to core into the sedimentary layers on the seafloor and underlying crust. Very little was known about the geology and structure of the ocean floor prior to drilling in the ocean basins and marginal seas. In addition, it was argued that deep-sea sediments would be the best archives of past climate change. The *Glomar Challenger* used a series of powerful thrusters located around the hull of the ship to maintain position over a drill site, even in heavy seas or strong currents. The pinging of a sonic beacon dropped to the seafloor at the pre-determined site location was detected by hull-mounted hydrophones, which relayed information to the ship's **dynamic positioning** computer, which in turn activated the thrusters as needed to maintain position within 3% of water depth (e.g., to within 90 m in 3000 m of water). This technology also allowed select holes to be reentered and deepened with a fresh drill bit. Such sites were equipped with a specially designed **reentry cone** with sonar reflectors fixed around the widest part of the funnel-shaped device so it could be "found" again once the drill string was removed from the hole and a new drill bit attached.

This is the re-entry cone that is positioned on the sea floor at the drilling site. The drill string is guided back into the hole by radio transmitters on the re-entry cone.

From 1968 to 1983, DSDP conducted 96 'legs' (drilling expeditions) of 6- to 9-weeks duration and drilled at 624 sites in all the major ocean basins. It began as a U.S.-funded program before launching the International Phase of Ocean Drilling (IPOD) in 1975. DSDP was instrumental in testing the hypothesis of seafloor spreading and cementing the theory of plate tectonics as the major new paradigm of geology during the 1960s and 70s.

DSDP ended in 1983 and was succeeded by the **Ocean Drilling Program** (ODP) in 1984 with a new home base of operations at Texas A&M University and a larger and more technically and scientifically advanced drillship, the *JOIDES Resolution* (JOIDES stands for Joint Oceanographic Institutions for Deep Earth Sampling). The **Integrated Ocean Drilling Program** (IODP) is the current international program featuring multiple drilling platforms including the *JOIDES Resolution* and newly constructed Japanese drilling vessel *Chikyu*, as well as mission-specific platforms ranging from ice-breakers to jack-up rigs for shallow water drilling.

Scientific ocean drilling has directly led to countless discoveries of the patterns and events that have shaped Earth history, and it has greatly contributed to our understanding of some of the most fundamental processes of Earth's integrated systems, i.e., the geosphere (solid Earth), hydrosphere (water of the continents and ocean), atmosphere (weather and climate), biosphere (marine, terrestrial, and subsurface life), and cryosphere (ice caps and ice sheets). For example, analysis of the changes in the types of sediments found in different parts of the ocean has helped develop a timetable for changes in ocean circulation that accompany the drifting of the continents. Through this process we know that the isthmus of Panama connected North and South America during the Pliocene Epoch, about 5 million years ago, and interrupted circulation from the Atlantic to the Pacific Ocean. As a result, there were major changes in the Earth's climate as it responded to the shifting patterns of ocean currents. Paramount in the successes of this research endeavor is 1) a growing understanding of mantle-crust-ocean-atmosphere interactions, including volcanism and complex geochemical exchanges between crustal rocks, sediments, and seawater, and 2) a deeper appreciation of the forcing mechanisms that drive the coupled ocean-climate system and the many clear examples of just how rapidly this system can be altered when pushed to some critical threshold.

The drilling ship JOIDES Resolution.

More recent discoveries provide insights into potentially important methane hydrate deposits along many continental margins, as well as the importance of life deeply buried in sediments and crustal rocks. Drilling has shown that the time around the Paleocene to Eocene transition some 54 million years ago was a period of extreme warmth throughout the Earth. One hypothesis to explain this period is that these methane hydrates turned into a gaseous form and released large amounts of this powerful greenhouse gas into the atmosphere. The new Integrated Ocean Drilling Program is focused on the following themes: Earth processes, environmental change, and the deep biosphere. Today we are exploring the deep biosphere, unraveling detailed records of past global change including times of abrupt changes in the ocean-climate system and marine biosphere, as well as the inner workings of the Earth's mantle and crust, geochemical cycling through the spreading centers and subduction zones, and the mechanics of earthquakes. Installation of seafloor observatories and a broad spectrum of drilling and logging technologies will allow the Earth science community to continue to press the frontiers of ocean exploration and discovery.

Food for Thought: Why is Earth so different?

Venus (left) and Earth (right) shown in true relative proportions. The image of Venus was obtained by radar that penetrates through the very thick atmosphere and clouds that normally obscure the surface. The light and dark areas of Venus are created by differences in topography, not differences in water. The entire surface is bone dry.

Our nearest planetary neighbor is Venus, which for many years was called the Earth's "sister planet" because of its general similarity in size and composition. Venus and Earth are two of the so-called rocky or terrestrial planets (the others are Mercury and Mars), which all apparently formed at the same time and from similar materials in the early Solar System. A question that has puzzled scientists for a long time is: why does the Earth have all this water in the ocean and Venus has none? Although you don't have the experience of planetary scientists in answering this question, can you come up with a couple of ideas why the Earth is so different? The accompanying table contains some data that can help guide you to some possible reasons.

For further information, you can also try the following web sites:
http://solarsystem.nasa.gov/planets/profile.cfm?Object=Venus
http://www.nineplanets.org/venus.html
http://www.daviddarling.info/encyclopedia/V/Venusatmos.html

	Venus	Earth
Average distance from the sun	1.08×10^8 km	1.50×10^8 km
Equatorial circumference	3.80×10^4 km	4.01×10^8 km
Density	5.24 g/cm^2	5.52 g/cm^2
Acceleration of gravity	8.87 m/s^2	9.77 m/s^2
Length of day	5,832 Earth hours	24 hours
Length of year	4,224.7 Earth days	365.24 days
Average surface temperature	462° C	25° C
Atmospheric gases	CO_2 (96.5%), N_2 (3.5%)	N_2 (80%), O_2 (20%)
Atmospheric pressure	90 atmospheres	1 atmosphere

A note about notation

In the table, and throughout this book, we will be using scientific notation to deal with very large (or very small) numbers. Scientific notation is designed to eliminate a lot of zeroes when writing these numbers, and in practice, it is very simple to use.

For example:

$$100 = 1.0 \times 10^2$$
$$1{,}000 = 1.0 \times 10^3$$
$$1{,}000{,}000 = 1.0 \times 10^6$$

In other words, the number of places that the decimal point must move to the ***left*** determines the exponent. In the table, the equatorial circumference of Venus could also be written as 38,000 km. For numbers smaller than one, the exponent becomes a negative number:

$$0.1 = 1.0 \times 10^{-1}$$
$$0.01 = 1.0 \times 10^{-2}$$
$$0.0001 = 1 \times 10^{-4}$$

In this case, the exponent is determined by the number of places the decimal point moves to the ***right*** in order to make the number greater than one. When you get used to this system, it really makes working with these numbers much easier.

Food for Thought: Meteorites and the Earth's Interior

The data from seismic waves gives us information about the density structure of the Earth's interior, but how do we know the chemical composition of these deep places that no one has visited? See if you can come up with an answer based upon the following pieces of information:

1. **Meteorites** that have fallen to Earth are remnants of the violent collisions that characterized our solar system in its early days as it formed from a collapsing cloud of interstellar gas and dust nearly 4.6 billion years ago. Radiometric dating of meteorites has revealed the age of our sun and its nine orbiting planets, including the "third rock from the sun", Earth.
2. **Iron meteorites** are composed of iron and nickel (Fe-Ni) and owe their origin to melting and separation from other elements during a phase of extreme heat, perhaps in the interior of an early planet that broke apart during the formation of the solar system. They are very dense, generally averaging 7-8 gm/cm^3.
3. **Stony meteorites**, on the other hand, are the most common type of meteorite found on Earth and consist of iron and magnesium-rich silicate minerals similar to those that found in ultramafic rocks.

So what can these meteorites tell us about the Earth's interior?

Follow-Up

The following web link will allow you to test your knowledge about the Earth's structure:
http://www3.Interscience.wiley.com:8100/legacy/college/skinner/0471152285/drag_dropacts/ch01/fig_1_13_fixed_size.htm

However, there are some mistakes in the program! See if you can determine which of the answers are incorrect!

Notes:

Name ______________________________

First three letters of last name

Investigation 2.1 Radiometric Dating and Geologic Time

The graph below shows the change in the ratio of stable isotope ^{207}Pb to the unstable isotope ^{235}U as ^{235}U decays to ^{207}Pb over time.

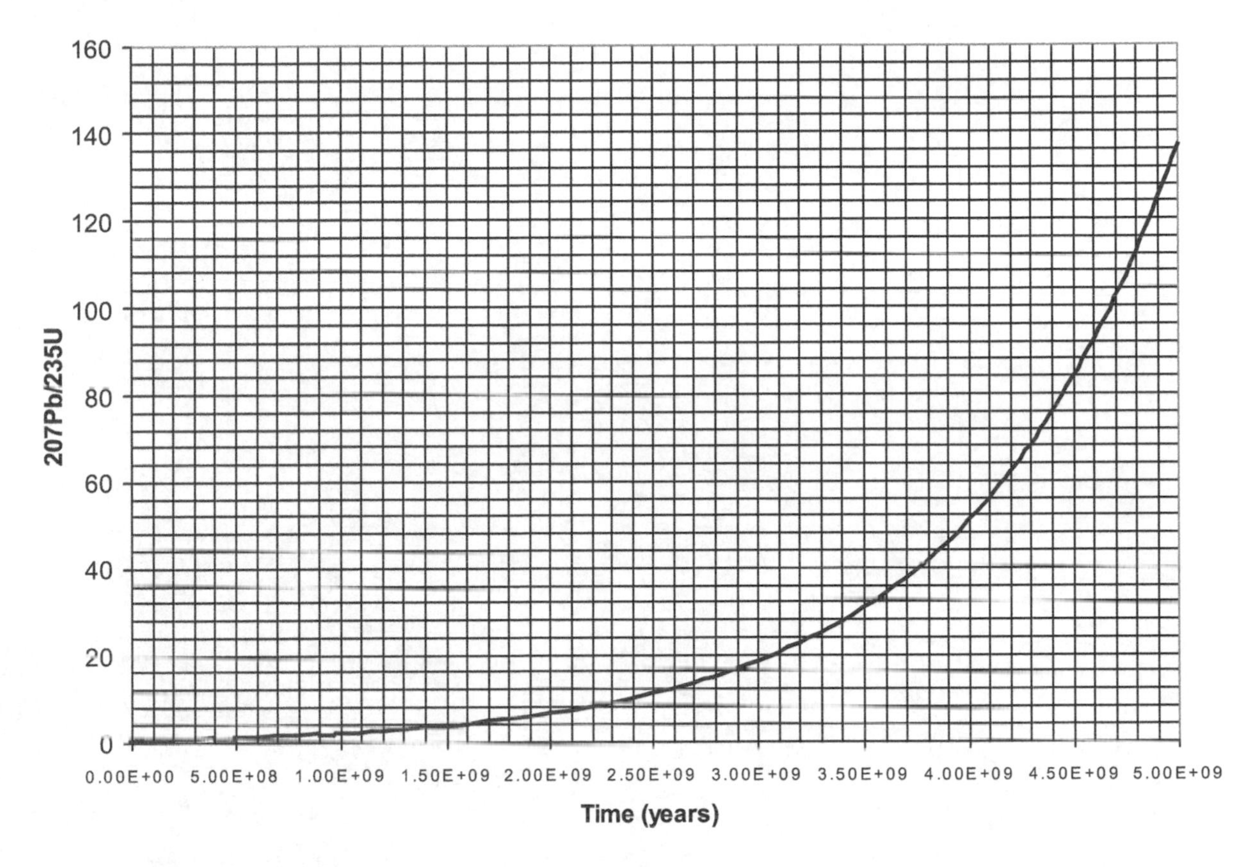

1). In words, explain why the graph has the shape it does.

2). The table below contains the results of several rock samples that were analyzed for their ^{207}Pb ad ^{235}U content. Determine the ages of these samples.

Sample #	$^{207}U/^{235}U$ Ratio	Age of Sample
1	22	
2	18	
3	31	
4	34	

Name ____________________________

First three letters of last name

Investigation 2.2 Correlating Ocean Cores

The two sediment cores diagramed below were obtained by the Ocean Drilling Program at two widely-spaced locations in the Pacific Ocean (see the map on the back of this page). Scientists on board the ship (JOIDES Resolution) studied the shells of microorganisms in the cores and documented that the species changed with depth in the cores. Shown in the diagram are the identifications of **nannoplankton**, very tiny organisms that live near the ocean surface whose shells accumulate in the sediment after they die.

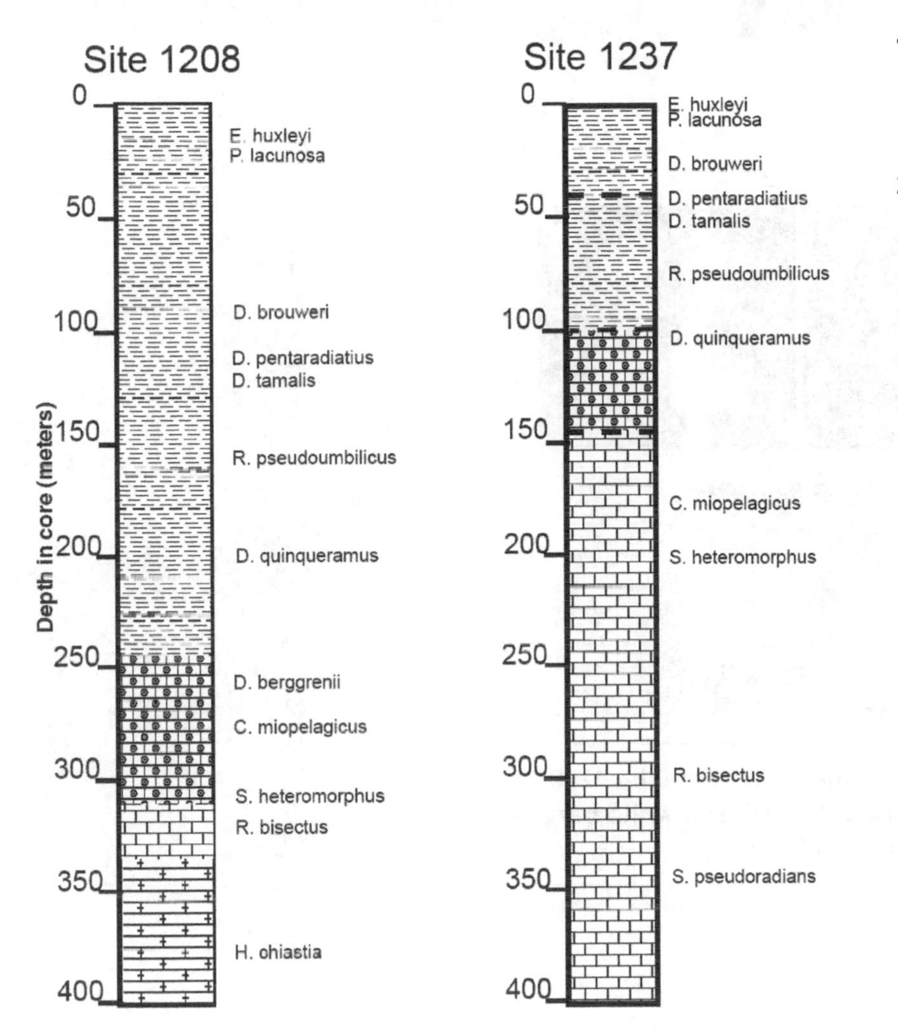

1). Correlate one core to the other based upon the distribution of these nannoplankton shells.

2). Which core contains the oldest sediment at a depth of 200 m in the core? How can you make this determination?

3). The nannoplankter *H. chiastia* at the bottom of Site 1208 was known to exist in the ocean 93.4 million years ago, and *S. pseudoradians* near the base of Site 1237 lived 29.1 million years ago. The species *S. heteromorphus*, found in both cores, has an age of 18.2 million years. Can you explain what happened at these locations around the time of *S. heteromorphus?*

For further information about these ocean cores:

http://www.oceanleadership.org/classroom/how_old_is_it_1

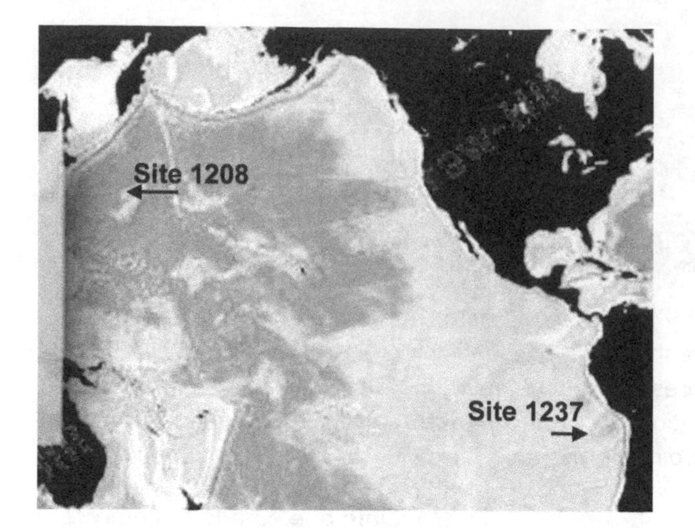

Locations of the cores. Site 1208 was drilled during Leg 198 of the Ocean Drilling Program, and Site 1237 was cored on Leg 202. Detailed information about these research cruises can be obtained at http://www-odp.tamu.edu/publications/

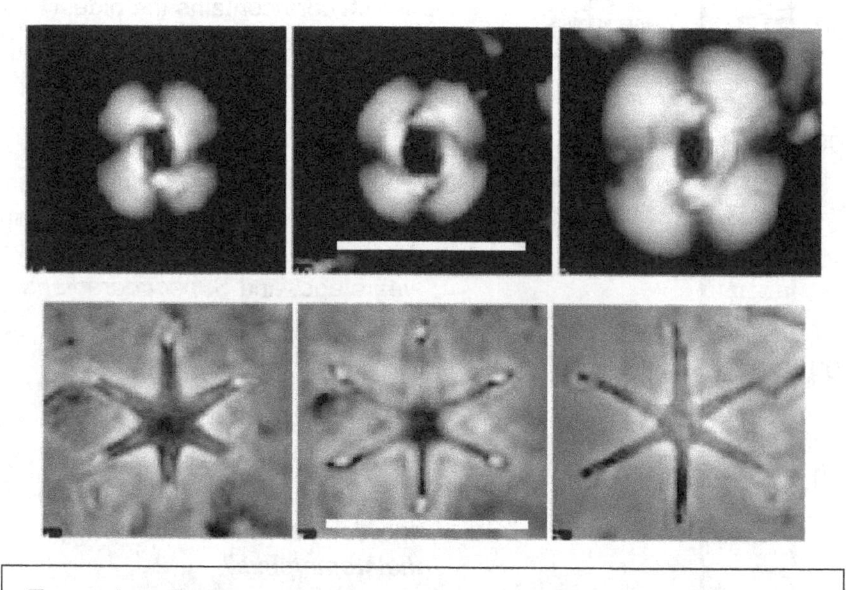

Examples of nannoplankton found in the core from Siite 1208. Top: *R. pseudoumbilicus* Bottom: *D. brouweri*. The white bar represents a distance of 10 micrometers (μm).

Name ______________________________

First three letters of last name

Investigation 2.3 Continents and Ocean Basins

1). Based upon your initial concepts of the Earth's structure, list one or two ideas that might explain why the Earth is divided into **continents** and **ocean basins**.

2). Your instructor will show you an experiment using blocks of spruce that may help you understand why these two areas exist on the Earth. What are **your observations** about how each block floats in water?

3). If the blocks of wood represent continents and ocean basins, what conclusion might you draw about the actual differences between these areas on Earth?

4). In this experiment, what assumptions are you making about the differences between the material of the Earth's crust and that in the Earth's interior?

5). A second experiment uses two different materials (different densities) of the same volume: one block of spruce and one block of oak. **Fill in the table below and calculate density** values for the spruce and oak blocks.

	volume (cm^3)	mass (g)	density (g/cm^3)
spruce block			
oak block			

6). What are your observations about how the different types of wood blocks float on water?

7). Your instructor will show you another experiment about measuring the density of rocks. Fill in the table below and **calculate the density of granite** (typical composition of continental crust) **and basalt** (typical composition of oceanic crust) from the last part of the experiment.

	volume (cm^3)	mass (g)	density (g/cm^3)
Granite (continental crust)			
Basalt (oceanic crust)			

8). Can you use this information to refine your ideas about why there are continents and ocean basins?

Name ______________________________

First three letters of last name

Investigation 2.4 **Isostasy**

1). The diagram on the right (also shown in Fig. 2.12) is a cross-section of the Earth down to the base of the lithosphere at 100 km depth. Come up with an explanation in your own words of what it might mean when we say: "the lithosphere is in isostatic equilibrium with the asthenosphere." Write your answer on the back of this page.

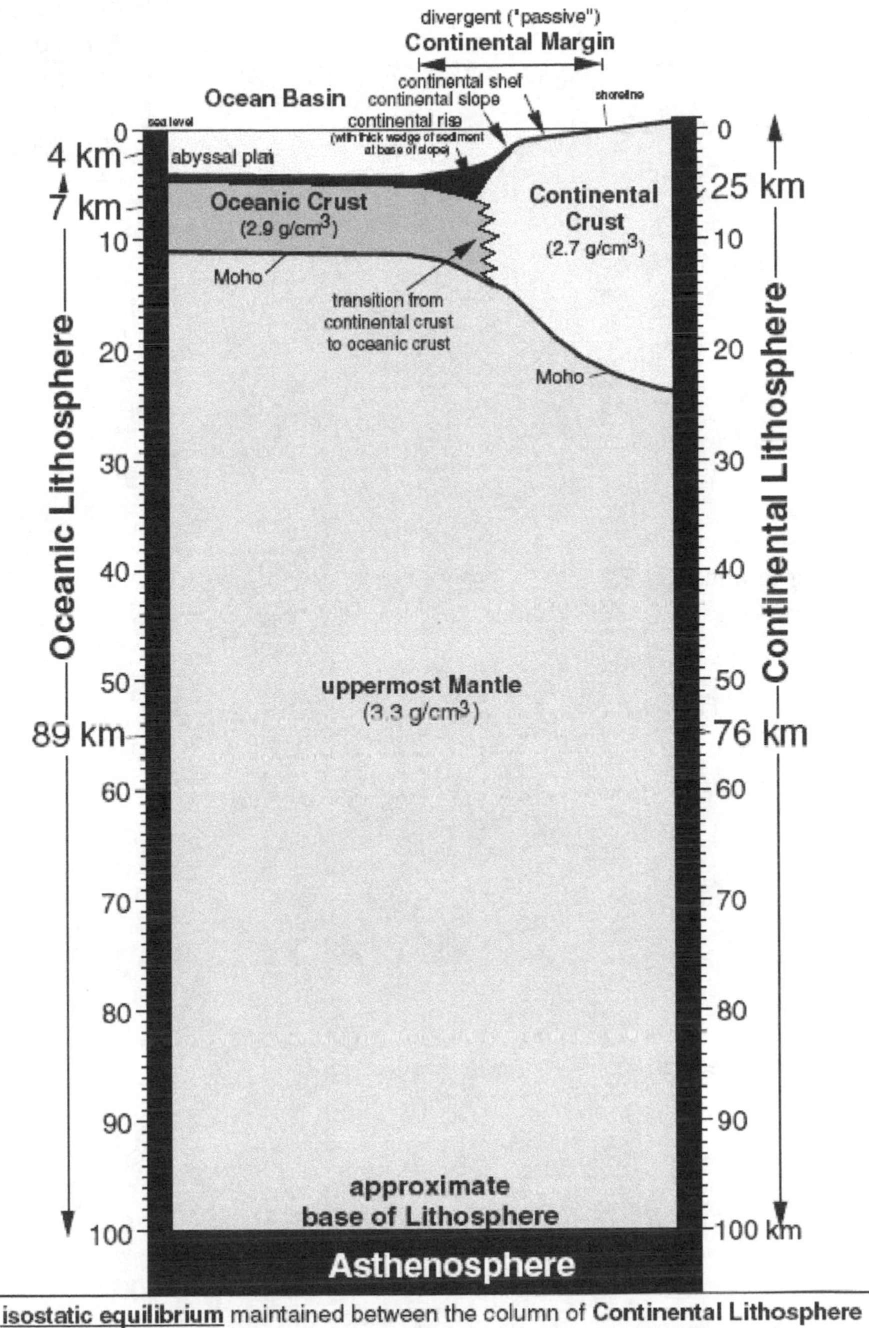

isostatic equilibrium maintained between the column of **Continental Lithosphere** and the column of **Oceanic Lithosphere** by the underlying **Asthenosphere**

2). From the information on the figure, calculate the total mass of material (in kg/m^2) from the Earth's surface to 100 km depth on both the left hand and the right hand side of the diagram.

3). Suppose that you are on top of Mount Everest, the highest elevation on Earth. Would the depth to the base of the crust (the "Moho") be greater or less than the depth to the Moho under Massachusetts? Explain your reasoning on the back of this page.

4). Now re-phrase your interpretation of isostatic equilibrium. Write your answer on the back of this page.

Answer to question 1:

Follow Up

Still uncertain about how isostasy works? Take a look at the following web site that shows what happens to a floating block as you change the block's thickness or the density of the underlying material. Notice how you can predict the ratio of the submerged portion of the block to the block's total thickness by noting the ratio of the densities of the materials:

http://discoverourearth.org/student/isostasy.html

Answer to question 2:

Answer to question 3:

Answer to question 4:

Name ______________________________

First three letters of last name

Investigation 2.5 Features of the Sea Floor

Find the following geographic and physiographic features of the ocean basins and margins seas. The term **physiography** means physical features of the Earth's surface; in this case we want to focus on features below sea level. Label the following features on the physiographic map of the world on the back of this page (a full-color version of this map is on the back cover of this book):

Atlantic Ocean
Mid-Atlantic Ridge
Puerto Rico Trench
South Sandwich Trench
Romanche Fracture Zone
Gibbs Fracture Zone
Gulf of Mexico

Indian Ocean
Mid-Indian Ridge
Java Trench
Ninety East Ridge
Owens Fracture Zone
Kerguelen Plateau
Red Sea
Gulf of Aden
Arabian Sea
Persian Gulf
Indus Cone

Pacific Ocean
East Pacific Rise
Chile Rise
Pacific-Antarctic Ridge
Juan de Fuca Ridge
Middle America Trench
Peru-Chile Trench
Marianas Trench
Aleutian Trench
Kuril Trench
Japan Trench
Kermadec-Tonga Trench
Mendocino Fracture Zone
Clipperton Fracture Zone
Eltanin Fracture Zone
Hawaiian Island Chain
Emperor Seamount Chain
Galapagos Islands
Great Barrier Reef

You may use any resource as sources of information to complete this exercise, but cite your sources (including URLs) on the back of this page.

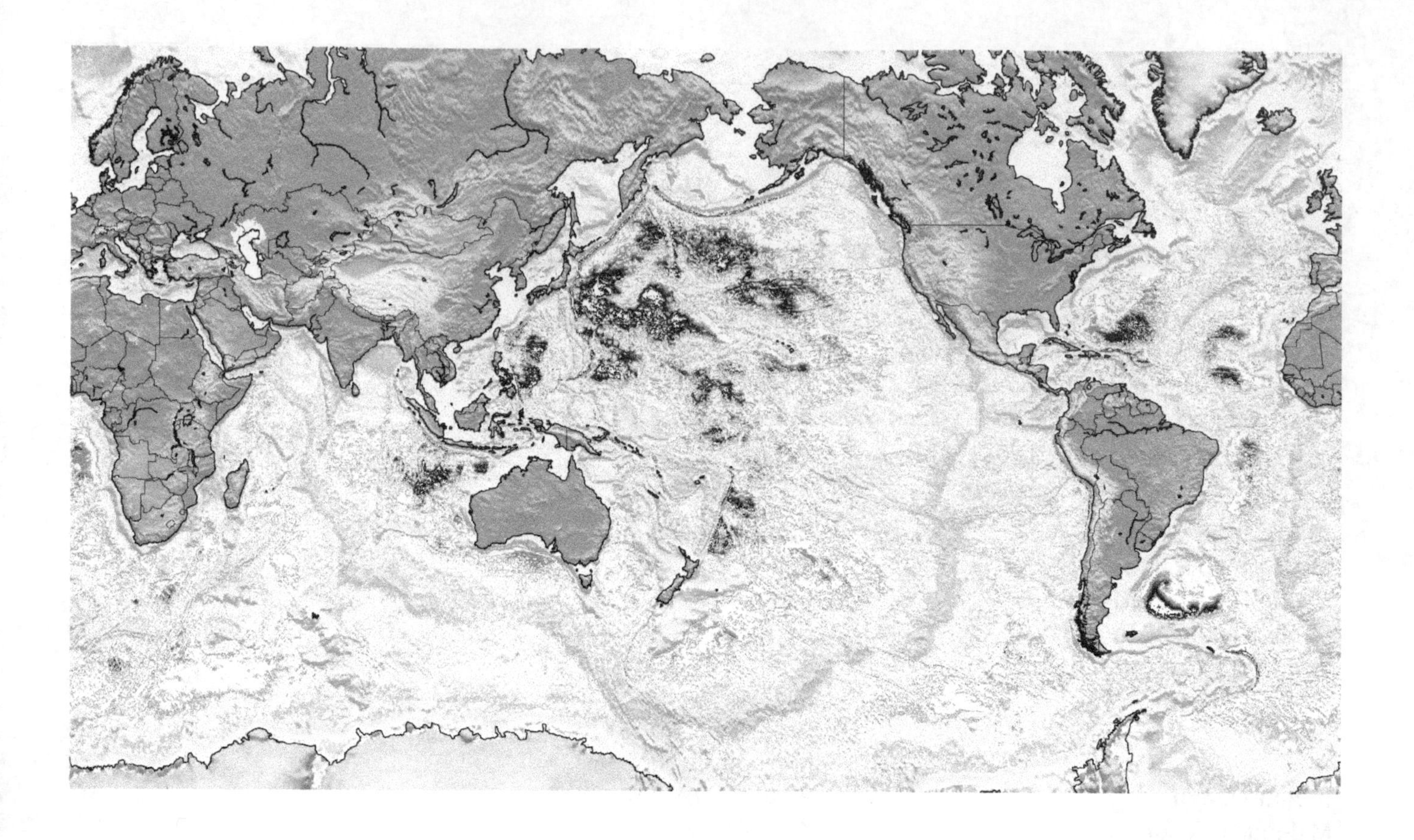

Name ______________________________

First three letters of last name

Investigation 2.6 Bathymetric Maps Revisited

A **bathymetric map** shows the three-dimensional features of the seafloor by using **contours**, or lines of equal depth, much the same way a **topographic map** depicts the features of the land above sea level. Contour lines that are close together represent a steep change in bathymetry (or topography), whereas widely spaced contours depict a gentle change in slope on the seafloor. The bathymetric map below has **contour lines** connecting points of equivalent depth. The **contour interval** of 50 m is 200 m. To help you visualize the seafloor features, an image based on side-scan sonar data has been superimposed on the map.

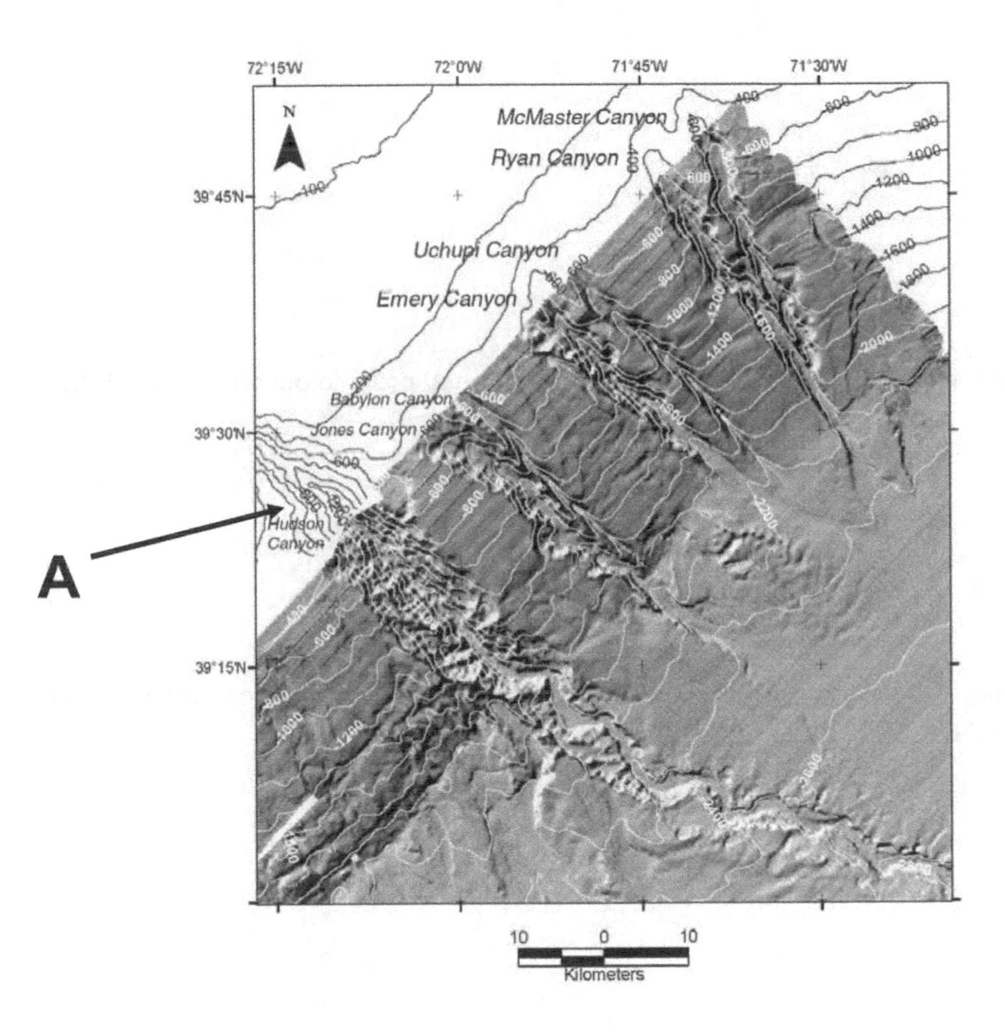

Examine this map and answer the questions on the back of this page.

After constructing bathymetric contours on the map and drawing a bathymetric profile across the area, answer the following questions:

1). What is the feature identified by point "A?"

2). What is the depth at the edge of the continental shelf?

3). At what depth does the relatively steep slope of the **continental slope** begin to flatten out?

4). What feature occurs at the base of the continental slope?

5). At what water depth would you predict to find the transition from **continental crust** to **oceanic crust**? Why there? Explain your answer.

6). What type of **continental margin** is this: active or passive? Explain the reasoning for your answer. What do you know? What more would you like to know?

Name ______________________________

First three letters of last name

Investigation 2.7 Earthquakes and Volcanoes

1). The maps on the back of this page illustrate the distribution of global seismicity (earthquake activity) and active volcanoes. Describe any geographic patterns you see and similarities or differences in the distribution of these phenomena.

2). Look carefully at the patterns in and around the Atlantic and Pacific Ocean basins. What are the similarities and differences?

3). If you had to draw a conclusion based on these observations, what would it be?

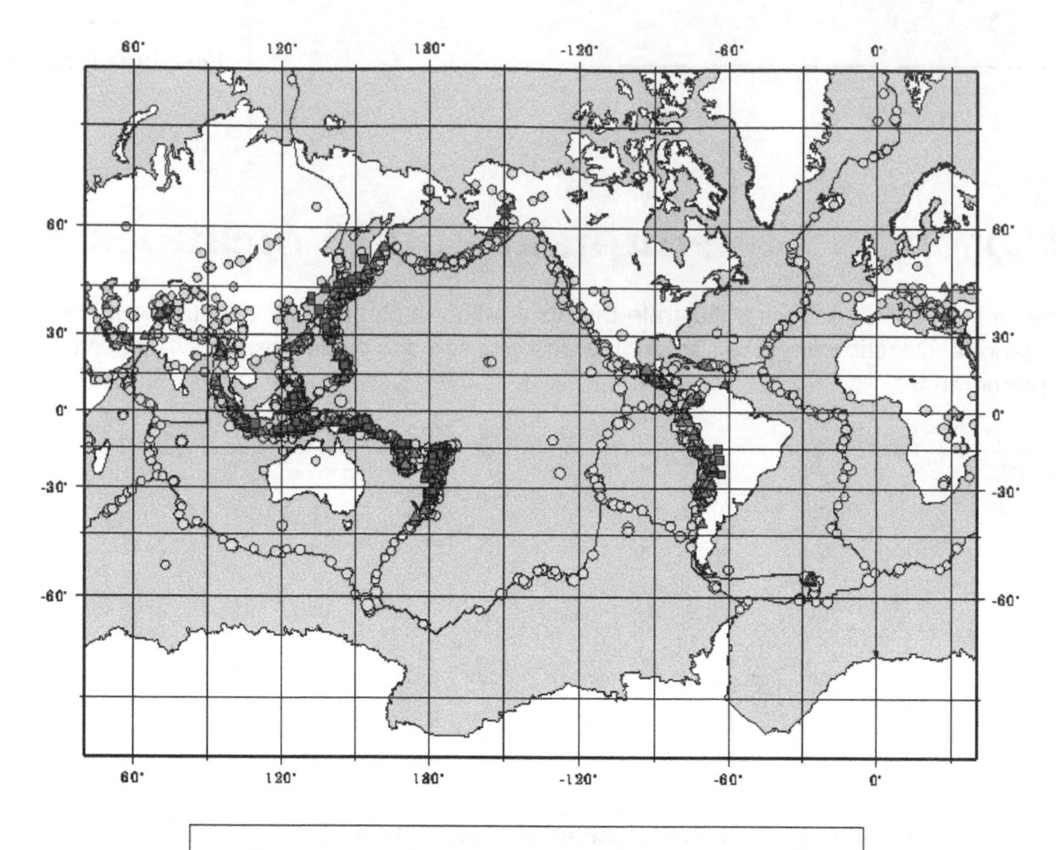

Worldwide earthquakes (seismicity) for 1995 with magnitude ≥ 5.0
(University of California, Berkeley)
http://seismo.berkeley.edu/istat/digiguide/TEMPLATE/merc_plate.gif

Active volcanoes of the world
(Smithsonian Institution Global Volcanism Program)
http://www.volcano.si.edu/world/find_regions.cfm

Name ____________________________

First three letters of last name

Investigation 2.9 **Plate Tectonics**

1). Use the physiographic map of the world provided on the next page (a full-color version of this map is on the back cover of this book).

- With a *green* colored pencil, draw along *divergent* plate boundaries (i.e., **oceanic ridges and rises** where new oceanic crust is formed, i.e., "spreading centers"),
- With a *red* colored pencil, draw along *convergent* plate boundaries (i.e., **trenches** where subduction occurs due to ocean-ocean and ocean-continent collision, and in major mountain ranges where continent-continent collision occurs),
- With a *blue* colored pencil, draw along *transform* plate boundaries (i.e., **strike-slip faults** such as offsets of oceanic ridges where two lithospheric plates slide past one another).

2). Label the following plates using the abbreviations provided.

- North American Plate (NAm)
- Caribbean Plate (Carib)
- South American Plate (SAm)
- Cocos Plate (Coc)
- Nazca Plate (Naz)
- Juan de Fuca Plate (JdF)
- Pacific Plate (Pac)
- Philippine Plate (Phil)
- Indo-Australian Plate (In-Au)
- Eurasian Plate (EurA)
- Antarctic Plate (Ant)s
- Scotian Plate (Scot)
- African Plate (Afr)
- Arabian Plate (Arab)

You may use any resource as sources of information to complete this exercise, but cite your sources (including URLs).

3). Using arrows, label the motion of the lithospheric plates (i.e., direction of motion) and the plate velocity in units of cm/yr (centimeters per year).

4). Approximately how fast is the Nazca Plate converging with the South American Plate? Your answer should be in units of cm/yr.

5). Approximately how fast (cm/yr) is the North Atlantic Ocean basin opening?

6). Approximately how far is Boston from the eastern edge of the North American Plate. Your answer should be in mi (miles) and in km (kilometers).

7). Approximately how far is Los Angeles from the western edge of the North American Plate (mi and km)?

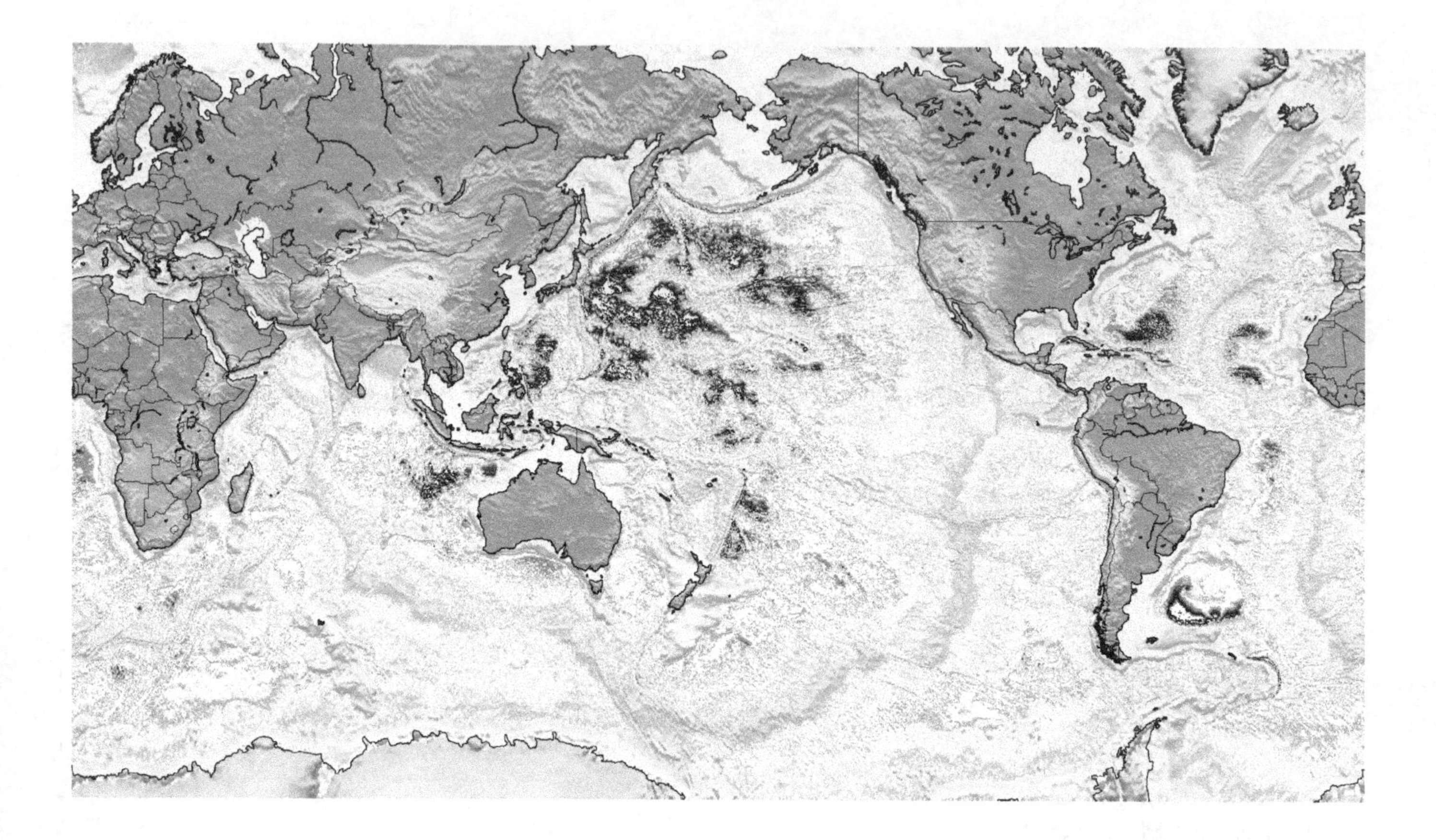

Follow-Up

Deep-focus earthquakes occur only along convergent margins, where the subducting plate is sliding back into the mantle. Go to the following web site http://neic.usgs.gov/neis/qed/ and plot on the map you just used the locations of all intermediate and deep-focus earthquakes (depths greater than 70 km) that have occurred over the past 30 days. Explain the patterns that you see.

Name ______________________________

First three letters of last name

Investigation 2.10 Hot-Spot Tracks

The figure on the other side of this page is a scaled map of the Pacific Ocean showing the Hawaiian Islands and the Emperor Seamount Chain.

1). Draw an arrow on the map that shows the direction that the Pacific plate is moving at the present time. Using a protractor and the North arrow as a reference, determine what direction (compass bearing) this is.

2). Put an arrow on the map indicating the direction that the Pacific plate was moving when the Emperor Seamount chain formed. Determine the compass bearing as before.

3). The date for the transition in plate motion is 43 million years, the date obtained for the seamount at the "kink" in the chain. Use the scale on the map together with this information to calculate the average rate of plate movement that formed the Hawaiian chain.

4). The oldest seamount in the Emperor Chain is 80 million years. What was the average rate of movement of the Pacific plate during the formation of the Emperor Seamount Chain?

Follow-Up

Do Hawaii and the Emperor Seamount Chain really represent the trace of a mantle plume? Look at the following references and see what you think! What has caused the "bend" anyway?
http://pubs.usgs.gov/gip/dynamic/Hawaiian.html
http://www.mantleplumes.org/Hawaii.html

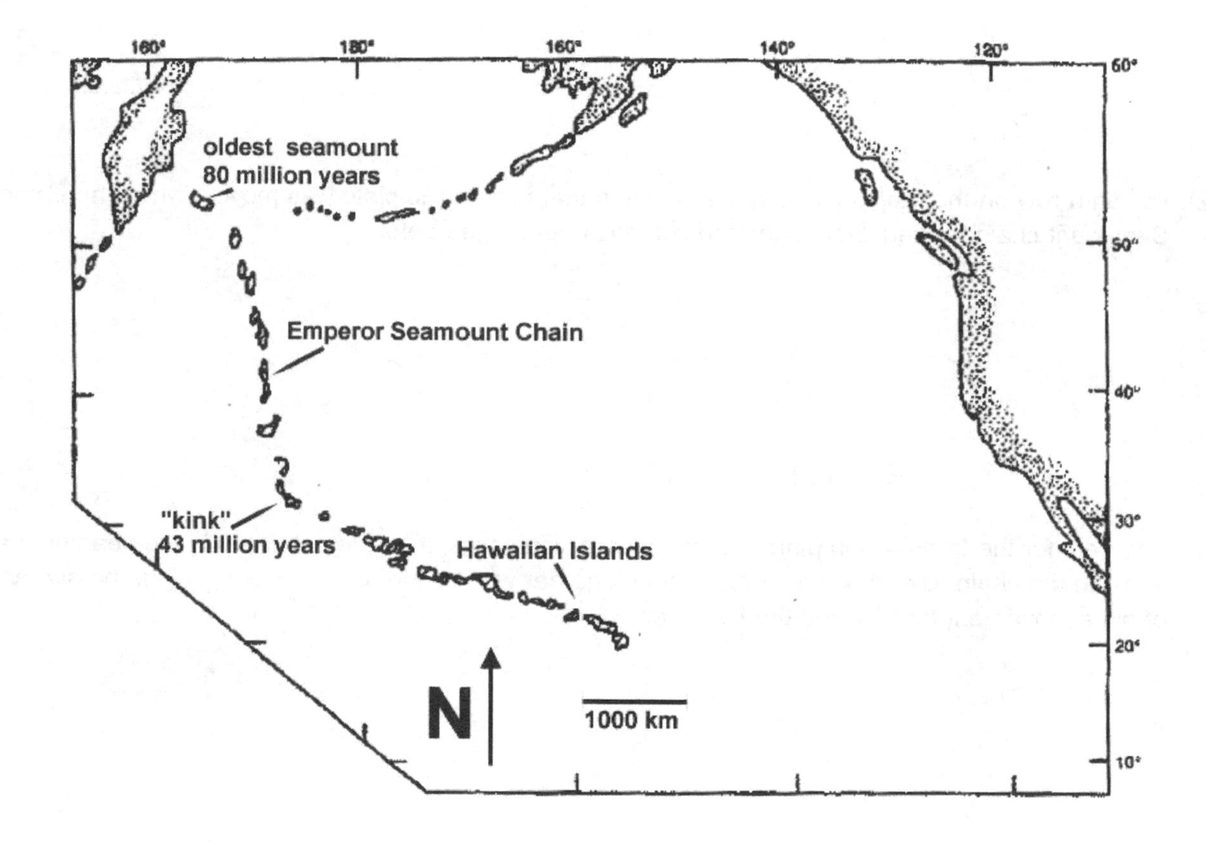

Name ______________________________

First three letters of last name

Investigation 2.11 Distribution of Ocean Sediments

1). Color the ocean basins of the physiographic map of the world on the back of this page according to the following sediment types:

- Use a **brown** colored pencil to depict the areas of the seafloor covered primarily by **terrigenous sediments** derived from the weathering of the continents (not including deep sea red clay or ice-rafted sediments),
- Use a **blue** colored pencil to depict the areas of the seafloor covered primarily by **calcareous ooze**.
- Use a **green** colored pencil to depict the areas of the seafloor covered primarily by **siliceous ooze**.
- Use a red colored pencil to depict the areas of the seafloor covered primarily by **red/brown clay**.
- Use a **yellow** colored pencil to depict the areas of the seafloor covered primarily by **ice-rafted terrigenous sediments**.

2). How would you characterize the distribution of calcareous ooze on the seafloor? (hint: carefully compare areas of the seafloor where calcareous ooze forms the predominant sediment type with areas where other sediment types predominate).

3). The Hawaiian Island Chain is a hotspot trace that depicts a straight line representing the direction of Pacific Plate motion to the west-northwest over the past 43 million years. If you were to drill into the seafloor at some location to the southeast of the big island of Hawaii, what would you predict the layers of sediments overlying basalt (oceanic crust) to consist of. Remember where the basalt formed and its original water depth relative to its present location and water depth. Is the pile of sediments of uniform or mixed composition? What sediments (sedimentary layers) might you encounter at your drill site, and why?

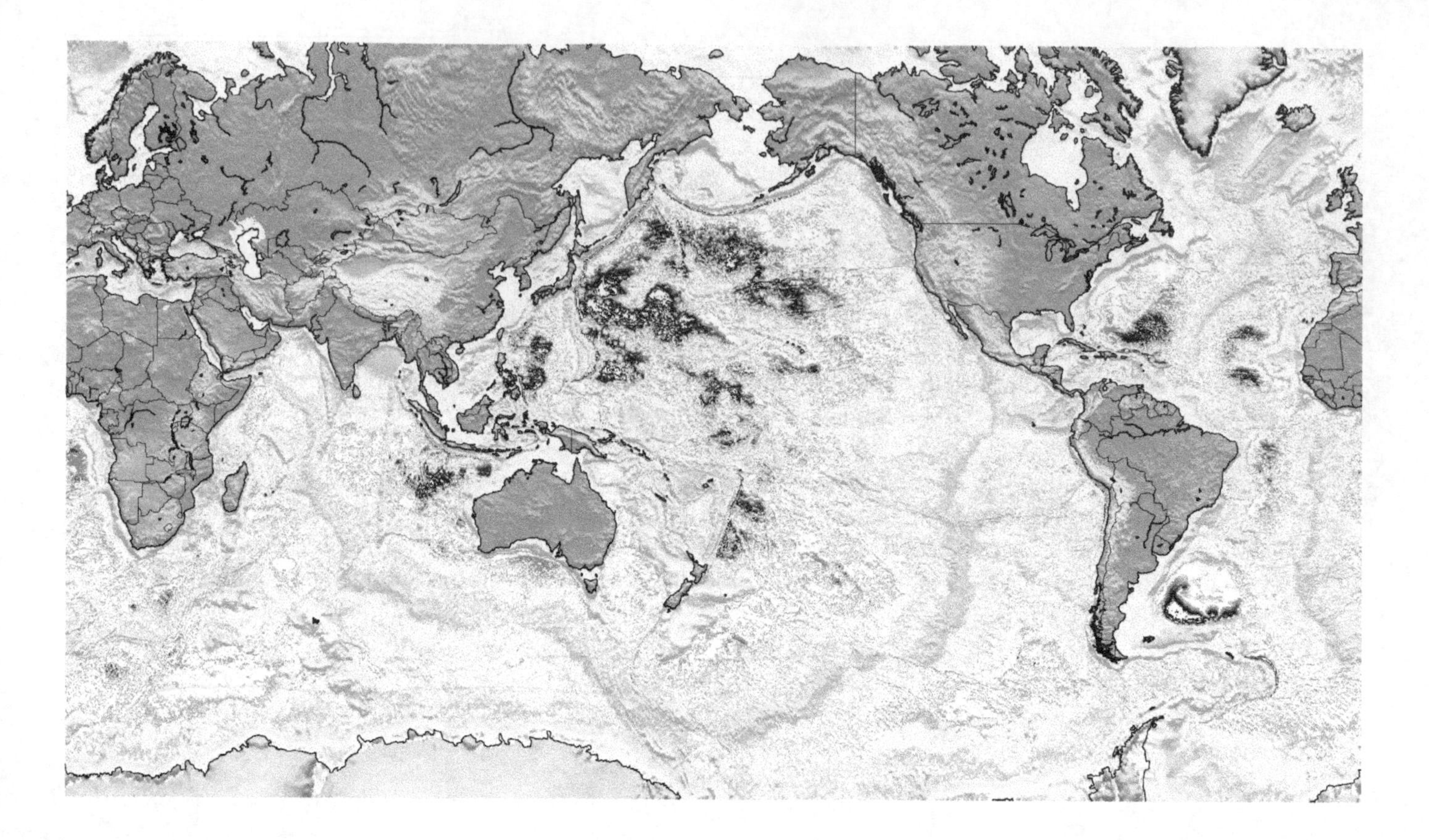

4). Antarctica has not always been covered by large ice sheets. Today, concentric rings of different sediment composition surround the continent due to ocean circulation patterns and climate: a belt of ice-rafted terrigenous sediment is closest to the continent, followed by a band of siliceous ooze, and finally calcareous ooze or red clay furthest away from Antarctica. Predict what sequence of sedimentary layers (like a layer cake) might be found if you were to drill into the seafloor near Antarctica and recover sediments dating back before Antarctica became glaciated about 34 million years ago.

PART 3

Water and the Ocean-Climate System

In the previous part of this book, we explored the materials and structures of the ocean basins, which constitute the "buckets" that hold the vast quantities of water that we call the ocean. Most of us, from personal experience, know that sea water is salty. However, we probably don't have much of a clue why there is so much salt in the ocean, and how it got that way. We may wonder if the salt content of the ocean will increase, or if there are regulating mechanisms that serve to keep everything fairly constant. Water itself is also a remarkable substance, unlike any other that is common in our solar system. The unique properties of water, such as the way it freezes or changes density with temperature, actually helps regulate the temperature of our planet. In addition, the temperature and salinity patterns of the water in ocean help explain the distribution of life in the sea. We will examine these relationships in the current chapter. The ocean is the supreme regulator of climate conditions on Planet Earth. The physical properties of water, especially its high heat capacity, allow it to absorb large amounts of energy without changing temperature very much. This heat energy is transferred back to the atmosphere by a variety of mechanisms, but the bottom line is that the relatively constant environmental conditions at the Earth surface, compared to other planets, are made possible by the large mass of water in the ocean. In the sections that follow we will examine how the ocean touches our lives on a daily basis, usually without us even being aware of its influence.

In this chapter you will learn:

- How water is different from most substances on Earth
- What kinds of salts there are in seawater and how long they stay there
- How solar energy stored by the ocean is moved around the planet
- How the Earth's rotation affects ocean circulation and weather patterns

3.1 The Unusual Structure of Water

Water is a substance that behaves differently from almost any other chemical compound that exists naturally. The differences begin with the basic arrangement of the atoms in a water molecule (H_2O), which gives it a **dipolar structure**. This means that the molecule has an uneven distribution of electrical charge owing to the asymmetrical shape of the water molecule. Instead of the two hydrogen (H) atoms being bonded on either side of the single oxygen (O) atom (i.e., 180° apart), the hydrogen atoms are 105° apart (Fig. 3.1). In this configuration the hydrogen-side of the molecule (H_2) has a net **positive charge** and the oxygen-side (O) has a net **negative charge.** This occurs because the negatively charged electrons spend more time in the vicinity of the O atom.

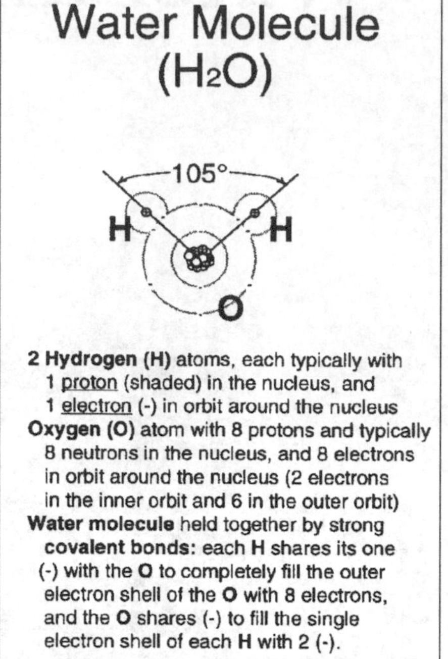

Figure 3.1 The structure of a water molecule.

Because of this asymmetrical distribution of electrical charge in the water molecule, the positively-charged ends of the water molecules are attracted to the negatively-charged ends of adjacent molecules. These are called **hydrogen bonds** (Fig 3.2). The proportion of water molecules bonded to other water molecules depends on the temperature, which in turn, controls the gain and loss of heat. At temperatures above the boiling point, water is a gas (steam) and there are only few hydrogen bonds (Fig. 3.3). When water is in its liquid state between 0° and 100°C, more hydrogen bonds develop among the molecules. When the temperature goes below freezing, water solidifies into ice and hydrogen bonds connect every molecule.

The dipolar structure of the water molecule and the formation of hydrogen bonds between water molecules are responsible for the many unique properties of water:

For an interesting animated look at the structure of the water molecule, and how this influences its behavior, go to http://www.johnkyrk.com/H_2O.html

1. **Water has a high surface tension (cohesion).**
   - Hydrogen bonds allow water to form droplets (e.g., raindrops)

2. **Water occurs in 3 states (phases) that occur over a relatively narrow range of temperature (Fig. 3.3).**
   - Water is the only naturally occurring substance at Earth's surface and atmosphere to exist simultaneously in all 3 phases: **solid**, **liquid**, and **gas**

3. **Water is a good solvent that allows it dissolve many other substances.**
   - The dipolar structure lets ionic compounds go into solution easily (e.g., NaCl forms Na^+ and Cl^-)

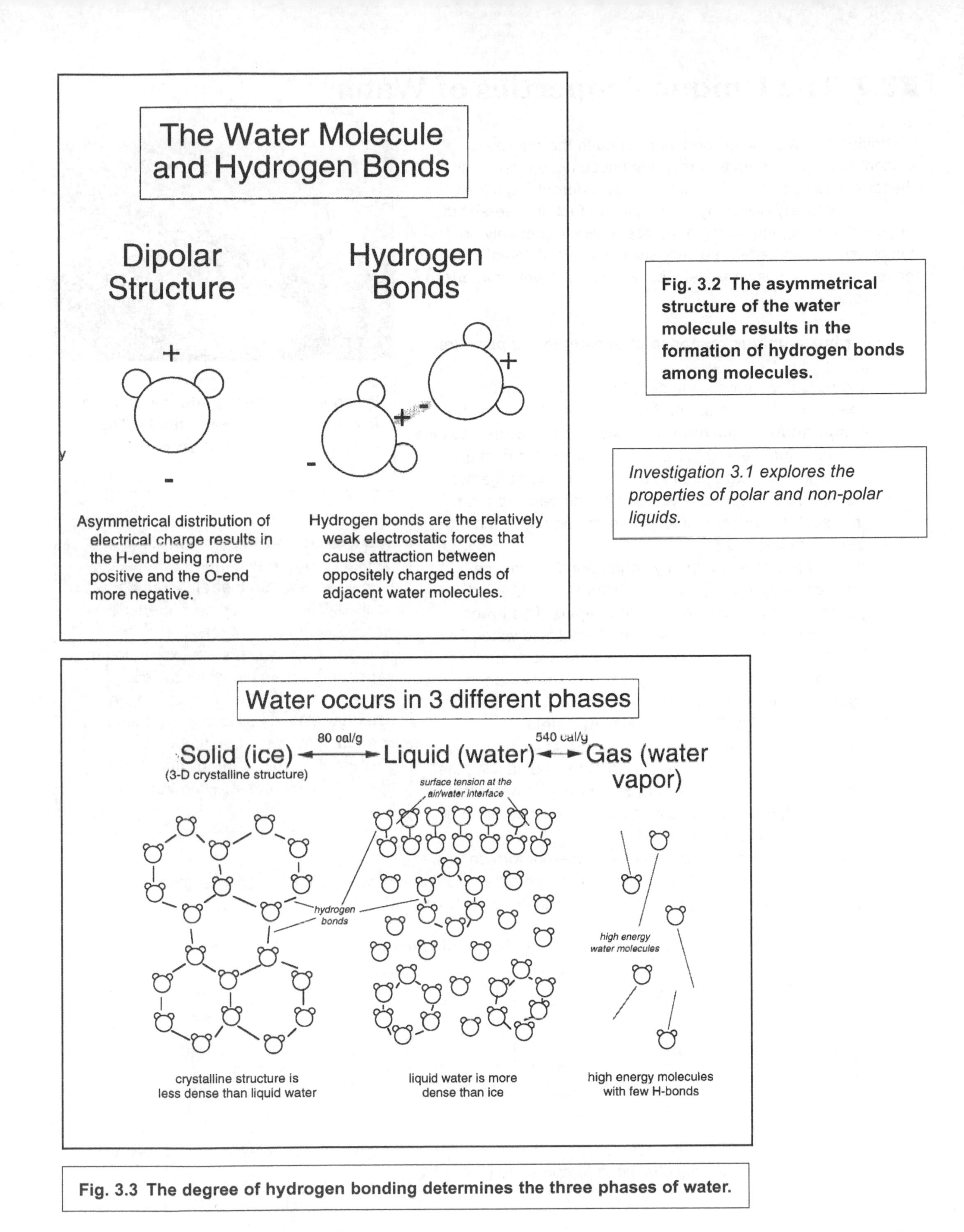

Fig. 3.2 The asymmetrical structure of the water molecule results in the formation of hydrogen bonds among molecules.

Investigation 3.1 explores the properties of polar and non-polar liquids.

Fig. 3.3 The degree of hydrogen bonding determines the three phases of water.

■3.2 The Unique Properties of Water

In addition to the basic properties outlined in the previous section, the dipolar structure of water causes it to respond to changes in temperature in fundamentally different ways than any other naturally-occurring compound. In fact, if it weren't for these differences, the water in the ocean would probably be completely frozen beneath a very shallow layer of liquid! Without these properties, it is very likely that life would never have arisen on Earth.

When water freezes into ice, it has a lower density so that it floats. This is one of the unusual properties of water.

1. **Water has a unique response of density to temperature (Fig 3.4)**
   - Liquid water increases in density as it cools until it reaches a temperature of 3.98°C. This is known as the **temperature of maximum density,** and it occurs because the vibrational energy of the water molecules is at a minimum allowing them to pack more closely together.
   - As water cools further, hydrogen bonds begin to form that push the water molecules apart and cause the density to decrease.
   - When water freezes, the hydrogen bonds in the ice form a hexagonal crystalline structure (Fig. 3.3) that pushes the molecules even farther apart. This lowers the density of the ice below that of the liquid water. As a consequence, **ice floats**. This is different from other substances, where the solid phase is denser than the liquid and sinks through it.
2. **Water has "high" boiling and freezing points**
   - Compared with other molecules having a similar chemical formula with 2 hydrogen atoms but lacking the dipolar structure (e.g., H_2S, H_2Se, and H_2Te) water is the only one that can exist as a liquid at the temperature of the Earth's surface. (Table 3.1)
   - In water, hydrogen bonds must be broken or formed to boil or freeze the liquid, and this requires more heat so that it occurs at much higher temperatures for water than for other H_2X molecules that do not have hydrogen bonds.

There are two ways that heat can be gained or lost by water or any substance, If liquid water from the refrigerator is put on the kitchen counter, it will gradually warm up to room temperature. This temperature change is the expression of **sensible heat** as the water molecules increase their energy of vibration. On the other hand as ice absorbs heat from the surroundings, it melts without changing temperature. This is **latent heat** that is causing the change of state from solid to liquid.

Table 3.1 Freezing and Boiling Points of Water and Related Compounds.

Property	*Water (H_2O)*	*H_2S*	*H_2Se*	*H_2Te*
Boiling Point	100°C	–62°C	–42°C	–4°C
Freezing Point	0°C	–83°C	–64°C	–51°C
Natural State	Liquid, vapor, solid	vapor	vapor	vapor

3. **Water has high heat capacity**
   - Compared with many other substances (liquid and solid), water absorbs and releases a considerable amount of heat with little change in temperature (Table 3.2)

- water's high heat capacity helps to moderate surface temperatures on Earth. Water retains the energy that it absorbs for a long time and releases it slowly into the atmosphere. For this reason, the coastal regions have a more moderate climate than the interior parts of continents.

Table 3.2 Heat Capacity of Water and Other Substances. The higher the number, the greater the ability of the substance to exchange heat with little change in temperature.

Substance	Heat Capacity
Water	1.00 cal/g/1°C
Ethyl Alcohol	0.58 cal/g/1°C
Aluminum	0.21 cal/g/1°C
Graphite	0.17 cal/g/1°C

4. Water has a high latent heat of vaporization, which is the amount of heat required to change water into steam, and it also has a high latent heat of fusion, which is the amount of heat needed to melt ice.

- considerable amounts of heat must be added or removed to convert water from one phase to another (**ice → water → vapor**)
- 540 calories/g are required to **evaporate water** and 80 calories/g are required to **melt ice**
- 540 calories/g of latent heat are released to the atmosphere when **water vapor condenses** to form clouds, rain, and snow, and 80 calories/g are released when **water freezes**

*Heat is measured in **calories** (calorie = amount of heat needed to raise the temperature of 1g of water by 1°C.*

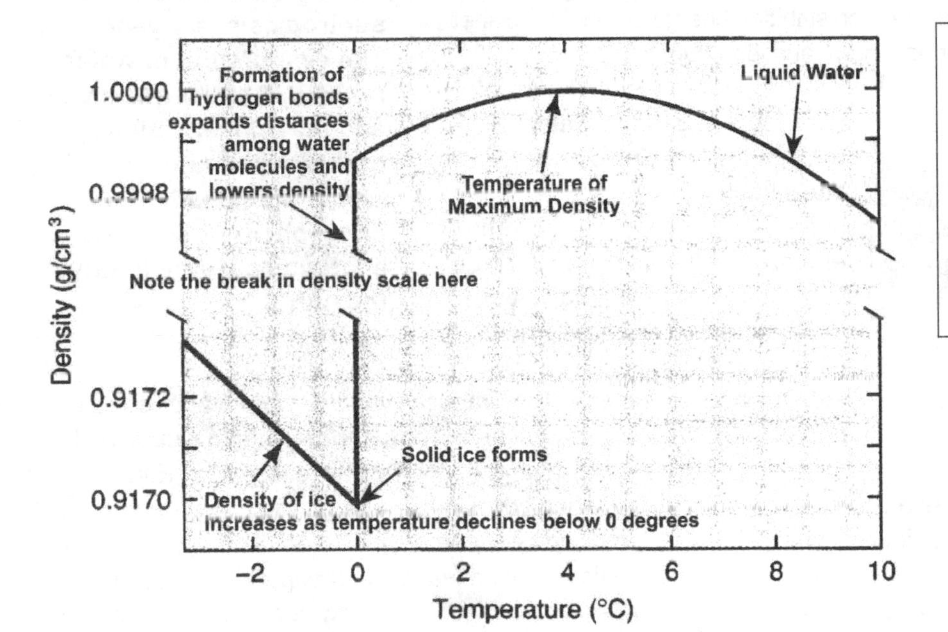

Fig. 3.4 The unique density change as water cools and then freezes is caused by hydrogen bonds. This graph shows the results for pure water. Adding salt, as in the ocean, will change the pattern somewhat.

Food for Thought: The ice-filled Ocean

Suppose that water behaved like other "normal" substances; that is that the solid phase (ice) is denser than the liquid (water). Now imagine what would happen to the ocean as ice formed in the cold seasons of the year. What kind of effects would this have on the ability of the ocean to support life?

Investigation 3.2 conducts an experiment to study the relationship between temperature and heat capacity.

■3.3 The Hydrologic Cycle and Heat Transfer

As water molecules absorb energy from the Sun or other source, some of the energy causes the water molecules to vibrate faster and this makes the water warmer (sensible heat). Some of the remaining solar energy can cause hydrogen bonds (H bonds) to be broken resulting in a change of phase (or state: solid-liquid-gas) without a change in temperature. The gradual melting of ice cubes in your soda or the evaporation of water from a puddle on the road are example of phase changes. These phase changes are the result of the absorption of latent heat. The opposite is true when water molecules are cooled: they vibrate less vigorously as they lose sensible heat, the temperature drops, and they release latent heat as H bonds are formed. Water vapor condenses to form water droplets and clouds, or liquid water begins to form ice crystals; both processes release heat.

Considerable heat energy is released to the atmosphere as hydrogen bonds form when water freezes (80 cal/g) or when water vapor condenses (540 cal/g) to form clouds or rain drops. In the opposite way, "extra" heat must be gained in order to break hydrogen bonds when ice melts (80 calories per gram of water, cal/g) or when water evaporates (540 cal/g). These are the **latent heat of fusion** and the **latent heat of vaporization** (Fig. 3.5). These processes are responsible for maintaining the ocean and atmosphere at reasonable temperatures. However, condensation of water vapor and evaporation of liquid water are much more important than freezing and melting because of the large amount of latent heat involved. The heat that is transferred by the evaporation and condensation of water is the engine that drives the **hydrologic cycle**. This ongoing process redistributes energy around the planet as water moves between the ocean, atmosphere, and land (Fig. 3.6).

Tropical cyclones (hurricanes and typhoons) represent safety valves for the release of excess heat that builds up in the tropics and subtropics every year. The evaporation of water in the eye of the hurricane and the condensation of this water vapor at higher altitudes in the atmosphere provide the energy necessary to drive the hurricane winds.

A large percentage of the water returned to the atmosphere from land areas comes from transpiration. This is a by-product of the photosynthesis of plants, which consume carbon dioxide and release oxygen and water vapor as by-products.

Let's follow a gram of water through the hydrologic cycle to see what happens. Water at the surface of the ocean will absorb energy from the sun and evaporate into the atmosphere. **Evaporation** will remove 540 calories of heat from the ocean and carry it into the atmosphere with the water vapor. When this water vapor cools in the upper parts of the atmosphere it can **condense** into clouds and raindrops, releasing the latent heat from the water vapor into the atmosphere. As the rainfall reaches the Earth's surface, some of it coalesces into rivers and streams or infiltrates into the soil zone as groundwater. A large portion of the rainfall evaporates from the land back into the atmosphere, removing heat energy with it. Additional water vapor is returned to the atmosphere through **transpiration**, a process by which plants release water vapor as a byproduct of photosynthesis. **Runoff** includes both surface (streams and rivers) and subsurface (groundwater) flow of liquid water toward the ocean under the influence of gravity or hydrostatic pressure. These processes of the hydrologic cycle help to redistribute excess tropical heat to colder regions by way of the global circulation of the atmosphere and day-to-day weather patterns. The atmosphere and ocean share about equally in the redistribution of heat around the planet through the processes of the hydrologic cycle (evaporation and precipitation) and surface currents.

For an excellent visualization and discussion of the hydrologic cycle, go online to the NASA Observatorium, which can be found at http://physics.ship.edu/~mrc/astro/NASA_Space_Science/observe.arc.nasa.gov/nasa/earth/hydrocycle/hydro2.html

Summary of latent heat versus sensible heat

- ***Latent heat*** *is the heat that is needed to change water from one phase to another; this occurs without a change in temperature because the energy gained (or lost) is used to break (or form) hydrogen bonds. When water on a stove is at a continuous boil, its temperature is not changing, even though the burner is on high. When you bring that water from room temperature to boiling, this increases the rate of vibration of water molecules, which is* ***sensible heat.***
- *540 calories of latent heat per gram of water are needed to evaporate water and thus 540 calories of heat are released to the atmosphere when water vapor condenses to form clouds, rain, or snow.*
- *80 calories of latent heat per gram of water are needed to melt ice and 80 calories are released to the atmosphere when water freezes.*
- *Latent heat is important for the hydrologic cycle, which moves moisture and heat around the planet.*

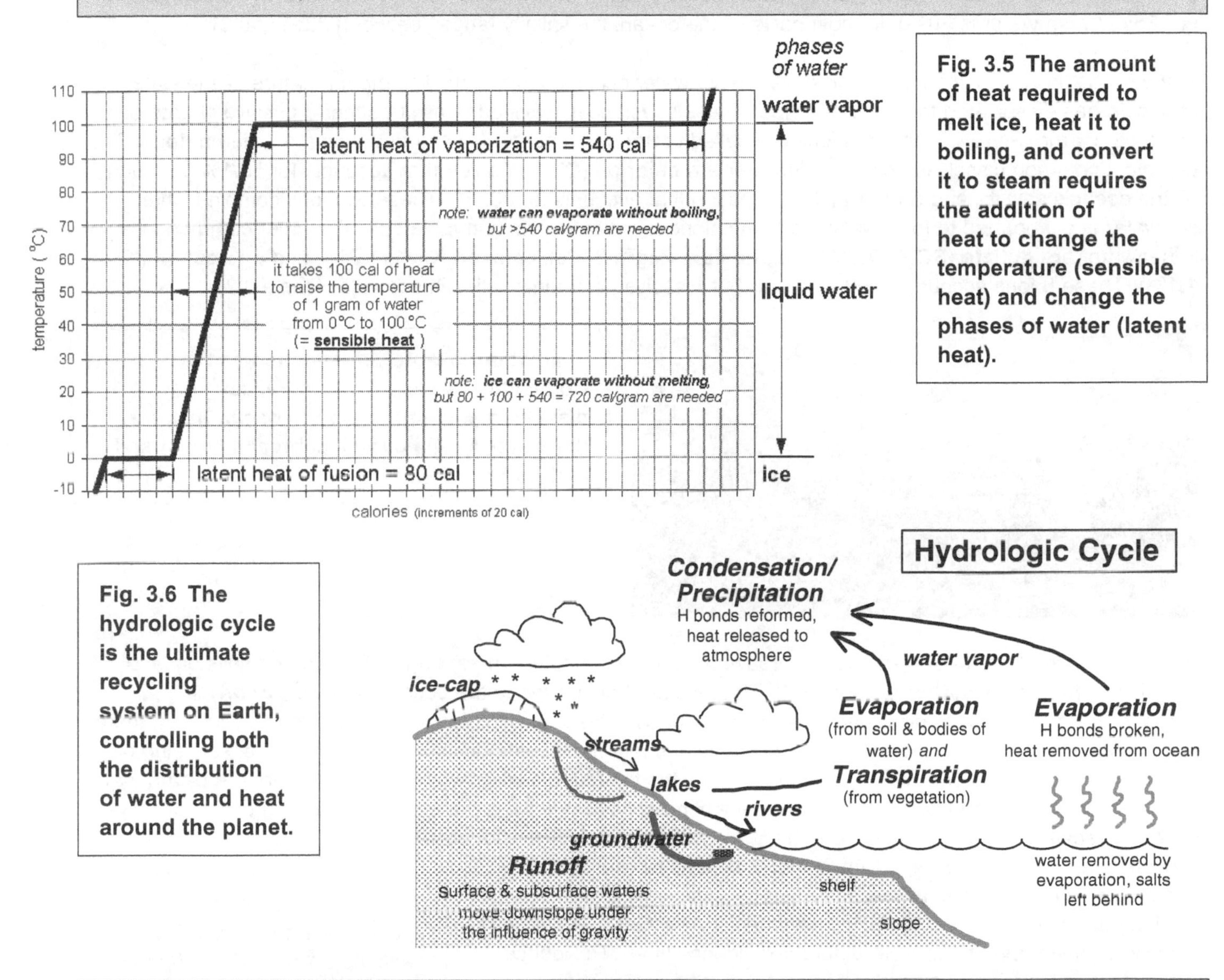

Fig. 3.5 The amount of heat required to melt ice, heat it to boiling, and convert it to steam requires the addition of heat to change the temperature (sensible heat) and change the phases of water (latent heat).

Fig. 3.6 The hydrologic cycle is the ultimate recycling system on Earth, controlling both the distribution of water and heat around the planet.

Food for Thought

The sun showers each square meter (m^2) of the ocean with approximately 1430 calories of energy every second. The surface area of the ocean is 361×10^{12} m^2 and the mass of water in it is 1.4×10^{24} g. If there were no way to remove this heat through the hydrologic cycle, how long would it take for the entire ocean to reach the boiling point from 0°C?

■3.4 Seawater Salinity: the Salt of the Ocean

Anyone who has gotten a mouthful of seawater while swimming in the ocean knows that it contains a lot of salt, which makes it undrinkable for us land-based creatures. **Salinity** refers to the total dissolved solids in water, and these are mostly the ions of mineral salts (such as sodium chloride, NaCl). However, since water is such a good solvent, there are many other substances dissolved in seawater including: 1) **gases** such as oxygen (O_2) and carbon dioxide (CO_2); 2) **nutrients** required by organisms, such as nitrates, phosphates, trace elements, and vitamins; and 3) dissolved **organic molecules**. Average seawater is 96.5% water and 3.5% total dissolved solids (freshwater, is essentially 100% water with only traces of dissolved substances). Oceanographers describe salinity with units of **parts per thousand** (‰; i.e., grams of dissolved solids per kilogram of water, g/kg) rather than percent (%), which is equivalent to parts per hundred. In other words ‰ = 10 x %. **Average ocean salinity is ~35‰** (fresh water is ~0‰). In most parts of the ocean, the salinity ranges between 33‰ and 37‰.

Many of the inorganic substances dissolved in seawater occur in ionic form. The dipolar nature of the water molecule has dissociated the bonds between these substances leaving them with either a positive charge or a negative charge. Positively charged ions are called **cations** and negatively charged ions are called **anions**. The two most common dissolved solids in seawater are **chloride (Cl^-)**, an anion that accounts for 55.1% by weight of the ocean's salinity, and **sodium (Na^+)**, a cation that accounts for 30.6%. These two ions combine when seawater is evaporated to form NaCl (sodium chloride), which is common table salt. The other common ions in seawater are **sulfate (SO_4^{2-}**, 7.7%), **magnesium (Mg^{2+}**, 3.7%), **calcium (Ca^{2+}**, 1.2%), and **potassium (K^+**, 1.1%). These 6 ions account for 99.4% of all the dissolved inorganic solids in seawater (Table 3.3).

In addition to water, rivers such as the Connecticut River shown here, carry dissolved substances to the ocean that are derived from the chemical breakdown of soil and rocks.

A major source of the dissolved solids in seawater is from the natural breakdown of rocks and soils on land known as **chemical weathering** (Fig. 3.7). The ions are transported to the ocean by rivers (**runoff**). If you compare the proportion of dissolved ions in seawater with the proportion found in rivers, you'll notice that there is a significant difference (Table 3.3). For example, the four most common ions in seawater (in descending order of abundance) are Cl^-, Na^+, SO_4^{2-}, and Mg^{2+}, while the top four dissolved components in rivers are bicarbonate (HCO_3^-), Ca^{2+}, SiO_2, and SO_4^{2-}. There are several reasons for this: 1) there are additional sources of dissolved solids in seawater besides runoff from the land, including **hydrothermal circulation** at the spreading centers and **volcanic emissions** (Fig. 3.7); 2) many of the elements and substances dissolved in seawater are used by organisms and 3) some of the ions are incorporated into marine sediments. As a result, the various dissolved ions in the ocean have different residence times. Residence time refers to the length of time an ion remains in seawater before it is used by organisms, buried in sediments, or removed by reaction with the ocean crust at subduction zones or spreading centers. Ions that are involved with biochemical cycles such as Ca^{2+}, HCO_3^-, SiO_2, and Fe (iron) have relatively short residence times (200 years to 2 million years) while the most common ions in seawater, Cl^- and Na^+, are very soluble

The different kinds of marine sediments are discussed in sections 2.14 and 2.15. Biogenic and authigenic sediments can remove large quantities of dissolved ions. The concept of residence time is explored in more detail in section 3.5.

and are not used in biological processes; therefore, they have very long residence times (hundreds of millions of years). The chemical composition of the ocean will have remained relatively constant for long periods of time if the input of dissolved solids into the ocean is the same as the output.

Table 3.3 The composition of seawater and average river water.

Dissolved Ion	Seawater	River Water (Runoff)
chloride (Cl^-)	19.3‰ (‰ = g/kg)	0.008‰ (= 7.8 ppm)
sodium (Na^+)	10.8‰	0.006‰ (6.3 ppm)
sulfate (SO_4^{2-})	2.7‰	0.011‰ (11.2 ppm)
magnesium (Mg^{2+})	1.3‰	0.004‰ (4.1 ppm)
calcium (Ca^{2+})	0.4‰	0.015‰ (15.0 ppm)
potassium (K^+)	0.4‰	0.002‰ (2.3 ppm)
bicarbonate (HCO_3^-)	0.1‰	0.058‰ (58.4 ppm)
silica (SiO_2)	0.003‰	0.013‰ (13.1 ppm)

1‰ (part per thousand) = 1 g salt/kg water (gram per thousand grams); 1‰ = 1000 ppm (part per million)

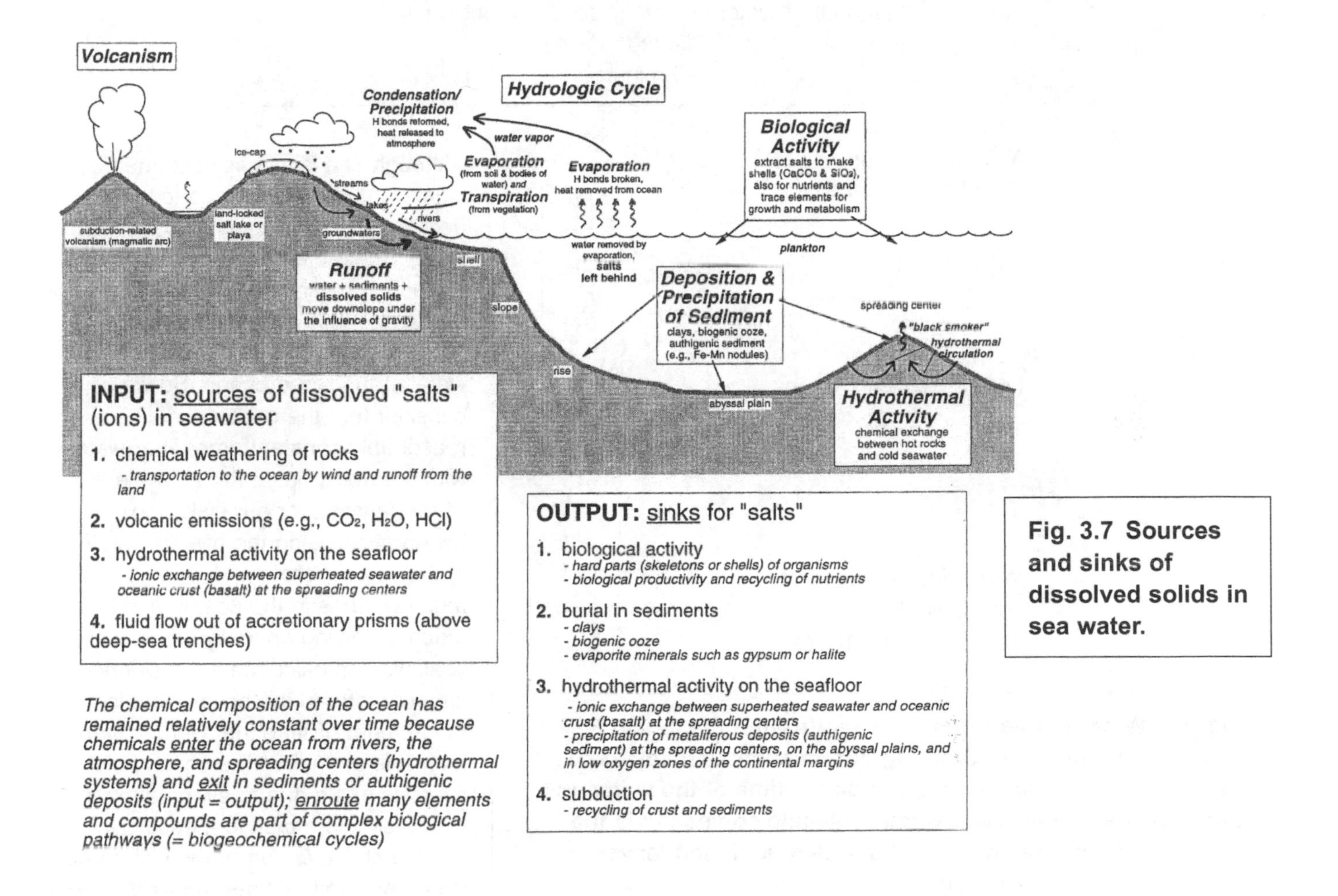

Fig. 3.7 Sources and sinks of dissolved solids in sea water.

Investigation 3.3 looks at the measurement and calculation of salinity.

■3.5 Residence Time of Water in the Ocean

We can observe that water flows into the ocean all the time from rivers great and small around the world. At the same time, we know that sea level stays relatively constant. There is even a passage in the Bible that states: "All the rivers run into the sea, yet the sea doth not overflow: unto the place from whence the rivers come, they return, to flow again." (Ecclesiastes 1:7). This is really an early statement of the hydrologic cycle: water that is transported to the sea by rivers and streams is evaporated into the atmosphere, so that sea level remains essentially constant. In other words, the ocean is in dynamic equilibrium with water; the amount coming in each year balances the amount going out by evaporation. We can reproduce this process in the bathroom sink (Fig. 3.8). Suppose that we fill up our sink until reaches the overflow drain near the rim of the sink. The water stops rising because the water is draining out of the sink at the same rate it is coming in from the faucet. If we turn on the faucet so that is delivering one liter per minute (1 l/min) of water, then the amount leaving via the overflow drain must also be one liter per minute. If our sink holds 10 liters when it is overflowing in this way, then we can calculate the **residence time** of the water in the sink from the following relationship:

Review the principles of the hydrologic cycle that were outlined in an earlier section.

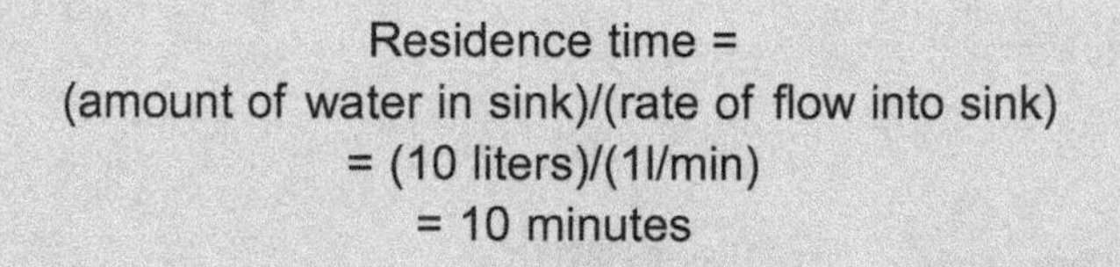

Residence time =
(amount of water in sink)/(rate of flow into sink)
= (10 liters)/(1l/min)
= 10 minutes

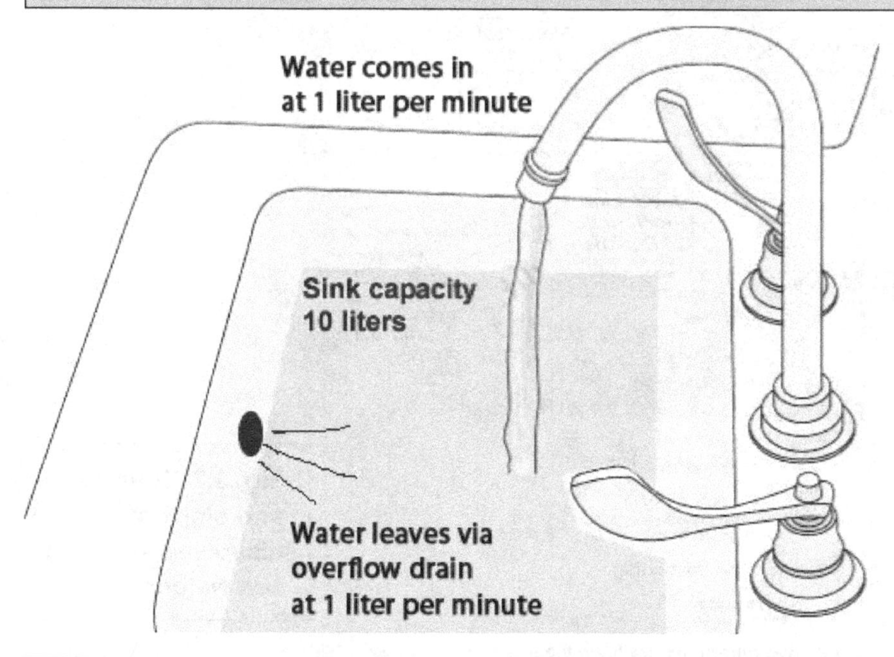

Fig. 3.8 Water coming into the sink through the faucet is balanced by the water draining out. In such a steady-state system we can calculate the residence time of the water. In other words, the average water molecule comes in via the faucet, stays in the sink for 10 minutes, and then leaves through the overflow drain.

Although sea level has fluctuated significantly over time due to the accumulation and melting of polar ice caps, and to changes in the volume of the ocean basins resulting from tectonic processes, this is a small amount in comparison to the total amount of water in the world ocean. So we can consider that the ocean contains a reasonably constant amount of water, with the rivers being the equivalent of the faucet over our sink, and evaporation being the overflow drain in the sink. Therefore, if we know how much water is in the ocean, and how much is flowing annually into it every year, we can calculate the residence time of water in the ocean, that is, the amount of time the average water molecule spends in the ocean before it leaves again due to evaporation. It's not as simple a task to measure the volume of the ocean or the worldwide river flow into it but several researchers have tried to estimate these values and they have come to a general agreement (Table 3.4). Note that the units here are in grams rather than liters, since the mass is a little easier to estimate than the volume. These numbers can be represented on a portion of the hydrologic cycle to provide a better idea as to how water moves around the globe (Fig. 3.9).

Table 3.4 Data for Calculating Residence Time of Water in the Ocean.

Mass of Water in Ocean	$13,700 \times 10^{20}$ g
Annual River Input to Ocean	3.8×10^{20} g/yr

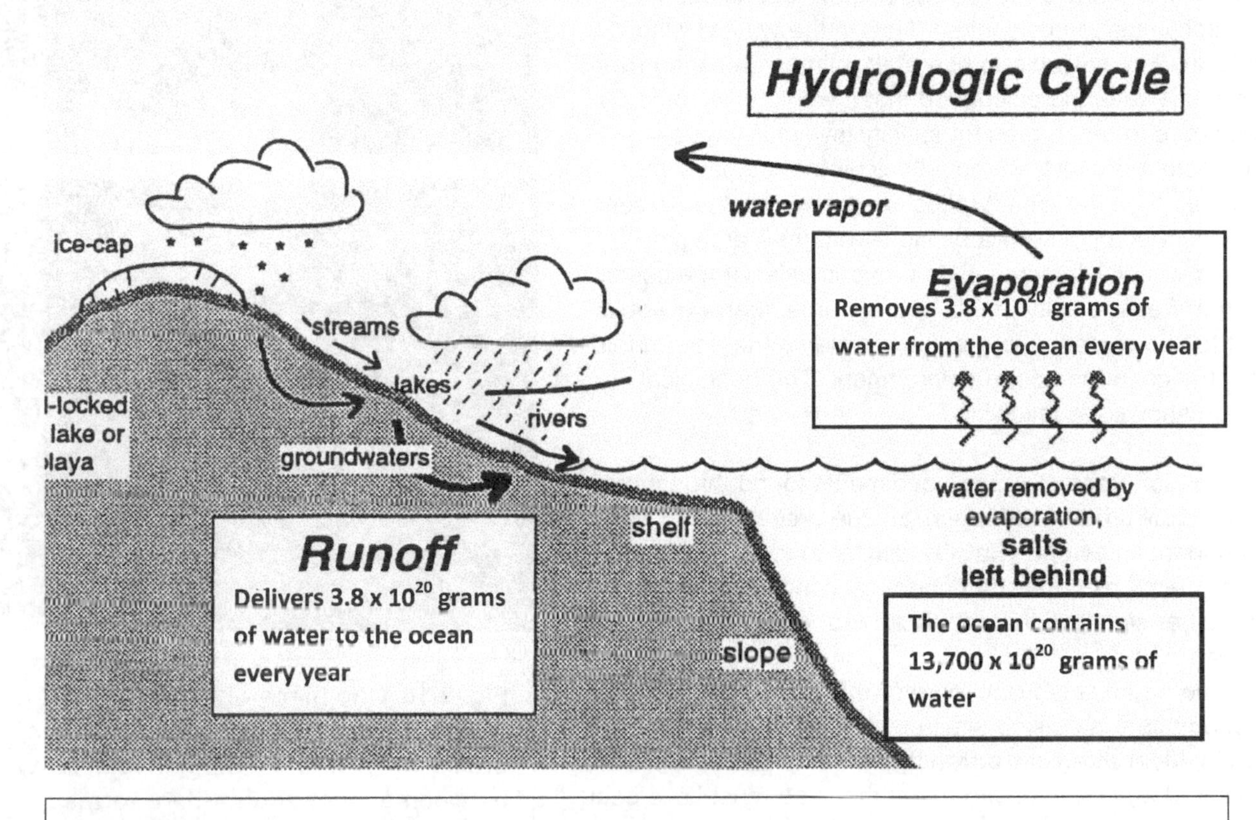

Fig. 3.9 The cycling of water into and out of the ocean is the basis for calculating residence time.

Follow-Up: Residence Time

1). There are 300 students in this room. If every minute during a 24-hour period, one student leaves and another arrives, how long does the average student stay in the room?

2). Calculate the residence time of water in the ocean using the information in table 3.4.

Investigation 3.4 looks at the calculation of residence times for a variety of salts in the ocean.

3.6 Element Cycling and the History of Seawater

As we have documented, seawater contains a high concentration of dissolved salts, mostly derived from the chemical breakdown of rocks and soils on the continents. The water evaporates as part of the hydrologic cycle but the salts are left behind to build up in the ocean. So does this mean that the ocean is getting increasingly salty over time? In 1899, Jon Joly proposed that if the ocean started out as a fresh-water body, we could figure out its age based on the accumulation of sodium (Na^+) in the water. Using the information available to him at that time comparing river water to seawater, he calculated that it would take some 90 million years to reach present salinity levels. If the ocean had no output of salts, we could calculate the age of the ocean based on the time it takes to accumulate the present-day concentration in seawater. However, there are some problems with Joly's original idea (hypothesis). If the ocean went from fresh to salty in this span of time, then we would expect to see evidence in marine sediments that record this major change in the ocean environment. The geological evidence shows the following:

Fig. 3.10 One piece of evidence for the relative constancy of the composition of sea water is the biological similarity between extinct and modern forms of marine life. The Cretaceous-age ammonite (a) has many similarities in form with the modern chambered nautilus (b).

1. The major types of marine sediments found throughout geological time are very similar. The presence of abundant limestone ($CaCO_3$: similar to today's calcareous ooze) requires consistent chemical conditions that do not differ significantly from those that exist in the present ocean.
2. Marine organisms from some of the earliest geological periods bear a striking similarity to modern sea life (Fig. 3.10). Most scientists agree that these organisms probably required an ocean environment that also must have been similar to the one that exists today. It is probably also true that the preservation and evolution of life is also favored by a constant chemical environment.
3. Salt deposits (Fig. 3.11) are found in many ancient marine deposits. These indicate that parts of the ocean were saline enough to precipitate salt in the past, and it also shows that salt can be removed from the ocean.

You can review the various kinds of marine sediments in section 2.14 and 2.15.

The dissolved salts in seawater apparently do not increase constantly over time. They are delivered to the ocean by rivers and accumulate until they are removed by other processes. Some, such as calcium (Ca^{2+}), are used by organisms for making shells. Others, such as sodium (Na^+), can only be removed by the precipitation of evaporite minerals (like common salt, NaCl), which occurs relatively infrequently in geological time. Just as we did for the analysis of water in the ocean, we can measure the input of the various dissolved salts by measuring the rate at which they are brought to the sea by the world's rivers. If we presume, as the evidence suggests, that the ocean stays relatively constant in its salinity, that means the input equals the output for dissolved salts as well as for water, and the residence time for salt can be calculated in a similar fashion. Estimated residence times for the major dissolved ions and their possible outputs (sinks) are shown in Table 3.5. The more reactive elements (mostly those used in biological processes) have the shorter residence times

Table 3.5 Residence times of major elements in seawater.

Dissolved Ion	Residence Time	Output (Sink)
chloride (Cl^-)	103 million years	Salt deposits
sodium (Na^+)	71 million years	Salt deposits, hydrothermal
sulfate (SO_4^{2-})	10 million years	Salt deposits, hydrothermal
magnesium (Mg^{2+})	14 million years	Hydrothermal, sediments
calcium (Ca^{2+})	1 million years	Biogenic ooze
potassium (K^+)	7 million years	Salt deposits, sediments
bicarbonate (HCO_3^-)	100,000 years	Biogenic ooze
silica (SiO_2)	20,000 years	Biogenic ooze, sediments

Fig. 3.11 Ocean salts can be removed periodically when parts of the sea are isolated by geologic processes and thick evaporite deposits form such as these from the Permian Castile Formation in New Mexico.

Food for Thought

Chloride has the longest residence time for any dissolved component in seawater (Table 3.5), yet this is only a fraction of the known age of Planet Earth. How does chloride get back into the ocean once it has been deposited as salt? Can you estimate how many times the average chloride ion has been cycled through the ocean during the Earth's 4.6 billion-year history?

Investigation 3.5 provides more information on the chemistry of seawater.

■3.7 Seawater Density: The Role of Heat & Salt

Temperature and salinity, together with pressure, control the density of seawater, and the relationship among the three variables is complex. For our purposes, we will focus on the effects of temperature and salinity. The more heat liquid water absorbs, the faster the water molecules vibrate (which becomes sensible heat or a temperature rise) and the further apart the molecules become. In this way, warm water is less dense than cold water. Therefore, warm water floats on cold water and accounts for the thermal and **density stratification** (layering) of the ocean in the tropical and temperate climate belts where there is sufficient solar radiation to warm the surface waters. In other words, warm, less dense water occurs as a surface layer over cold, dense deep waters in the low to mid-latitudes.

Table 3.6 Density of water (in g/cm³) as a function of temperature and salinity.

°C	*0‰*	*20‰*	*25‰*	*30‰*	*35‰*
0	0.99984	1.01607	1.02008	1.02410	1.02813
5	0.99996	1.01586	1.01980	1.02374	1.02770
10	0.99970	1.01532	1.01920	1.02308	1.02697
15	0.99910	1.01450	1.01832	1.02215	1.02599
20	0.99820	1.01342	1.01720	1.02098	1.02478

Substances dissolved in water also make the water denser. Salt water is denser than freshwater. The higher the salinity, the greater is the density of seawater (Table 3.6). Furthermore, the addition of salt changes some of the fundamental physical properties of water. Of greatest significance for the ocean, it lowers the freezing point, such that water with the salinity of the ocean can exist as a liquid down to temperatures as low as –2°C. This lowering of the freezing point is the reason why salt is used to de-ice roads in the winter. As we saw in our earlier discussion in section 3.1, salt also changes the temperature of maximum density, making the coldest water the densest so that it naturally settles to the bottom of the ocean basin. In places where precipitation and runoff from the land are high, river water (freshwater) can greatly dilute coastal waters making them less salty and less dense than average seawater. Surface water salinities are also diluted in tropical areas of the open ocean where there is abundant rainfall. In places where evaporation from the surface of the ocean is high, such as in the subtropics, surface water salinities are typically higher. In the Mediterranean Sea, for example, excessive evaporation creates warm, salty waters which become dense enough to sink and flow out of the Mediterranean and into the North Atlantic where it forms an important intermediate water mass called Mediterranean Intermediate Water or MIW.

Estuaries are places where rivers meet the sea, and different degrees of mixing between fresh water and seawater occur here. In some situations the less dense river water may mix with the seawater, and in other places it may flow seaward above the more dense seawater. These environments are examined more fully in section 6.3.

We will examine the phenomenon of density layering in the next section.

When water becomes denser by cooling or by processes of the **hydrologic cycle**, such as evaporation or sea ice formation, it may sink to become a distinct intermediate or deep water mass. A **water mass** is a body of water that can be identified by its physical and chemical characteristics (temperature, salinity, density, dissolved gases, and dissolved nutrients) (Fig. 3.12). Intermediate and deep waters sink to their level of **neutral buoyancy** (equilibrium) below the sun-warmed surface waters.

Density is mass (quantity of matter) per unit volume. A typical unit of density is g/cm³ (grams per cubic centimeter) or kg/m³ (kilograms per cubic meter). Pure water (freshwater) at a temperature of 25°C has a density of 1.000 g/cm³ (or 1000 kg/m³). The density of seawater, which contains dissolved solids, varies between **1.022** and **1.028 g/cm³**. Because both salinity and temperature control density, warm tropical surface waters are closer to 1.022 g/cm³ whereas cold polar surface waters and deep waters are closer to 1.028 g/cm³. Oceanographers prefer a less cumbersome unit than g/cm³ or kg/m³ because of the important but subtle differences in seawater density. They use **σ_t (sigma tee)** which can be calculated by the equation:

In section 4.11 we will learn more about how density controlled by salinity and temperature forms specific water masses that are major features of global ocean circulation

$$\sigma_t = [\text{density, (g/cm}^3) - 1.000] \times 1000.$$

Therefore, typical ocean density values range between **22.0** and **28.0 σ_t** units (σ_t is based on measured temperature, measured salinity, and atmospheric pressure; it has not been corrected for pressure) (Fig. 3.12).

Fig 3.12 The T-S-σ_t diagram shows how the density of seawater varies in response to changes in temperature and salinity.

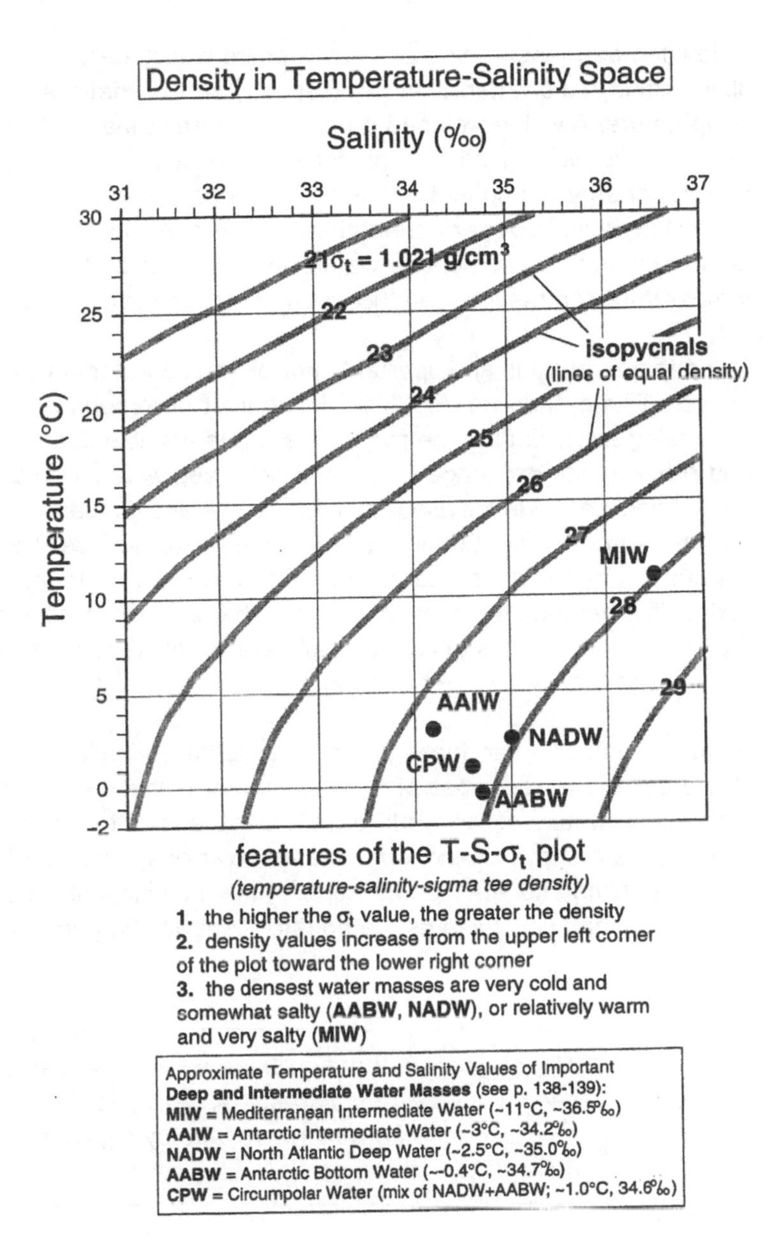

Follow-Up

For further information about seawater density and salinity (plus a fun activity), go to http://www.windows.ucar.edu/tour/link=/earth/Water/density.html&edu=high

Investigation 3.6 looks at ways to determine the density of seawater.

3.8 Density Layering in the Ocean

Variations in temperature and salinity team up to create layers of different density in the ocean that are related to the location in latitude. As solar energy heats the surface waters in the low to mid-latitudes (0° to 45°), it creates a warm, less dense surface layer over very cold deep waters (Fig. 3.13). This **permanent thermocline** is the interval through which temperature decreases rapidly with increasing water depth. The thermocline extends from the base of the **mixed layer**, at a depth of about 50 to100 meters to approximately 900-1000 m. The depth of the surface mixed layer depends upon the mixing (homogenization) of the warmed surface waters by the day-to-day winds and storms, waves and surface currents. In the middle latitudes, winter storms tend to be bigger than summer storms; therefore the mixed layer is usually deeper during the winter months. Summer heating causes the creation of a **seasonal thermocline** (a steeper temperature gradient than during the winter).

Below the permanent thermocline the entire world ocean is filled with icy cold waters that possess only small variations in temperature. A well-developed permanent thermocline exists in the low latitudes and into the mid-latitudes because of the strength of solar energy, although the temperature gradient weakens with increasing latitude. A permanent thermocline does not exist in polar regions because surface waters are *very cold* and deep waters are *very cold*. Therefore, there is little temperature contrast/gradient between polar surface and deep waters.

In section 3.19 and 3.20 we will see how the sinking of cold, saline water at poles is an important part of global ocean circulation.

Since temperature is an important control on sea water density, the thermal barrier can also be a density barrier as well. This pycnocline (Fig. 3.14) is the interval through which seawater density (g/cm^3) increases rapidly with increasing water depth. The pycnocline forms a stable density barrier between surface and deep water masses, and prevents the exchange of nutrient-rich deep waters with the surface ocean. Like the permanent thermocline, the pycnocline is well-developed in the tropics and temperate latitudes, and the top of the pycnocline can be anywhere from 50 to 150 meters below the ocean surface. The top of the pycnocline corresponds to the base of the surface mixed layer. The base of the pycnocline is around 1000 meters in the low to mid-latitudes. Density varies little beneath the pycnocline. As with the thermocline, there is no pycnocline in the polar regions, allowing the deep ocean waters to rise and fall freely in these regions. As we noted in section 3.7, oceanographers use σ_t units to describe seawater density.

Relatively limited solar heating in the high latitudes inhibits the development of a permanent thermocline and stable pycnocline. Because of the absence of stable density stratification, the high latitudes are the doorways to the deep waters of the world ocean. Deep and bottom waters, those water masses below the permanent thermocline and pycnocline, originate as polar or subpolar surface waters. During the long winter months, intense cooling and sea ice formation cause the high latitude surface waters to become denser. These dense waters sink and flow towards the equator beneath the permanent thermocline and pycnocline.

The permanent thermocline is an effective barrier that prevents the mixing of cold, deep water with the surface mixed layer. This limits the amount of nutrients that can be brought up from below for use by organisms. We will examine these processes more thoroughly in section 4.6.

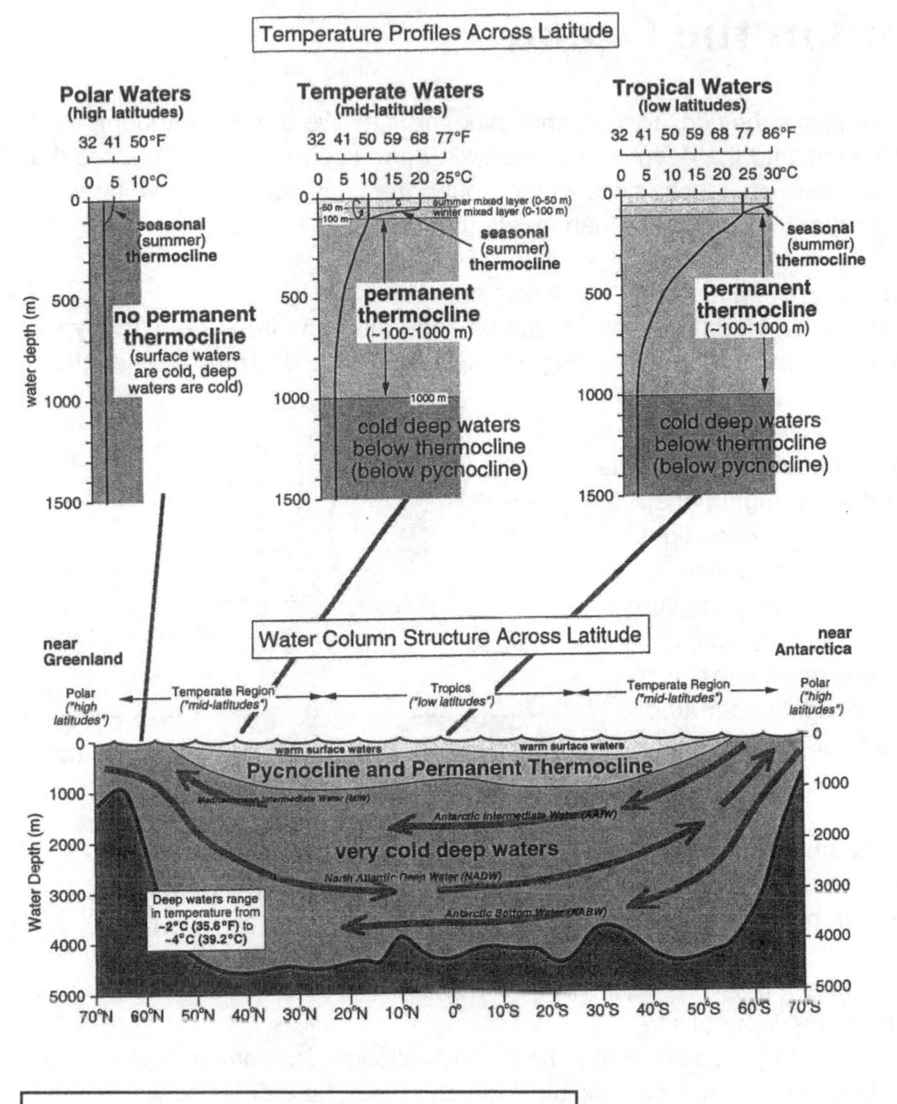

Fig. 3.13 The world ocean is well-stratified (layered) in the low to mid-latitudes due to solar heating of surface waters and the formation of a permanent thermocline. The thermocline separates warm (less dense) surface waters from icy cold (much more dense) deep waters. The pycnocline represents this density barrier between surface and deep waters. Insufficient solar heating in the high latitudes inhibits the formation of a permanent thermocline and pycnocline.

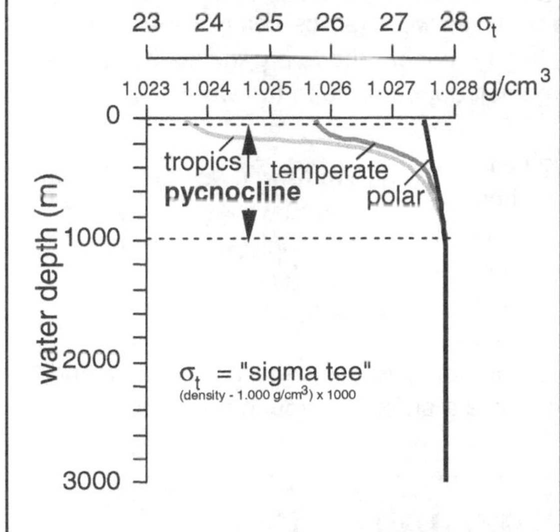

Fig. 3.14 The pycnocline is the vertical interval in the ocean where density increases rapidly with depth. The pycnocline is very well developed in the tropics, but almost absent in the polar ocean.

Investigation 3.7 focuses on the nature and location of the thermocline and pycnocline in the ocean.

■3.9 Light and Sound in the Ocean

Everyone knows the color of the ocean, or thinks they do. The ocean is blue, or is it? We are all thoroughly familiar with the azure blue of the tropical seas and the deep blue of the wide-open ocean, but what causes the variability in the shades of this color? Even more so, much of the water around the coastlines of the world is more green than blue. So clearly, there is more to ocean color than meets the eye.

The color we see depends upon the interaction of light energy with water molecules.
As you know, sunlight is actually composed of various colors, which can be separated one from the other by passing sunlight through a prism or diffraction grating and generating a spectrum. These different wavelengths of light interact with water molecules in different ways. The red and orange colors, those at long-wavelength end of the spectrum, are readily absorbed by water. The energy of these wavelengths is converted to heat. In the ocean, the red wavelength penetrates only to about 10 m below the surface (Fig. 3.15). Yellow light is completely absorbed by 100 m. Only green and blue wavelengths penetrate deeper than this. The intensity of light at great depths is very low. In general, only 1% of all light energy reaches depths of ~100 m, and this region is the **euphotic zone**, where photosynthesis can occur. In general, no sunlight penetrates below a depth of about 1000 m (the **photic zone**). Much of the ocean is completely dark.

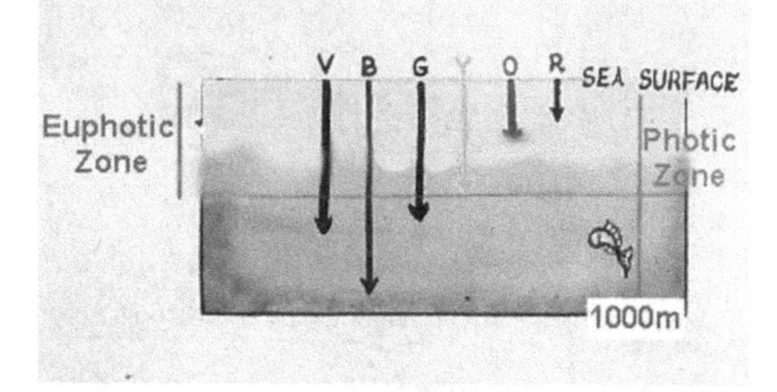

Fig. 3.15 Blue light can reach greater depth in the ocean than other colors. The euphotic zone is where light energy is intense enough for photosynthesis to take place. The base of the photic zone is where light energy disappears entirely.

Life in the ocean depends upon the availability of light energy to drive the process of photosynthesis or primary productivity. We will examine this further in section 4.4.

The depth to which light can penetrate is very variable. The numbers cited above are typical of clear water in the open ocean, but in coastal waters, the depth of the euphotic and photic zones can be much shallower. Suspended sediment or an abundance of microscopic plankton can restrict the depth to which light will penetrate. Moreover, these particles will alter the color of the water. Chlorophyll is a green photosynthetic pigment in many plankton. In large numbers these organisms will scatter the solar radiation in the yellow and green wavelengths to give a greenish appearance to the water.

Sound travels more than four times faster through water than through air, 1,480 meters per second (m/s) in water versus about 340 m/s in air. There is some variability due to temperature. Because the density of water is much greater than that of air, the molecules of water are much closer together and sound waves can be transmitted over longer distances in water. This allows sound waves to be used effectively to determine the depth of the ocean and also allows ships to listen for submarines at great distances. Whales and dolphins communicate using sound, and the plaintive call of the humpback whale is a well known sound that is a subject of much research.

We saw in section 1.7 how sound waves are used in the application of echo sounding.

Food for Thought: Underwater Photography

If you have tried to take pictures underwater, you may have noticed that everything has a bluish cast. Can you explain why this happens? Many professional photographers use a red filter when filming or photographing in the ocean. Explain why this improves picture quality.

Follow Up: Are We Making the Ocean Too Noisy for Whales?

Over the past several years a heated debate has sprung up over the sensitivity of marine mammals to noises that are introduced as part of ocean research and military exercises. The most contentious of these involved an experiment proposed in 1994 to test whether the ocean is undergoing a measurable temperature increase in response to the Earth's changing climate. The plan was to put low-frequency loudspeakers underwater off the the coast of California and Hawaii and track changes in the time that these transmissions reached receivers in other parts of the Pacific. In theory, if the ocean is heating up, then the speed of these sound waves will increase over time. This experiment was opposed by marine biologists who study whales and other marine mammals. Their concern was that the low-frequency sound waves could interfere with the ability of whales to navigate in the ocean. Whales and other marine mammals use echolocation to determine distance and find food, and the presence of this new sound source could jeopardize their very survival, in violation of the Marine Mammal Protection Act of 1972. The dispute led to Congressional hearings, and the sound experiment was never carried out.

More recently, in 2003, the U.S. Navy wanted to experiment with a new low-frequency sonar system that would be better able to detect the quieter generation of submarines that are being developed. Environmental groups claimed that earlier sonar operations had killed and severely injured numerous animals. In March, 2000, hours after a sonar experiment was conducted in the Caribbean, at least 18 whales and dolphins beached themselves in the Bahamas. Several died. In addition, British and Spanish researchers reported the deaths of 14 whales that beached themselves in the Canary Islands after a sonar experiment in that part of the world. Autopsies on these whales indicated that they developed gas bubbles in their organs and blood vessels, a condition similar to the "bends" that divers get if they surface too quickly. The researchers thought that the acoustic signals from the sonar may have caused them to become disoriented and rise from deep waters too quickly, resulting in the formation of the gas bubbles. A court order ultimately restricted the Navy to test its sonar system in restricted areas away from the presence of marine mammals.

In October of 2005, another lawsuit was filed against the Navy, contending that mid-frequency sonar was responsible for the deaths of 37 whales on the Outer Banks of North Carolina. The suit wants the navy to monitor for the presence of marine mammals before it uses this equipment. This suit is still pending.

Research on this topic is continuing. We use sound waves in the ocean for many purposes: determining its depth, exploring for oil and gas, analyzing the layering of the sediments on the sea floor. In addition, the noise from ships and other marine operations could be of equal or greater significance in affecting whales and other marine mammals, and further studies of these sources is also needed.

For Further Information

"2 Environmental Camps Feud Over Noisy Ocean Experiment" New York Times, April 5, 1994.

"Judge Limits Navy's Use of Sonar" CBSNews.com, August 27, 2003.

"Whale Deaths Linked to Sonar" New York Times, October 15, 2003.

"Navy is Sued on Use of Sonar in Exercises", New York Times, October 20, 2005.

http://news.nationalgeographic.com/news/2007/05/070502-whales-video.html

http://news.nationalgeographic.com/news/2003/10/1008_031008_whalebends.html

■3.10 Solar Energy, Winds, and Ocean Currents

The energy that powers the surface processes of the Earth comes from the sun. The sun evaporates the water, which generates the winds that move the currents and waves, and, of course, the energy from the sun drives photosynthesis in plants. The sun is approximately 93 million miles (~150 million km) from Earth and its diameter is ~100 times greater than that of the Earth. Because of its great distance and size, solar energy reaches the Earth as parallel rays. However, the distribution of incoming solar radiation (**insolation**) across Earth's surface is uneven because of the spherical shape of the planet. There are also significant seasonal changes in the amount of solar radiation received at any given latitude because Earth's axis of rotation is tilted 23.5° relative to its orbital plane around the Sun, known as the **plane of the ecliptic**.

The low latitudes (the tropical climate belt from 0° to ~23.5 north and south latitude) receive abundant solar radiation throughout the year because of the high angle of solar incidence. In these low latitudes, the sun is high in the sky at mid-day (Fig. 3.16). More solar radiation is received during daylight hours than is radiated back into space at night, so there is a net gain of insolation (Fig 3.17). In fact, if the annual solar surplus were not removed in some way, the tropical oceans would reach the boiling point.

The high latitudes (the polar climate belt that extends from 60° north or south to the poles) experience a net loss of insolation over the course of a year (Fig. 3.17) because of the lower angle of solar incidence. During the summer months, the sun is low in the sky at mid-day and there can be total darkness during some of the winter months. The same amount of solar energy that strikes the low latitudes is dispersed across a much larger surface area in the high latitudes (Fig. 3.16). Heat absorbed by the ocean and atmosphere in the high latitudes is less than the energy radiated back to space. Without a way to add heat to the polar regions, the ocean there would be frozen solid.

We will investigate the mechanisms on the Earth that generate the prevailing winds in section 3.12. The specifics of the large-scale circulation patterns in the ocean are the subject of sections 3.16 and 3.17.

We discuss the tilt of the Earth's axis and its effect on global climate in section 3.11.

Differences between temperature or pressure in the atmosphere or ocean across the globe cause the air or water to move in directions that correct the unequal heat distribution. Water masses and air masses move from areas of high pressure to areas of low pressure. In general, global high pressure zones exist in the tropical regions, with low pressures persisting over the poles. The ocean and atmosphere share about equally in redistributing the excess heat of the tropics toward the heat-deficient Polar Regions.

1. The evaporation of water during the hydrologic cycle is the first step in transferring heat from the ocean to the atmosphere. Hydrogen bonds are broken during the evaporation of water and latent heat is removed from the ocean. As moisture-rich air masses cool, condensation of water vapor causes tiny water droplets to form, clouds to build, and precipitation to fall. During the process of condensation, hydrogen bonds form between water molecules and latent heat is released to the atmosphere. Prevailing winds carry this heat to other parts of the globe and in this way tropical heat is redistributed to the higher latitudes.

2. The ocean also transports heat by large surface currents of the upper water masses. For example, the **subtropical gyres** are circular patterns of currents that transport warm waters toward the pole along the western sides of the ocean basins and cool waters toward the equator along the eastern sides. Examples of this circulation pattern include the **Gulf Stream** (warm) and **Canary Current** (cool) in the North Atlantic, and the **Kuroshio Current** (warm) and **California Current** (cool) in the North Pacific.

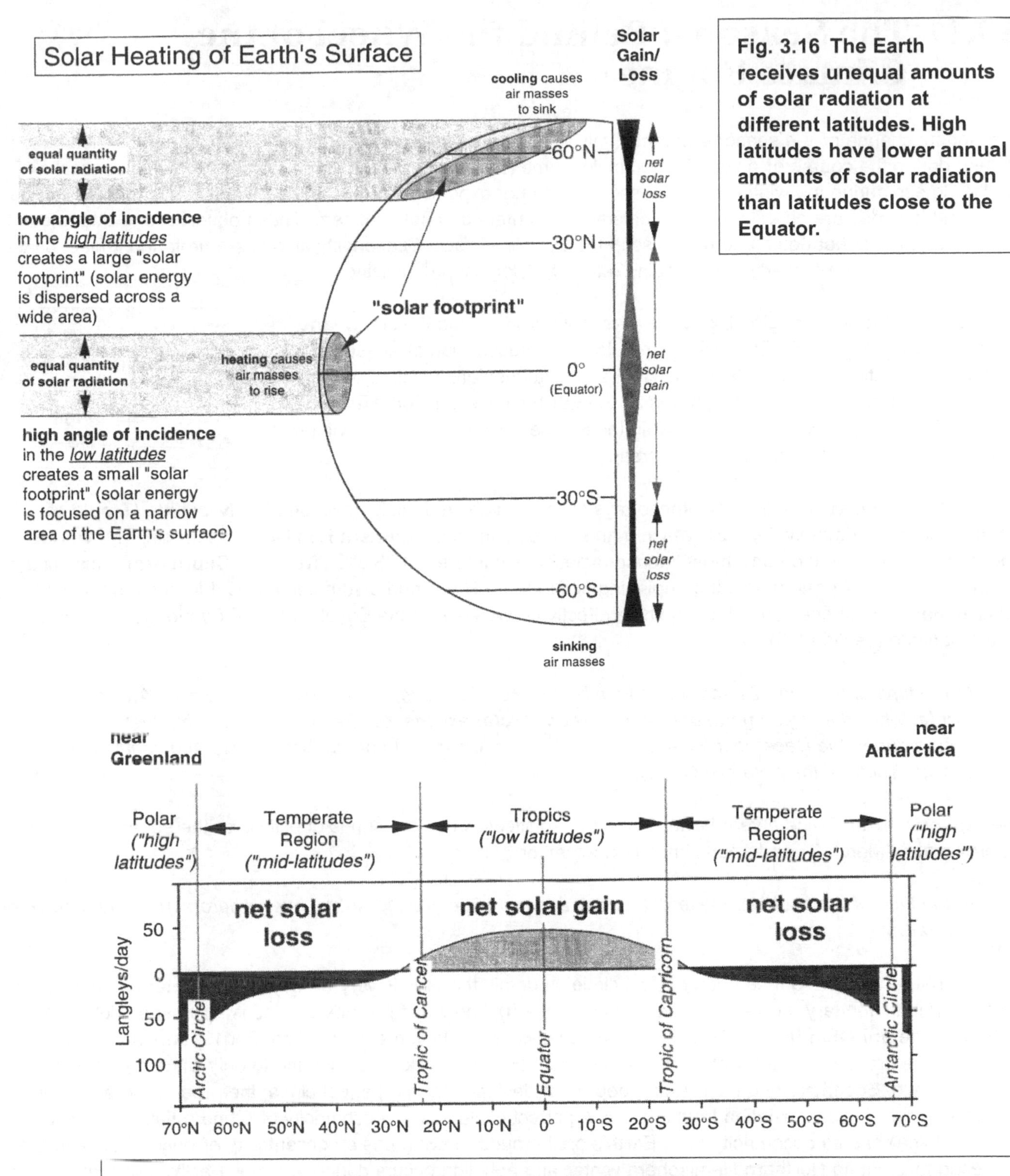

Fig. 3.16 The Earth receives unequal amounts of solar radiation at different latitudes. High latitudes have lower annual amounts of solar radiation than latitudes close to the Equator.

Fig. 3.17 The tropical ocean receives more solar energy than it loses; the reverse is true in the temperate and polar latitudes. Some mechanism for redistributing this energy must exist or else the ocean would boil in the tropics and permanently freeze at the poles.

Investigation 3.8 probes the relationship among latitude, the time of year, and the height of the sun in the sky.

■3.11 The Seasons: Behind the Wheel of the Climate Engine

The annual change of the seasons–summer, fall, winter, and spring–has a profound influence on the distribution of heat during the course of a year. For example, some localities in the very high latitudes experience weeks of total darkness during the winter, and then six months later experience weeks without night, while many localities in the mid-latitudes are characterized by bitterly cold winters and hot summers. These observations illustrate the yearly extremes of heat gain and heat loss at the Earth's surface. Seasonality also has a profound impact on the Earth's biosphere, particularly the changing rates of biological productivity.

The Earth is tilted at an angle of **23.5**° relative to its orbit around the sun (**plane of the ecliptic**) (Fig. 3.18). This axial tilt results in the succession of seasons because distribution of most intense sunlight and solar insolation shifts between the Northern and Southern Hemispheres as the Earth moves in its orbit around the sun. For example, when it is summer in the Northern Hemisphere, it is winter in the Southern Hemisphere *(and vise versa)*.

In sections 4.4 and 4.6, we will look further at how the changes in seasons affect the ability of the ocean to support life.

At the **summer solstice**, the most intense rays of the sun shine directly down on 23.5°N latitude (**Tropic of Cancer)** on approximately June 21, which marks the beginning of Northern Hemisphere summer. The **winter solstice** occurs when the sun's most intense radiation is centered at 23.5°S (**Tropic of Capricorn)**. This occurs around December 21 and marks the beginning of Southern Hemisphere summer. It was during the summer solstice that Eratosthenes saw the sun shine directly down a well in the Egyptian city of Syene, which is at 23.5°N latitude (section 1.6).

> *At the time of the June 21 solstice, no sunlight strikes the Earth's surface south of 66.5°S (**Antarctic Circle**) while the region north of 66.5°N (**Arctic Circle**) experiences 24 hours of daylight. Just the reverse occurs during the December 21 solstice (i.e., total darkness north of the Arctic Circle and continuous sunlight south of the Antarctic Circle).*

The **equinox** occurs twice a year between the two solstices, when the sun is directly over the equator, 0° (approximately March 21 and approximately September 21).

> *At the time of the equinox, the length of day and night is equal (12 hours) everywhere across the surface of the Earth.*

Earth's orbit around the Sun is not a perfect circle. In detail, the orbit is very slightly elliptical. Earth is closest to the Sun around January 3 (at a distance of 147 x 10^6 km), known as **perihelion**, and is farthest on July 6 (152 x 10^6 km), the **aphelion** (Fig 3.19). The difference between perihelion and aphelion (5 x 10^6 km) is very small relative to the greatest diameter of Earth's orbital path (~299 x 10^6 km), amounting to only a 3% deviation from a perfect circle. **Eccentricity** describes the degree of deviation from a perfect circle; the greater the eccentricity, the greater the elliptical deviation from a circle. A perfect circle has an eccentricity of 0 and a flattened circle (= straight line) has an eccentricity of 1. Earth's orbit around the Sun has an eccentricity of only 0.017, and the perihelion falls during Northern Hemisphere winter, and aphelion occurs during summer. Earth's eccentricity has a minimal effect on yearly changes in insolation across latitude and so, contrary to a common misconception, the distance of the Earth from the sun has almost no effect on the changing of the seasons.

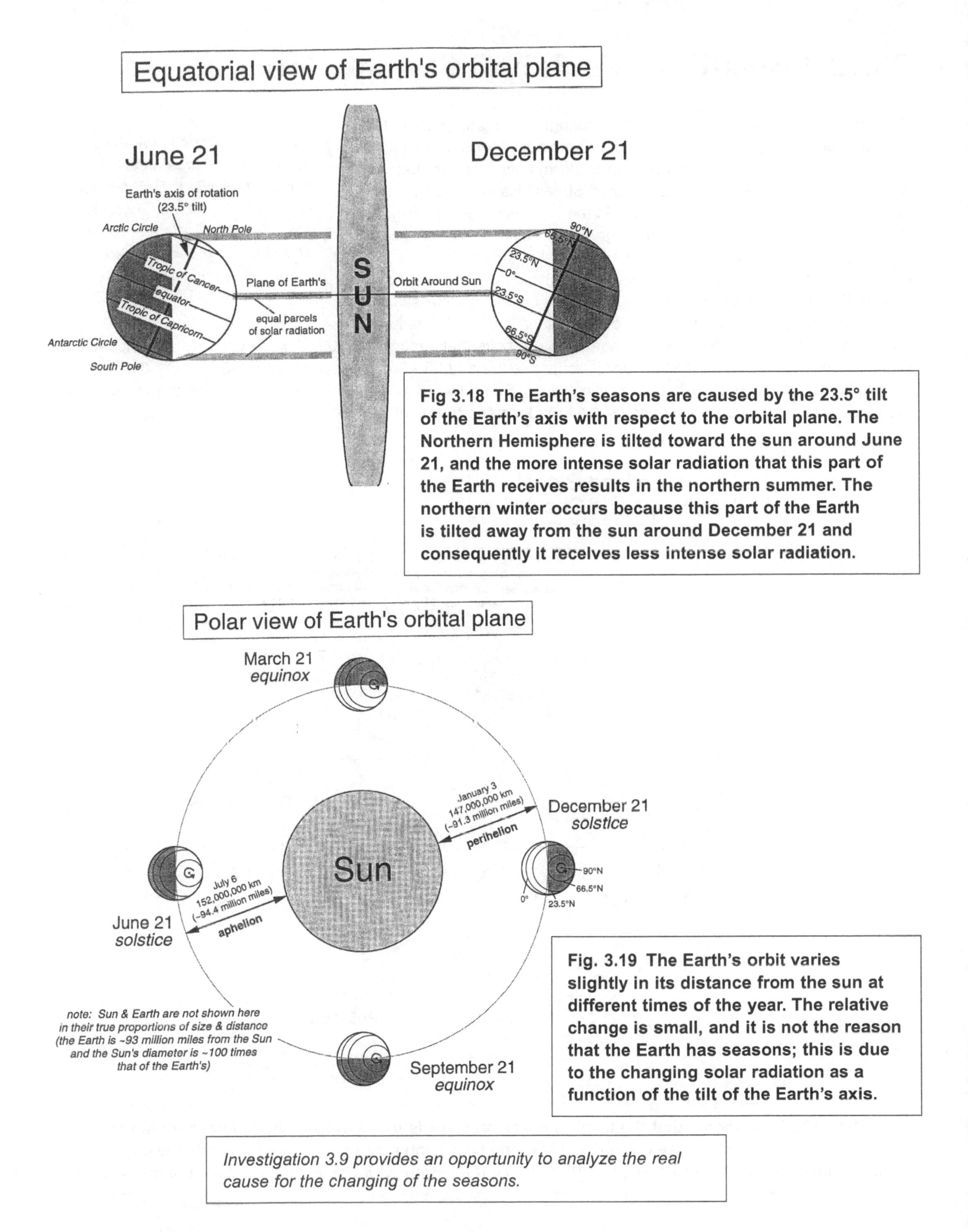

Fig 3.18 The Earth's seasons are caused by the 23.5° tilt of the Earth's axis with respect to the orbital plane. The Northern Hemisphere is tilted toward the sun around June 21, and the more intense solar radiation that this part of the Earth receives results in the northern summer. The northern winter occurs because this part of the Earth is tilted away from the sun around December 21 and consequently it receives less intense solar radiation.

Fig. 3.19 The Earth's orbit varies slightly in its distance from the sun at different times of the year. The relative change is small, and it is not the reason that the Earth has seasons; this is due to the changing solar radiation as a function of the tilt of the Earth's axis.

Investigation 3.9 provides an opportunity to analyze the real cause for the changing of the seasons.

■3.12 Prevailing Winds and Climate Zones

The Trade Winds in the Pacific can decrease substantially during an El Niño. The monsoon pattern in the Indian Ocean can also alter the Trade Winds there. These phenomena are explored more fully in section 3.15.

We are all familiar with how the weather changes during the different seasons, but have you ever noticed on TV weather reports how weather patterns (zones of high and low pressure, storm tracks, and fronts) move from west to east across the United States? Have you ever noticed the general path of hurricanes in the Northern Hemisphere, first migrating west in the tropics and then gradually hooking to the right as these cyclones move away from their tropical birthplace? These phenomena are due to zonal wind patterns that we call the **prevailing winds** (Fig. 3.20). These are not the day-to-day or hour-to-hour shifting of the local winds. Instead, these are distinct global zones of weather development and migration. These zones comprise belts that stretch around the globe between specific latitudes, like the tropical zone (0°–~23.5° latitude), temperate zone (23.5°–66.5°), or polar zone (66.5°–90°). These zones are each characterized by distinct prevailing winds. Storm tracks move from east to west in the tropics and near the poles, and from west to east across the broad temperate belt of the mid-latitudes.

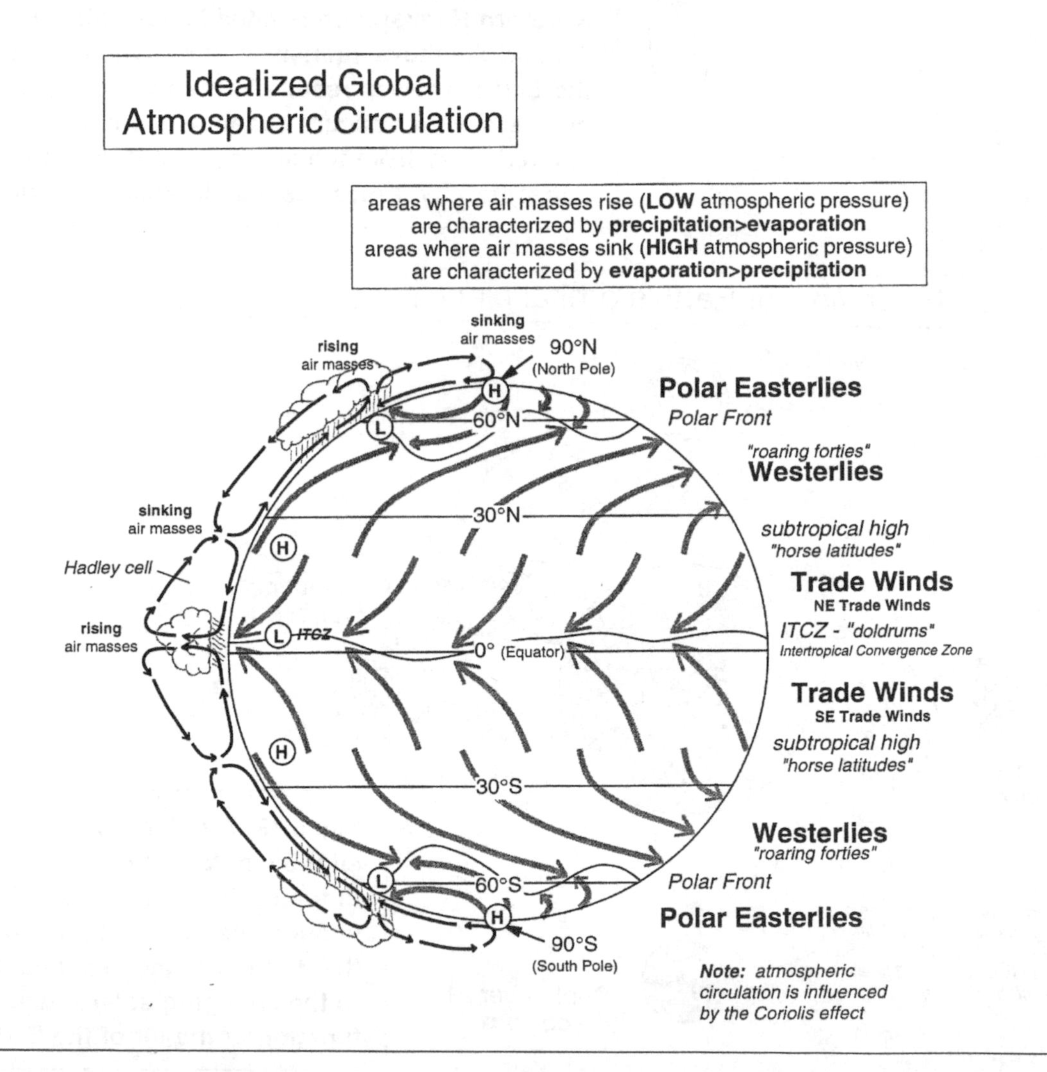

Fig. 3.20 The heat energy that the tropical ocean receives is transferred to the atmosphere at the Equator. This warmed air rises, forming a low-pressure center, and winds blow towards the equator to replace this air. This Hadley cell circulation drives the pattern of surface winds across the entire globe.

The atmosphere is heated most intensely by the sun in the tropics. The molecules in the warmed air vibrate faster and move farther apart, and as a result, the density of the warmed air decreases a bit. These lower-density air masses rise and cause a regional low atmospheric pressure because rising air masses exert less pressure on Earth's surface. Surface winds rush in to replace the rising air. These surface winds are called the **Northeast Trade Winds** north of the Equator and **Southeast Trade Winds** south of the Equator, and they represent the prevailing winds of the tropics. The Trade Winds are among the most constant winds on the planet, except in the Pacific during an **El Niño** event. The meeting (convergence) of the NE Trades and the SE Trades near the equator is the **Intertropical Convergence Zone** (**ITCZ**). As hot, moist air masses rise in the ITCZ, these air masses cool and water vapor condenses to produce abundant precipitation (Fig. 3.20). Sailors sometimes refer to this region as the **"doldrums"** because of extended periods of slack winds alternating with tropical squalls. Air masses generally rise at the ITCZ, except for the downdrafts associated with thunderstorms, which provide the wind to fill the sails. The position of the ITCZ moves seasonally and is north of the equator in most regions due to the unequal distribution of land and sea between the Northern and Southern Hemisphere. The region between eastern Africa and southeast Asia experiences the greatest seasonal shifts in the position of the ITCZ. An extended period of rain associated with the seasonal movement of the ITCZ and a resultant shift in the prevailing winds is called a **monsoon**. The tropical rain forests are in regions of the globe traversed by the seasonal movement of the ITCZ.

Notice that the Trade Winds, the Westerlies, and the Polar Easterlies do not blow directly north or south as one might expect from our discussion. This is a function of the rotation of the Earth on its axis, and this deflection is the ***Coriolis Effect.*** *We will examine this process in section 3.13.*

Once in the upper troposphere (~16 km above Earth's surface), the air masses, now largely devoid of their moisture, move toward the poles. As they flow north and south, they continue to cool, which increases the relative density of the air masses. Between ~20° to 35°N and S latitude, the dense, dry air masses sink toward the Earth's surface and create high atmospheric pressure because sinking air masses exert more pressure on Earth's surface. This region is at the transition between the tropical and temperate belts, and is known as the **subtropics**. These dry air masses are associated with little precipitation, and the highest rates of evaporation in the ocean and regions of deserts on land. Mariners sailing from Europe would refer to this area of the North Atlantic as the **"horse latitudes"** because the horses on board their ships would often die of dehydration, and they would throw the carcasses overboard. The area is characterized by light winds and hot and dry conditions that increased the sailing times for wind-powered ships. At the surface, air masses diverge to supply the Trade Winds that flow toward the equator and the poleward-flowing **Westerlies** (Fig. 3.20). The Westerlies drive the weather patterns of much of the U.S., Europe, and central Asia.

The **Hadley Cell** describes the conveyor-like flow of air masses in the tropics as they rise at the ITCZ, diverge and move poleward, sink in the subtropics, and are drawn back toward the ITCZ as the surface winds we call the NE and SE Trade Winds (Fig. 3.20).

In the mid-latitudes, between ~35° to 60°N and S latitude, the Westerlies converge with the **Polar Easterlies**. This is where tropical air clashes with polar air along the **Polar Front**. Rising air masses create areas of low atmospheric pressure and year-round precipitation. Sailors sometimes refer to this region of the ocean as the **"roaring forties"** because of the strong winter storms that whip-up large, irregular waves. This region is characterized by highly seasonal and variable weather patterns as the Polar Front meanders north and south as a planetary-scale wave. Think of this meandering front as an unattended fire hose that is thrashing about uncontrollably (but in super slow motion!) due to the great water pressure. Near the poles, cold dry air descends once again giving birth to the Polar Easterlies at the surface. The Polar Regions are characterized by little precipitation.

Investigation 3.10 looks more closely at the wind belts of the globe and the associated weather patterns.

3.13 Earth's Rotation and the Coriolis Effect

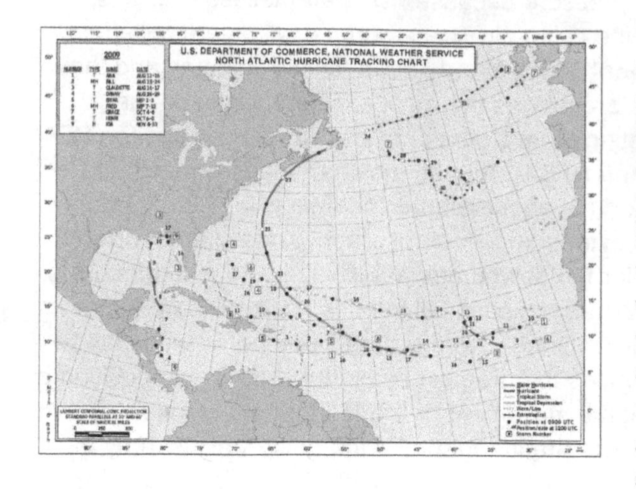

The path of hurricanes, as shown in this map, is influenced by the Coriolis Effect.

The Earth rotates on its axis once every 24 hours. Because our planet is a sphere, the actual distance (circumference around the planetary sphere) that one point on the surface will move through space during this 24-hour period is dependent upon latitude. If you were standing exactly on the Equator, in one day you would circle the Earth around its widest circumference, or ~38,400 km. In contrast, if you were standing at 60°N latitude, you would travel in a circle with a circumference of ~19,200 km (Fig. 3.21). Accordingly, the velocity of the Earth's surface at these two latitudes is different: 38,400 km/24 hr = 1600 km/hr at the Equator and 19,200km/24 hr = 800 km/hr at 60°N. None of this makes any difference as long as you remain attached to the Earth's surface. But as soon as you are airborne in an airplane or jet aircraft, you continue to travel eastward through space with the same velocity as the point of your departure. Since the ground beneath you is moving at a velocity that differs from that of your point of origin, your airborne path takes on an apparent deflection known as the **Coriolis Effect**.

Suppose that four aircraft take-off from 40°N latitude 90°W longitude (north of St. Louis) and four aircraft take-off from 40°S, 90°W (west of Chile in the southeast Pacific), each set of aircraft with headings of due north, east, south, and west (Fig. 3.21). As the aircraft fly in their straight initial bearings, the Earth rotates beneath them. As described above, each aircraft has a component of velocity to the east that represents the velocity of Earth's rotation at the point of take-off. This **velocity** at Earth's surface varies across latitude: it is faster in the lower latitudes (tropical belt) and progressively slower towards the higher latitudes (temperate and polar belts):

- 1600 km/hr (994 mi/hr) at the equator (0°)
- 1400 km/hr (869 mi/hr) at 30°N&S
- 800 km/hr (497 mi/hr) at 60°N&S
- 0 km/hr at the poles (90°N&S)

If the pilots do not correct for the Earth's rotation, then the aircraft will head in a direction to the right of their original direction in the Northern Hemisphere, and to the left in the Southern Hemisphere. This apparent deflection is called the **Coriolis Effect**. The Coriolis Effect influences all freely moving objects, including the motion of fluids, such as air masses and water masses.

To see how angular velocity, and hence Coriolis deflection differs across latitude, compare velocities between latitudes:

- 0° to 30°: 1600 km/hr – 1400 km/hr = 200 km/hr difference
- 30° to 60°: 1400 km/hr – 800 km/hr = 600 km/hr difference
- 60° to 90°: 800 km/hr – 0 km = 800 km/hr difference

The greater the difference between velocities, the greater is the Coriolis Effect, so you can see that it's influence is greatest in the higher latitudes. The Coriolis Effect goes to zero at the equator where there is a change is sign: deflection of moving objects goes from the right in the Northern Hemisphere to the left in the Southern Hemisphere.

The resulting curved paths could just as well illustrate the flow of fluids on the planet, specifically the motion of air masses and water masses. Moving air masses are deflected towards the right of their original direction in the Northern Hemisphere. This is why the Trade Winds in the Northern Hemisphere blow from the Northeast towards the Southwest: they start out moving south toward the low-pressure area in the tropics, but are deflected to the right of their travel direction (in this case, that is to the west). In the same fashion, the northward traveling Westerlies are deflected to the right (east) in the Northern Hemisphere. An air mass or water mass moving across latitude in the tropics (lower latitudes) experiences less difference, and therefore less Coriolis deflection, than in the mid- to high latitudes.

We can summarize the Coriolis Effect with the following points: 1) the Coriolis Effect is caused by the Earth's rotation; 2) air masses and water masses are deflected to the right of the direction of travel in the Northern Hemisphere and to the left in the Southern Hemisphere, and 3) there is greater deflection towards the higher latitudes and no effect at the equator.

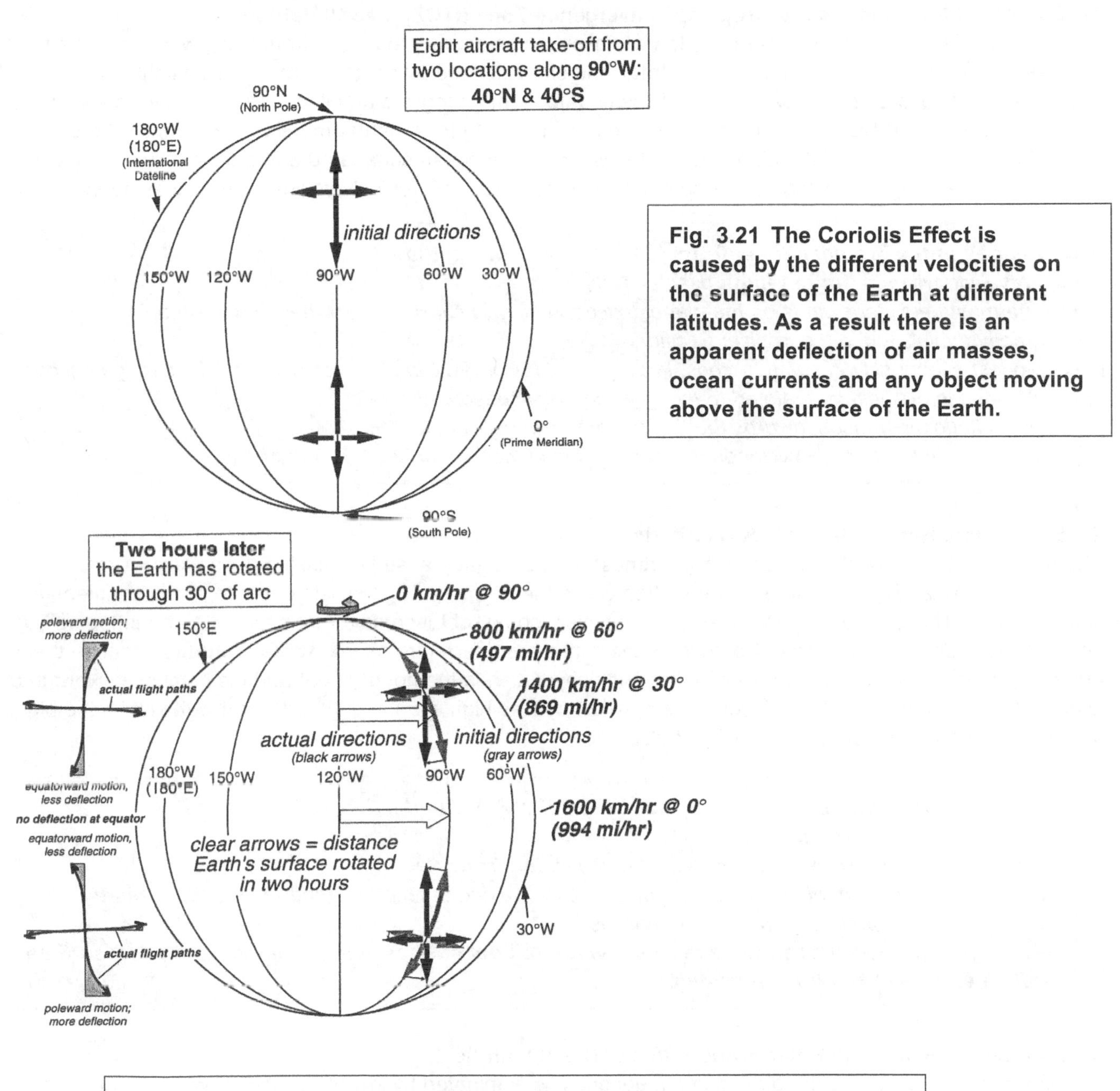

Fig. 3.21 The Coriolis Effect is caused by the different velocities on the surface of the Earth at different latitudes. As a result there is an apparent deflection of air masses, ocean currents and any object moving above the surface of the Earth.

Investigation 3.11 examines some additional implications of the Coriolis Effect.

■3.14 The Influence of the Ocean on Global Climate

Now we can put together the information that we have accumulated from our earlier analyses into a comprehensive picture of how the ocean regulates global climate. The high heat capacity of the ocean, together with the imbalance in the amount of solar radiation across latitude, and the resulting wind belts create natural climate zones that are governed by differing atmospheric and oceanic conditions. Each zone (or belt) is bordered by prevailing atmospheric high- or low-pressure centers that dictate wind movement and precipitation regimes (Fig. 3.22).

You can review the importance of heat capacity and the variable solar radiation that the Earth receives in sections 3.1 and 4.2.

1) Equatorial Low and the Intertropical Convergence Zone (ITCZ): near 0° latitude
This region of the ocean is dominated by low atmospheric pressure that results from rising warm, moist air masses. It is sometimes referred to as the **doldrums** characterized by hot temperatures with light variable winds and occasional squalls. The ITCZ is north of the equator in most regions and it shifts seasonally, especially over the Indian Ocean and SE Asia resulting in monsoon rains during the summer months. The abundant precipitation that falls within this equatorial region causes the waters at the ocean surface here to have relatively low salinity (Fig. 3.23). The rising air masses can also result in the formation of tropical cyclones (hurricanes, typhoons).

Conditions in the Tropical Zone: 0° to ~23.5° N & S ("low latitudes")
- *Prevailing winds = **<u>Trade Winds</u>** (Hadley Cell)*
- *The most persistent winds on the planet, except during **El Niño events** when Trade Wind strength is greatly diminished in the tropical Pacific*
- *Modest seasonality in some regions, large excursions of ITCZ in other regions produce strong seasonal changes in precipitation related to <u>the monsoon</u> (dry season/rainy season)*
- *Precipitation increases towards the ITCZ (warm to very warm surface waters)*
- *The area where tropical cyclones (hurricanes, typhoons) can grow and strengthen*

2) Subtropical High: ~20–35° N & S latitude
The middle latitudes are dominated by high atmospheric pressure caused by sinking dense, dry air masses. For example, a regional high pressure system, often called the Bermuda High, exists offshore of the southeastern United States. These areas of the ocean are characterized by light, sporadic winds that often stranded sailing ships for days or weeks at a time. Sometimes the zones are referred to as the **horse latitudes** because the horses aboard these ships would die of thirst and dehydration in the hot dry heat and the carcasses were thrown overboard. The dryness lasts in all year round, which causes high evaporation and warm waters with the highest surface salinities of the open ocean (Fig. 3.23).

Conditions in the Temperate Zone: ~23.5° to ~66.5° N & S ("mid-latitudes")
- *Prevailing winds = **<u>Westerlies</u>***
- *Strong seasonality (related to movement of the **Polar Front**)*
- *A fast moving current of air (the jet stream)meanders along the steep temperature and pressure gradients where polar and tropical air masses meet*
- *Ample precipitation in all seasons results in **warm to cool surface waters** with **relatively low surface salinities away from the subtropics***

3) Subpolar Low and the Polar Front: ~35–60° N & S latitude
This is where tropical and polar air masses meet and it is dominated by low atmospheric pressure. Such low pressure areas occur near the Aleutian Islands of Alaska in the Pacific Ocean and near Iceland in the Atlantic

Ocean. The Polar Front often meanders from day to day, or week to week and its position shifts north-south with the seasons. Abundant precipitation is associated with the front and this results in relatively low salinity and warm to cold surface waters (Fig. 3.23). The low pressure area is also the source of extratropical cyclones especially in winter. These are the fabled nor'easters that wreak havoc along the coast of New England.

An area of high atmospheric pressure exists over the north and south poles. This results from the sinking of dry, dense air masses. Precipitation is sparse, and the sea at the North Pole is covered by ice. There is no ocean directly at the South Pole; the continent of Antarctica is there.

Conditions in the Polar Zone: ~66.5° to 90° N & S ("high latitudes")

- *Prevailing winds = **Polar Easterlies***
- *Precipitation decreases towards the poles*
- *Sea-ice formation during winter from the icy old seas of the Arctic and Antarctic*
- *Polar High: ~90° N & S ("poles")*

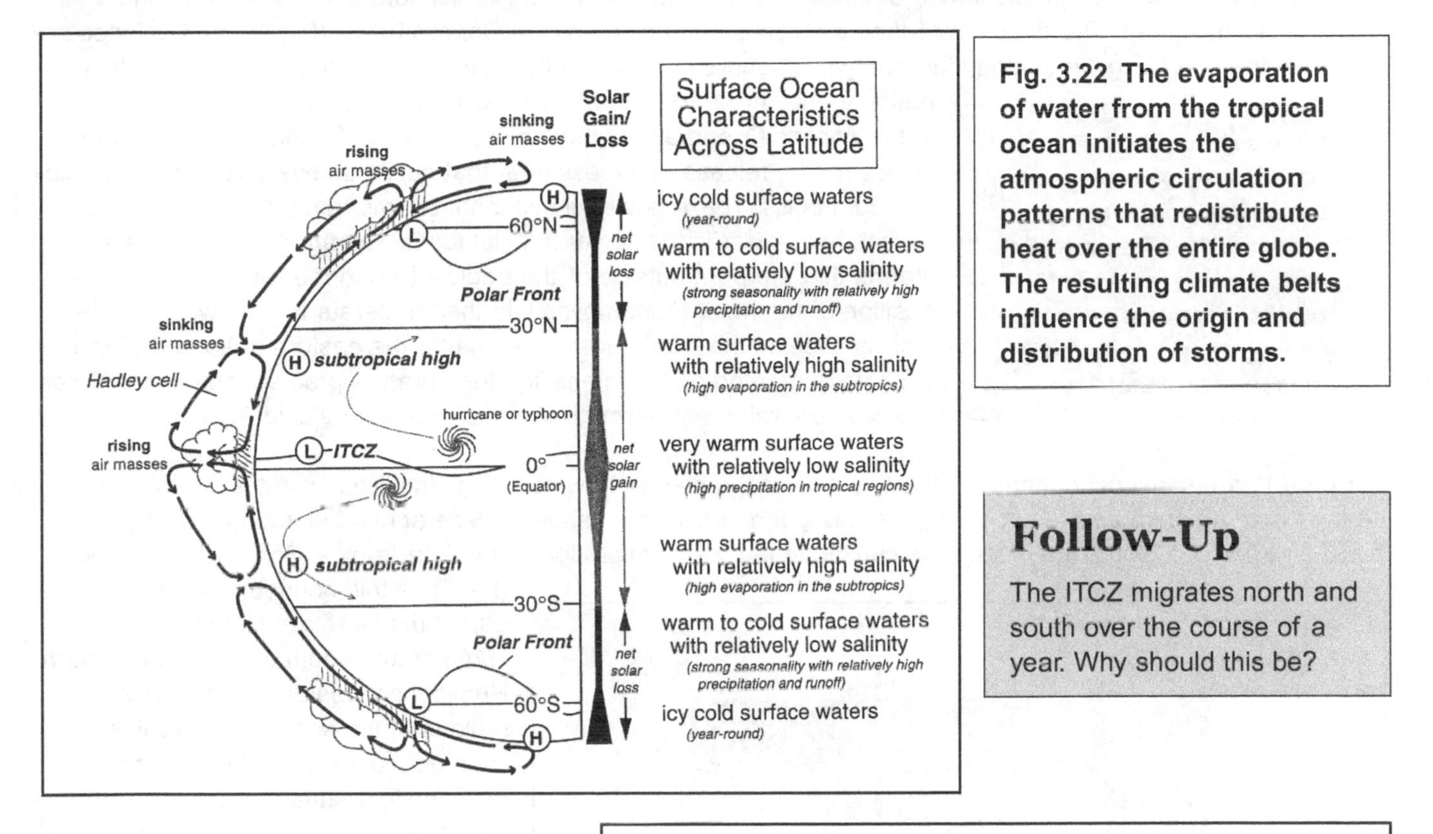

Fig. 3.22 The evaporation of water from the tropical ocean initiates the atmospheric circulation patterns that redistribute heat over the entire globe. The resulting climate belts influence the origin and distribution of storms.

Follow-Up

The ITCZ migrates north and south over the course of a year. Why should this be?

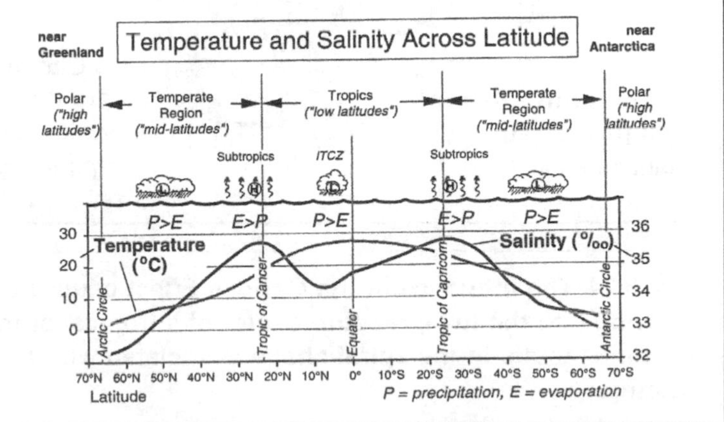

Fig. 3.23 The difference in the evaporation of sea water and the amount of precipitation at various latitudes controls the salinity of seawater at the ocean surface.

■3.15 Natural Climate Variability: Cyclones, Monsoons & El Niño

Have you ever noticed how some summers seem hotter and drier than others, or that some winters produce much more precipitation than "average"? **Weather** refers to the day-to-day changes in our atmosphere, while **climate** describes the long-term patterns of weather for each region of the Earth. The different climate zones that we have discussed (e.g., tropical, temperate, polar) experience a characteristic progression of weather patterns and seasonal extremes of temperature and precipitation as the amount of solar radiation increases and decreases during the course of a year. But no two years are exactly alike. If we are to fully understand our ocean-climate system, we must understand the natural extremes of climate from one region to another and from one year to the next.

Storms are an important part of seasonal weather. A cyclone is a major storm that grows around a low pressure area. The winds blow counterclockwise around cyclones in the Northern Hemisphere and clockwise in the Southern Hemisphere. The direction of their rotation is determined by the Coriolis Effect (Fig. 3.24). Cyclones are driven by the prevailing winds and steered by the Coriolis effect and other low and high pressure cells in their paths as they move to higher latitudes. Tropical cyclones (called hurricanes in the Atlantic Ocean and typhoons in the Pacific Ocean) represent safety valves for the release of excess heat that builds up every year in the tropics and subtropics. These powerful seasonal storms transport much of this excess heat towards the cooler high latitudes. Extratropical cyclones are storms that are born outside of the tropics. During the winter months, the position of the Polar Front moves into the temperate belt. Powerful winter storms such as the "Nor'easters" that batter the eastern seaboard of the U.S. are generated by the intensified temperature gradient across the Polar Front, where relatively warm air clashes with bitterly cold Arctic air.

We investigated the unequal distribution of solar radiation and resulting heat energy in section 3.10. The excess heat that accumulates in the tropical and subtropical ocean is partially removed by the formation of cyclones.

Monsoons are seasonal changes in the direction of the prevailing winds. In a simplistic way, it is similar to the change from an onshore breeze during the daylight hours to an offshore breeze at night along the coast (Fig. 3.25). In tropical regions, monsoons are caused to the yearly migration of the Intertropical Convergence Zone (ITCZ) as this boundary shifts north during the Northern Hemisphere summer and south during the Northern Hemisphere winter. Mountainous regions at the edge of the tropics, such as the southwest U.S., also experience a summer monsoon. The term "monsoon" is commonly applied to the season that experiences increased precipitation. The seasonal movement of the ITCZ is particularly pronounced in the region of the Indian Ocean: from east Africa to southeast Asia. Places like India and the Philippines experience months of torrential rains during the monsoon followed by months with little rain.

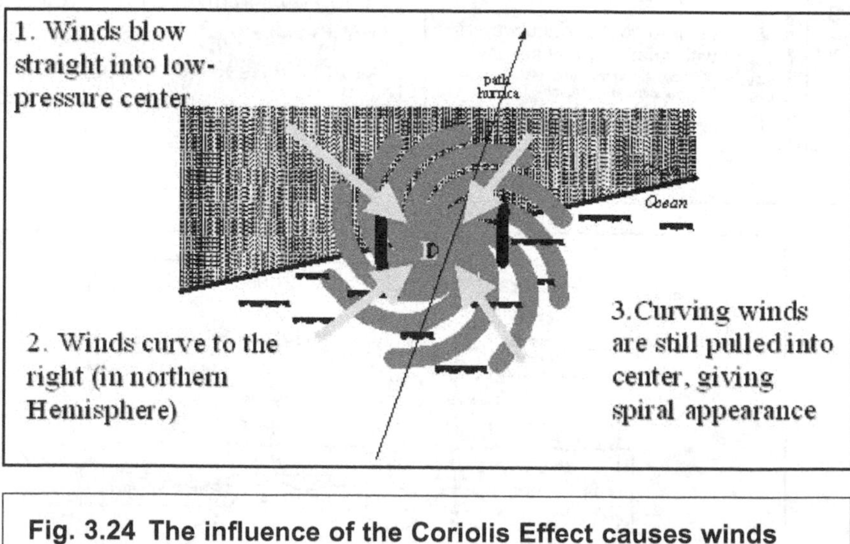

Fig. 3.24 The influence of the Coriolis Effect causes winds blowing into the low-pressure center of a tropical storm or cyclone results in the spiral shape associated with these storms.

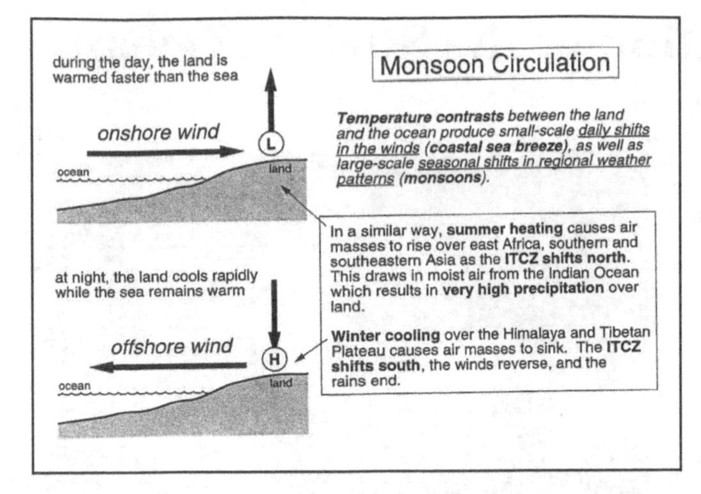

Fig. 3.25 The seasonal monsoon is related to the changes in air pressure that draws moist air to the continents during the summer season.

The **El Niño Southern Oscillation** (ENSO) is a prime example of natural variability in the ocean-climate system over longer time spans (Fig. 3.26). An El Niño event occurs every 3 to 7 years and it can greatly perturb the "expected" seasonal progression in weather patterns across the globe. During a normal year, there is a strong atmospheric pressure gradient between the Southeast Pacific regional high pressure area and the regional low that is located between Indonesia and Australia.

We will explore the very important process of upwelling, where cold, nutrient-rich sea water rises to the surface, in section 3.18.

This results in strong Trade Winds, which cause warm water to pile-up (thicken) in the western equatorial Pacific due to the relatively constricted flow through the passages between Australia and Indonesia. The resultant thick layer of tropical water is called the **Western Pacific Warm Pool**. However, during an El Niño event, the atmospheric pressure gradient across the tropical Pacific weakens, Trade Wind strength slackens, and warm water expands eastward to cap the normally cool, nutrient-rich waters that upwell along the equator and continental margin of Peru and Ecuador. The warm current shows up around Christmas time and results in a reduced population and harvest of fish, flooding rains in the normally arid region of western South America, and economic disaster for the local people. The effects of a severe El Niño event are also felt beyond the eastern tropical Pacific, including widespread droughts in some regions, floods in others, severe winter storms along the California coast, and milder winters in the northeast U.S. Sometimes the reverse happens: the Trade Winds blow more vigorously, increasing the Warm Pacific Pool and causing more robust upwelling of cold, deep water along the equatorial region. These La Niña events have generally the opposite effects of El Niño on the climate system. The causes El Niño and La Niña are presently unknown, but oceanographic research is improving the prediction of these events, which will allow for better planning and management strategies for the climatic consequences.

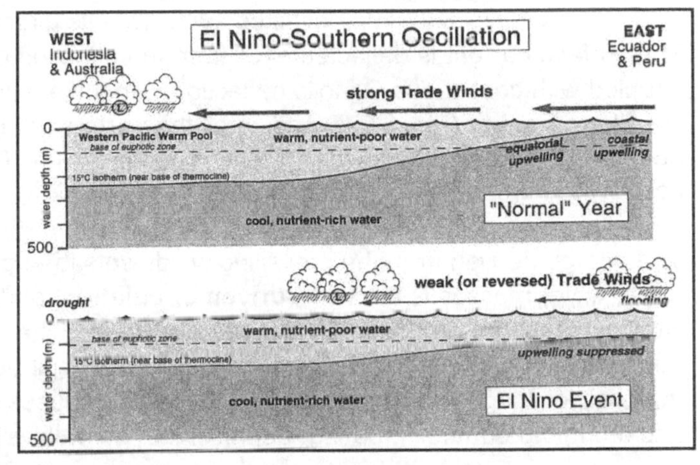

Figure 3.26 Changing wind patterns also affect ocean circulation to produce the periodic phenomenon of El Niño.

Food for Thought

Look at an animation from the NOAA Earth System Research Laboratory that shows ocean temperatures over the last year:

http://www.esrl.noaa.gov/psd/map/clim/sst.anim.year.html

Based on these data, make your best estimate of current conditions and discuss the following question: ***Do you think we are in an El Niño or La Niña event now, entering one or the other, or are conditions "normal"?***

■3.16 Wind-Driven Circulation of the Surface Ocean

We have seen how the unequal heating of the Earth and its rotation on its axis gives rise to the various wind belts around the globe. These prevailing winds create a drag (wind stress) on the ocean surface, and some of this momentum is transferred to the water, causing it to move. As the surface water moves, friction among the water molecules causes the momentum to be transferred deeper into the water column, but energy is lost with increasing depth. As a result, the velocity of the current at the surface decreases with greater depth. Interestingly, not only the velocity, but the direction of the current changes with depth as well. This is the result of the Coriolis Effect, which will affect moving water in the same way that it does the winds. The Coriolis Effect causes the moving water to be deflected away from its direction of travel (to the right in the Northern Hemisphere). The surface current is deflected ~45° from the direction of the prevailing wind. A decrease in current speed, coupled with continuous Coriolis deflection with increasing depth an apparent spiral of moving water called the **Ekman spiral** (Fig. 3.27). Adding all the vectors (magnitude and direction) of the Ekman spiral yields a net current direction that is ~90° to the prevailing wind. This composite current is the **Ekman transport** and it controls the motion of the surface ocean.

Review the basic principles behind the Coriolis Effect in section 3.13.

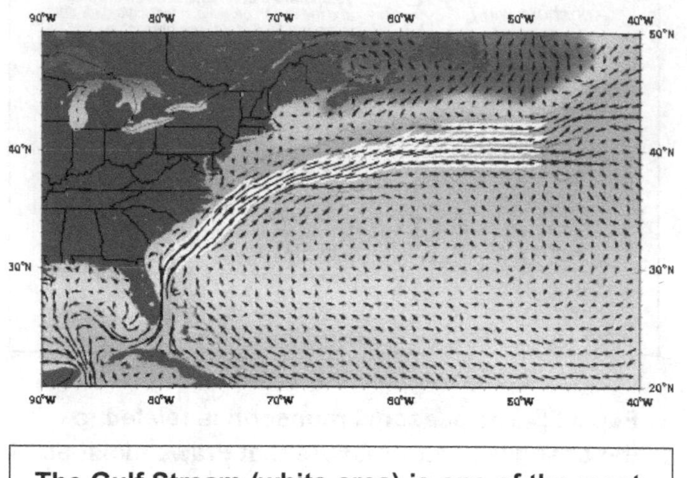

The Gulf Stream (white area) is one of the most important features of ocean circulation in the North Atlantic.

The energy derived from the prevailing winds sets the uppermost water column in motion. This movement of the upper water masses is the **wind-driven circulation**, and the motion is in a direction to the right of the prevailing winds in the Northern Hemisphere and to the left of the prevailing winds in the Southern Hemisphere. Ekman transport causes near-surface waters to **converge** (pile-up) in subtropical regions thereby creating subtle "hills", "domes", or "ridges" on the ocean surface, and it causes waters to **diverge** (move apart) in subpolar regions and along the equator, creating "depressions" or "valleys" (Fig. 3.28). These subtle highs and lows on the ocean surface are not visible because the relief is less than 2 meters (<6.6 ft.) higher or lower than the average level of the sea over broad areas of the ocean.

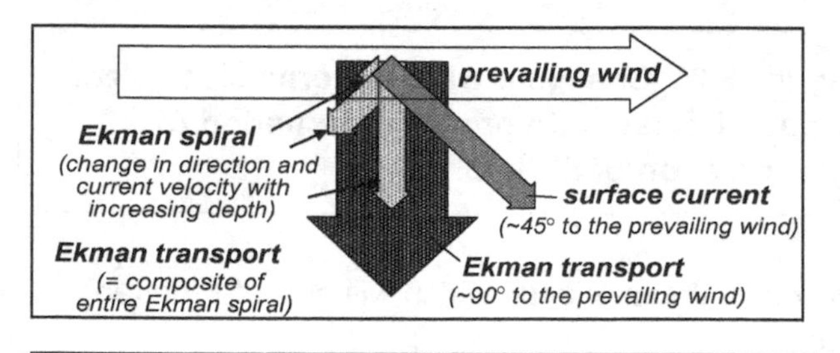

Fig. 3.27 The prevailing wind moves water at the ocean surface, and this ocean current is deflected at an angle to the wind as determined by the Coriolis Effect. Water flowing at greater depths is also deflected, so that the net transport (Ekman Transport) of water is at right angles to the prevailing wind.

Gyres are the large horizontal wind-driven current systems that circulate around the subtle domes and depressions on the ocean surface. For example, the **subtropical gyres** represent large circulation cells around the hills created by convergence in the subtropics. The subtropical gyre in the North Atlantic starts when the Trade Winds blow out of the northeast towards the Equator and initiate the westward-flowing North Equatorial Current. When this current encounters the Caribbean

Divergence of water masses causes upwelling of deeper waters, a process we will examine in section 3.18.

Islands and North America, the Coriolis Effect deflects the current to the right (north) as the Gulf Stream (Fig. 3.29). This eventually becomes the North Atlantic Current that flows towards Europe, and is deflected to the right (south) as the Canary Current. Subtropical gyres transport warm waters toward the pole along the western sides of the ocean basins and cool waters toward the equator along the eastern sides. Subtropical gyres are prominent features of circulation in the North and South Atlantic, North and South Pacific, and the Indian Ocean.

We explored the layering of the ocean caused by temperature, salinity, and density in section 3.8.

Wind-driven circulation affects only the upper ocean to a depth of about 150 meters because the pycnocline (or permanent thermocline) provides a stable density barrier between the less dense (warmer) near-surface waters and the more dense (very cold) deep waters.

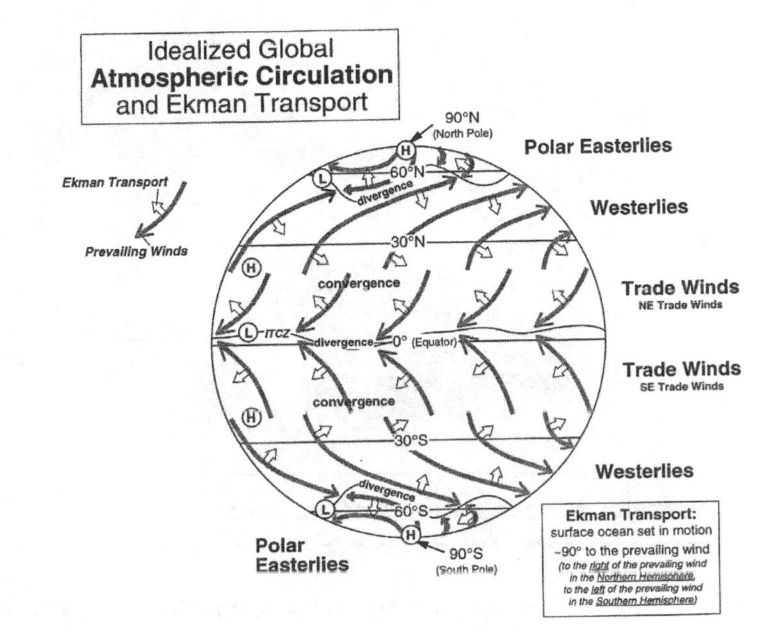

Fig. 3.28 Ekman Transport as caused by the Coriolis Effect causes ocean water to "pile up" in some areas of the globe (convergence) and flow away from other regions (divergence).

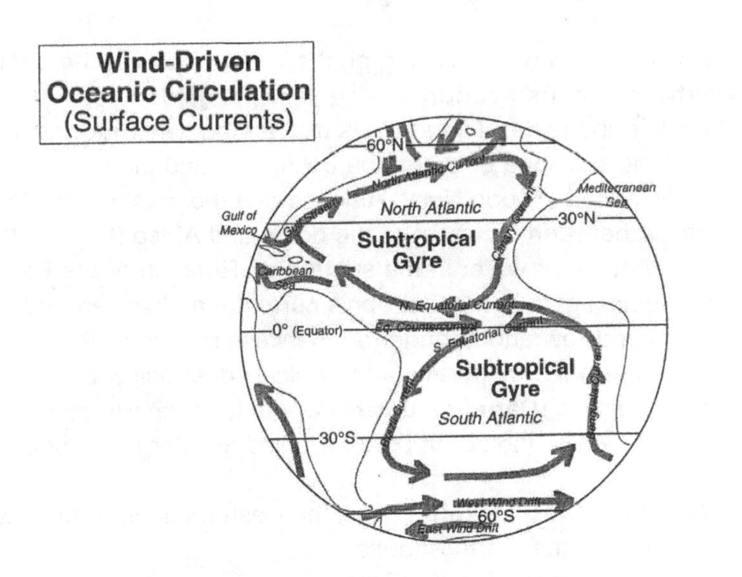

Fig. 3.29 The presence of continents restricts the wind-driven circulation of the ocean to individual basins. The Coriolis Effect drives these circulating currents to form loops or gyres.

Investigation 3.12 analyzes the relationship between prevailing winds and surface current directions.

■3.17 Ocean Currents: Coriolis & Gravity in Balance

The prevailing winds provide the energy to drive the surface currents of the world ocean. Ekman transport and the Coriolis Effect cause surface waters to converge ("pile-up") in the subtropics and diverge (move apart) at the equator and in subpolar waters. This creates subtle "hills" and "valleys" on the ocean surface of < 2 meters (<6.6 ft.). Gravity acts on the water to pull it back from these hills or into these valleys. This continuous tug-of-war between opposing forces results in a. partial balance or equilibrium that keeps water moving around these subtle domes and valleys. This **geostrophic flow** is represented by most surface currents in the ocean. For example, the subtropical gyres are geostrophic currents that represent the flow of upper water and in the Indian Ocean.

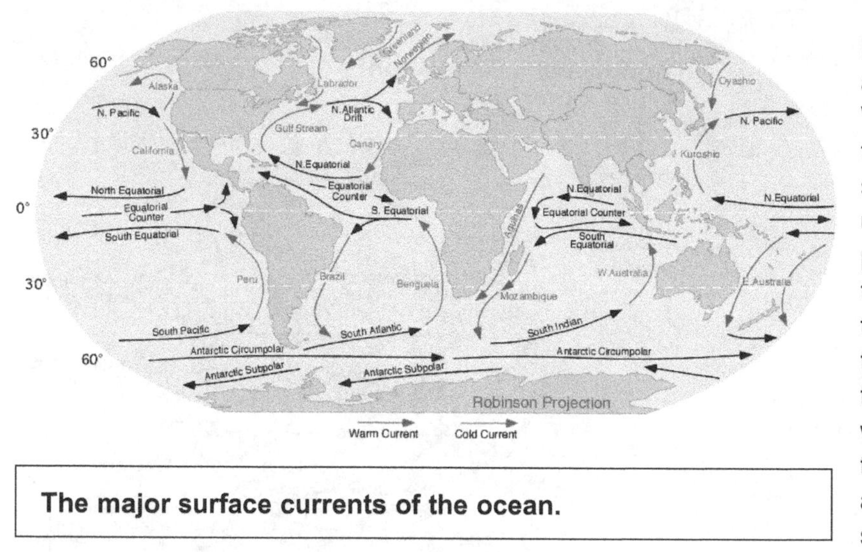

The major surface currents of the ocean.

Earth's rotation from west to east, assisted by the typically strong Trade Winds in the tropics, causes the water in the ocean to "pile-up" towards the western sides of the ocean basins. This is not unlike what happens when you push a pan or pail of water across the room; the water rises on the side you pushed from, and it will sometimes slosh out of the bucket if you push hard enough. As the Earth rotates from west to east, the water in the ocean starts to slosh toward the western sides of the basins ("pan") and therefore, the ocean surface stands slightly higher on the western sides of the ocean basins. In this way, the dome of water created by convergence in the subtropics is not located in the center of the ocean basin, but is instead displaced toward the western side (Fig. 3.30).

This offset dome causes water flowing on the western side of the dome to flow faster than the eastern side. This is called **westward intensification**. It's like taking a garden hose and partially constricting the flow; the water shoots out farther and faster. The same is true for the water moving in the ocean: the surface currents are forced through a narrower passage between the continents and the crest of the dome causing them to flow faster. For example, the distance between North America and the crest of the dome in the **Sargasso Sea** is much narrower than the distance between the crest of the dome and Africa (Fig. 3.30). In this illustration, convergence of surface waters creates a dome of water in the subtropics. Rotation of the Earth causes the dome to be displaced to the west. The subtropical gyre is a geostrophic current that flows around the elevated water toward the center of the basin. The flow is narrow and stronger on the western side of the gyre (such as the **Gulf Stream** in the North Atlantic Ocean) where it transports warm tropical water poleward. The flow is wide and much weaker on the eastern side of the gyre (**Canary Current)** where it transports cool water towards the equator. The subtropical gyre isolates a portion of the North Atlantic called the Sargasso Sea.

Strong **western boundary currents** mark the western sides of the subtropical gyres:

- **Gulf Stream** in the North Atlantic
- **Brazil Current** in the South Atlantic
- **Kuroshio Current** in the North Pacific

- **East Australian Current** in the South Pacific
- **Agulhas Current** in the Indian Ocean

These currents play an important role in transporting tropical heat to the cooler high latitudes. For example, the **Gulf Stream** ultimately becomes the **North Atlantic Current** (also called **North Atlantic Drift**) and moderates the climate of northern Europe.

The flow of the Gulf Stream is like a wide meandering river, although its course is not as rigidly constrained by river banks. Occasionally, the meander loops become pinched-off, creating eddies of rotating water called warm-core rings or cold-core rings, depending upon which side of the Gulf Stream they are on (Fig. 3.31).

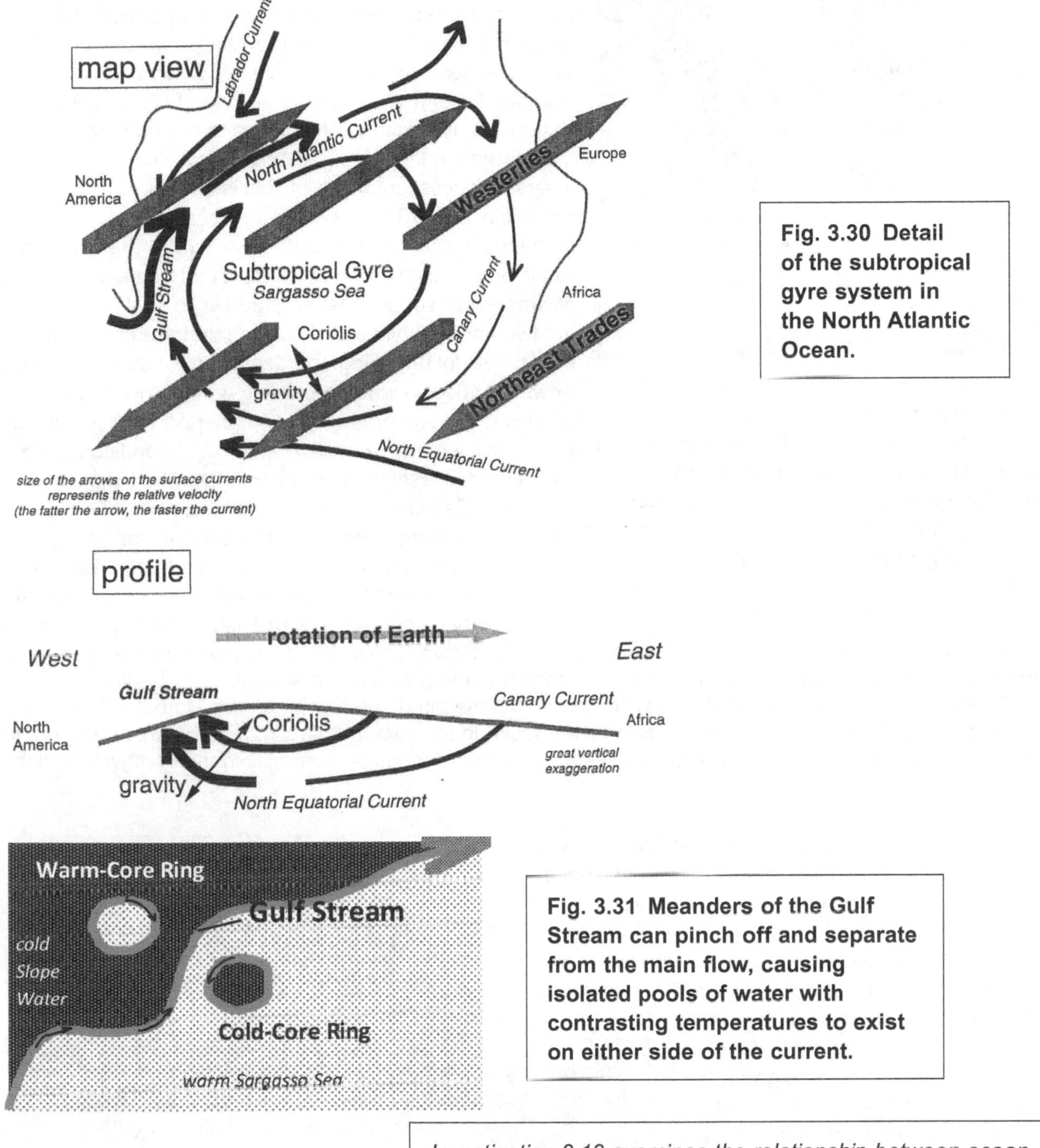

Fig. 3.30 Detail of the subtropical gyre system in the North Atlantic Ocean.

Fig. 3.31 Meanders of the Gulf Stream can pinch off and separate from the main flow, causing isolated pools of water with contrasting temperatures to exist on either side of the current.

Investigation 3.13 examines the relationship between ocean topography and current flow.

■3.18 Wind-Driven Upwelling: Gateway to Biological Productivity

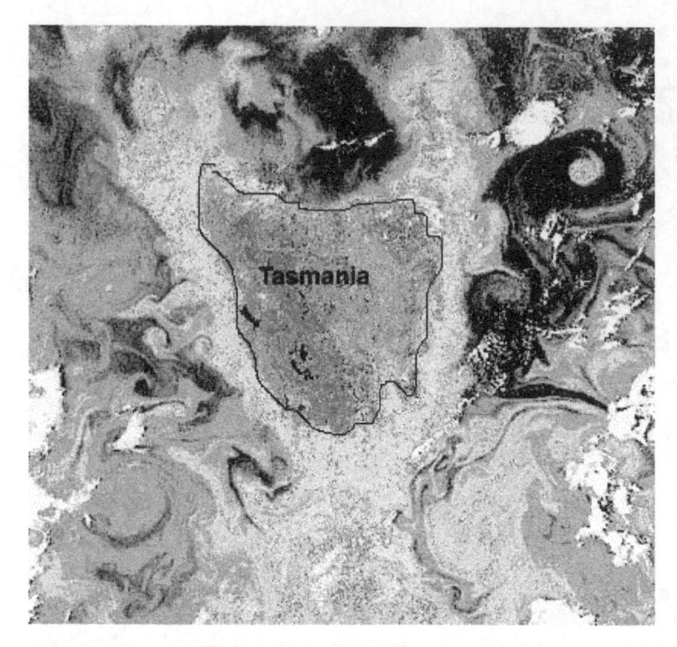

This image from space shows the distribution of chlorophyll in the ocean around the island of Tasmania, south of Australia. Bright areas show high biological productivity (abundant chlorophyll) caused by the upwelling of nutrient-rich water around the coast.

The wind-driven surface currents of the world ocean, including the gyres, represent the horizontal flow of water masses. However, water can move vertically as well. **Upwelling** and **downwelling** are the processes that describe this vertical movement of water masses in the world ocean. **Downwelling** is the sinking of cold, dense water in the high latitudes of the Atlantic to form deep water masses such as North Atlantic Deep Water and Antarctic Bottom Water, or the sinking of warm, salty water emerging from the Mediterranean Sea to form Mediterranean Intermediate Water. **Upwelling** is the reverse process, but much of this is directly caused by prevailing winds. The upward movement of water results from the displacement of surface waters by the prevailing winds and resultant Ekman transport that creates a divergence of surface waters (see section 3.17). There are two principal types of upwelling that are caused by winds: coastal upwelling and oceanic divergence. **Coastal upwelling** occurs when prevailing winds blow roughly parallel to the shore and Ekman transport pushes surface waters away from the coast (Fig. 3.32). In addition, since the western coastline of continents face the sluggish and broad Eastern Boundary Currents, winds blowing offshore can more easily drive the currents farther out to sea. Deeper, nutrient-rich waters come up to replace displaced surface waters. This results in **high biological productivity** by primary producers (plankton) which in turn supports a greater abundance of fish and other marine life. Coastal upwelling is prevalent on the eastern sides of the ocean basins (western margins of the continents). In many areas, the strength of upwelling varies seasonally. Examples of seasonal coastal upwelling include the margin off northwest Africa (Morocco, Spanish Sahara, Mauritania, Senegal) and west Africa (Namibia, Angola) in the eastern Atlantic, off California and Peru in the eastern Pacific, and along the Somalia, South Yemen, and Oman margins (summer) in the northwest Indian Ocean.

We examined the changes in the Trade Winds and surface currents in the Pacific Ocean that give rise to El Niño in section 3.15.

Oceanic divergence also results in the upwelling of deeper, nutrient-rich waters. The resulting elevated rates of primary productivity support larger communities of animals. Divergence is created where prevailing winds converge but the resulting Ekman transport causes the near-surface waters to diverge, forcing deeper waters to rise to the surface (Fig. 3.32). This occurs in subpolar waters of the North Atlantic and North Pacific, and around the continent of Antarctica. These are rich feeding grounds for a number of whale species. Upwelling also occurs along the equator where the sign of the Coriolis changes direction from Ekman transport to the right of the prevailing wind

Downwelling is a large-scale process that is not caused by winds, but rather by density differences among water masses. These water masses can be identified by their temperature and salinity characteristics. We will examine this process more fully in section 3.19.

(Northern Hemisphere) to left of the prevailing wind (Southern Hemisphere). This latter example is **equatorial upwelling**. The Galapagos Islands, famous for the research of Charles Darwin and his evolutionary theory of natural selection, are located on the equator in the eastern Pacific and are characterized by the diverse and abundant marine life that is supported by equatorial upwelling. In the Pacific Ocean, El Niño affects the rate of equatorial upwelling. When the Trade Winds decrease during an El Niño event, the intensity of the upwelling along the equator also decreases, leading to a lowered nutrient supply to the surface and a corresponding decline in biological productivity.

Food for Thought

We associate high biological productivity with warm temperatures. Look at the satellite image of biological productivity in the Atlantic Ocean. High biological productivity is indicated by the orange and red colors; low productivity is shown by blue and violet. Do you expect this distribution and how can you explain what you see?

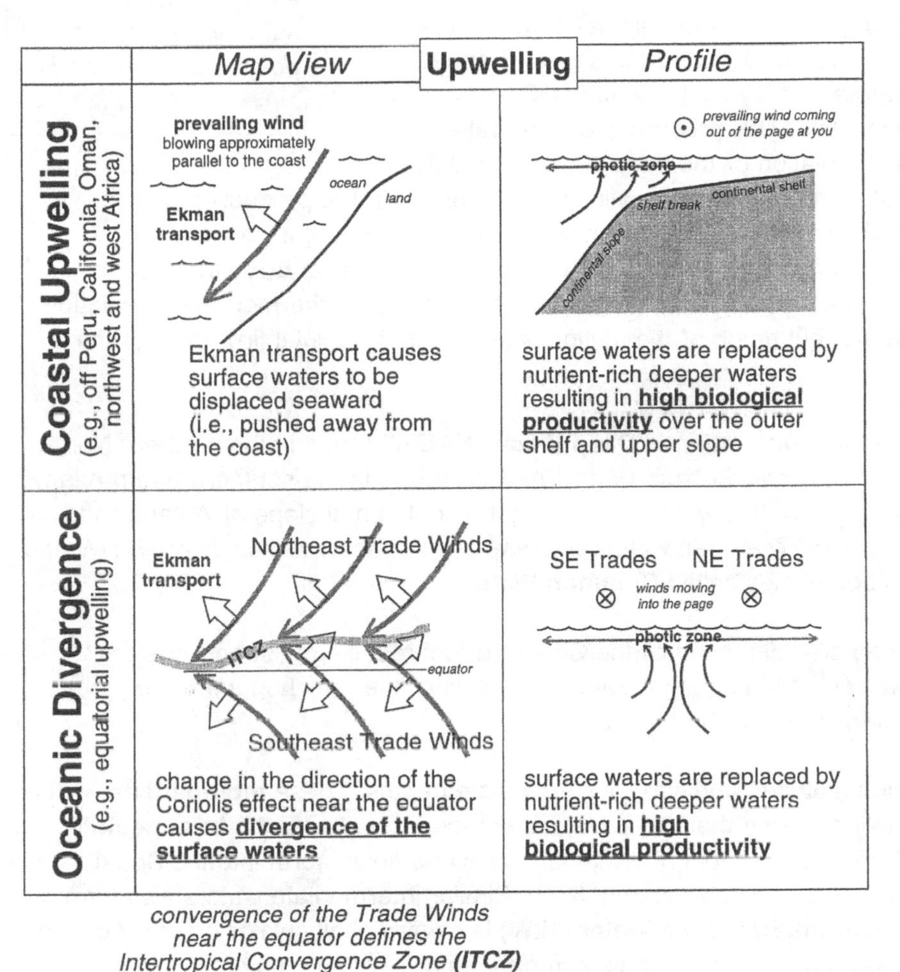

Ekman Transport:
surface ocean set in motion ~90° to the prevailing wind
(to the right in the Northern Hemisphere, to the left in the Southern Hemisphere)

Fig. 3.32 Upwelling results when the movement of surface currents causes the water to be replaced by colder, nutrient-rich water from deeper in the ocean.

■3.19 Density-Driven Downwelling & Thermohaline Circulation

Up to the present time, we have been focusing our attention on how the surface ocean moves, driven largely by the energy of the prevailing winds. However, the stark differences in temperature and salinity that can occur among different oceanic water masses stimulate a very different kind of circulation system. Intense winter cooling and sea-ice formation in polar seas during the several months of darkness that prevails in high latitudes results in the formation of cold, dense waters. These waters sink to the sea floor, since the absence of a pycnocline (density barrier) in the polar regions allows free interchange between surface and deep water. These dense waters move toward the equator beneath the pycnocline as "deep" or "bottom" waters and icy cold waters (<4°C, or <40°F) fill the entire world ocean below the pycnocline. This process is **thermohaline circulation**, which is the density-driven circulation of the deep ocean (Fig. 3.33). The term "thermohaline" implies that both temperature and salinity are important in the production of deep and intermediate water masses. Thermohaline circulation also includes the production and circulation of "intermediate" water masses. Intermediate and deep waters sink to their level of **neutral buoyancy** (density equilibrium) below the solar-warmed surface waters. There is a vertical component of thermohaline circulation related to the downwelling of dense waters, but much of the motion is related to horizontal flow through the ocean basins of the world.

Review the differences in temperature and salinity structure of surface waters and deep water masses in section 3.7 and 3.8.

Deep waters form only in the Atlantic today. **North Atlantic Deep Water** (**NADW**) forms in the northern North Atlantic (Greenland-Norwegian Sea) and **Antarctic Bottom Water** (**AABW**) forms in the southern South Atlantic (Weddell Sea of Antarctica) (Fig. 3.33). Some of this water flows along the continental slope of Antarctica to enter the Indian Ocean and the Pacific Ocean. The deep waters of these ocean basins are a mix of NADW and AABW called **Circumpolar Water** (also sometimes called **Common Water**).

Deep water masses, like surface currents, are influenced by the Coriolis Effect resulting in strong western boundary currents. As deep waters flow toward the equator beneath the pycnocline they hug the lower continental slopes and rises on the western sides of the ocean basins.

Other waters also form in the mid- to high latitudes and sink to intermediate depths. These **intermediate waters** are less dense and are produced in smaller volume than deep waters. For example, **Antarctic Intermediate Water** (**AAIW**) forms at the Antarctic Convergence (Polar Front), then sinks and flows north into the South Atlantic, Caribbean Sea, Gulf of Mexico and North Atlantic (Fig. 3.33). Similar intermediate waters also form in the North and South Pacific. **Mediterranean Intermediate Water** (**MIW**) is a warm, salty water mass produced in the Mediterranean Sea due to high evaporation rates in the subtropics. MIW is among the densest waters formed in the ocean today. However, it doesn't sink to become deep or bottom water because the relatively small volume of water that spills over the Gibraltar sill into the North Atlantic mixes with other water masses to dilute its originally dense character. MIW sinks to about 1000 m and turns toward the north due to the Coriolis Effect where it provides an important source of salt for the winter production of North Atlantic Deep Water.

Thermohaline circulation is important because it ventilates (oxygenates) the entire water column of the world ocean below the pycnocline. The motion of intermediate, deep, and bottom waters redistributes heat, salt, dissolved gases, and nutrients. Thermohaline circulation is relatively slow compared to wind-driven surface circulation. For example, it takes approximately 1000 years from the time a parcel of water sinks in the Arctic to form NADW before it surfaces in the North Pacific at the end of its long migration. Thermohaline circulation is intimately linked with wind-driven circulation above the pycnocline to create a **"global conveyor"** of world ocean circulation, which we will examine more fully in the next section. The seasonal formation of sea-ice releases latent heat to the atmosphere in the high latitudes. Salts supplied by intermediate waters like MIW, or by western boundary currents such as the Gulf Stream help the surface waters of the northern North Atlantic sink to become NADW. In addition to playing the major role in the global conveyor, thermohaline circulation also carries away some of the excess CO_2 and other greenhouse gases that have been rapidly building-up in our atmosphere due to the burning of fossil fuel.

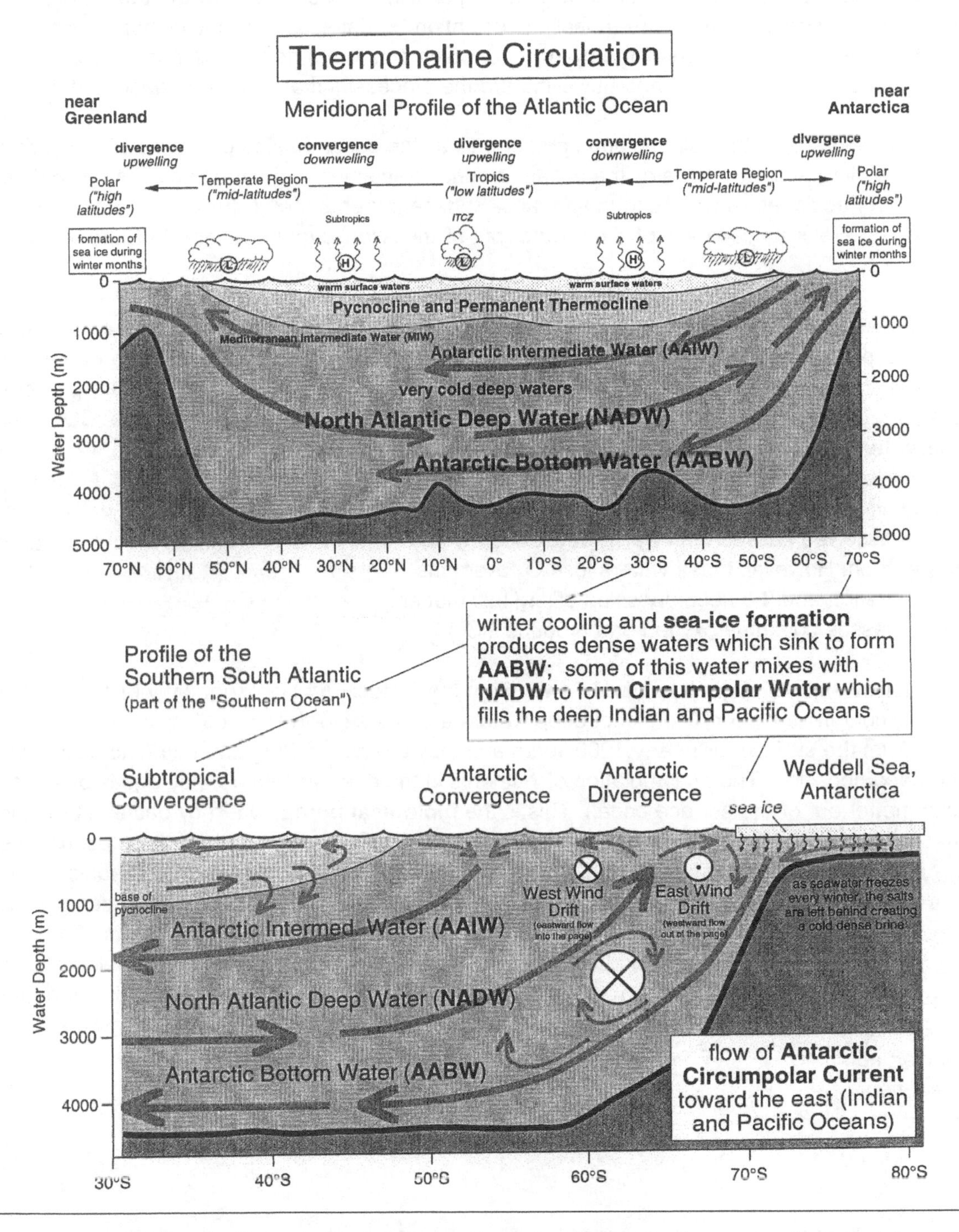

Fig. 3.33 Thermohaline circulation is vertical circulation in the ocean that is driven by temperature and salinity differences in the various ocean water masses.

3.20 The Global Conveyor: World Ocean Circulation

The **global conveyor** describes the complete circuit of global ocean circulation involving horizontal flow of surface and deep waters, and the vertical flow of downwelling and upwelling. Waters of the thermocline and surface mixed layer move under the influence of wind-driven circulation; waters below the permanent thermocline (and pycnocline) move by density-driven thermohaline circulation. Surface waters move independently of bottom, deep, and intermediate waters because of the pycnocline, which acts like a density barrier to separate surface and deeper water masses. Downwelling and upwelling are the processes that link the surface and deep ocean.

Surface waters cool and sink in the Atlantic and spread to fill all the ocean basins of the world with cold deep waters. Coastal upwelling at the margins of the ocean, around the continent of Antarctica (Antarctic Divergence), and in the equatorial Pacific return waters to the surface. Surface currents then return these waters back to the Atlantic (Fig. 3.34). There is a net export of deep water out of the Atlantic and net import of surface water into the Atlantic.

Deep and intermediate water masses acquire their physical and chemical characteristics at the surface where they formed. These properties include temperature, salinity, and density, which are considered **conservative** properties because they are modified only by diffusion or mixing with other water masses. Other properties acquired at the surface include nutrients and dissolved gases (oxygen, O_2, and carbon dioxide, CO_2). These are **non-conservative properties** because they are modified by biogeochemical cycles, even though the water mass retrains its temperature and salinity signature. For example, because cold water holds more dissolved gasses than warm water, deep waters are initially oxygen-rich. However, these waters lose O_2 over time due to animal respiration and the decomposition of organic matter (both of these processes consume oxygen and produce CO_2).

We will investigate the biogeochemical cycles in the ocean, including the biological pump that cycles carbon in the ocean, in section 4.5.

The older the water mass, the longer it has been away from the surface, and consequently its O_2 content is lower and the CO_2 content is higher. The oldest deep waters are in the North Pacific (Fig. 3.34). These waters have been away from the surface for nearly 1000 years and they are rich in CO_2 and nutrients accumulated by respiration and decomposition. The accumulation of nutrients in the deep waters as they age is due to the rain (flux) of organic matter out of the surface ocean. This is the **biological pump**, whereby bacteria breakdown the organic matter thereby releasing CO_2 and nutrients in the process. The accumulation of CO_2 in the deep waters generates acidity (carbonic acid) that dissolves the rain of calcareous shells of microscopic plankton descending from the surface waters (Fig. 3.35). This process is responsible for the Carbonate Compensation Depth (CCD), which marks the depth at which calcareous materials disappear from the bottom sediments. The CCD occurs at shallower depths in the parts of the ocean, such as the North Pacific, where the bottom water is older and, therefore, contains more dissolved CO_2.

You can see from this analysis how ocean currents and the distribution of carbonate sediments are related. See section 2.14 for more information about carbonate sediments.

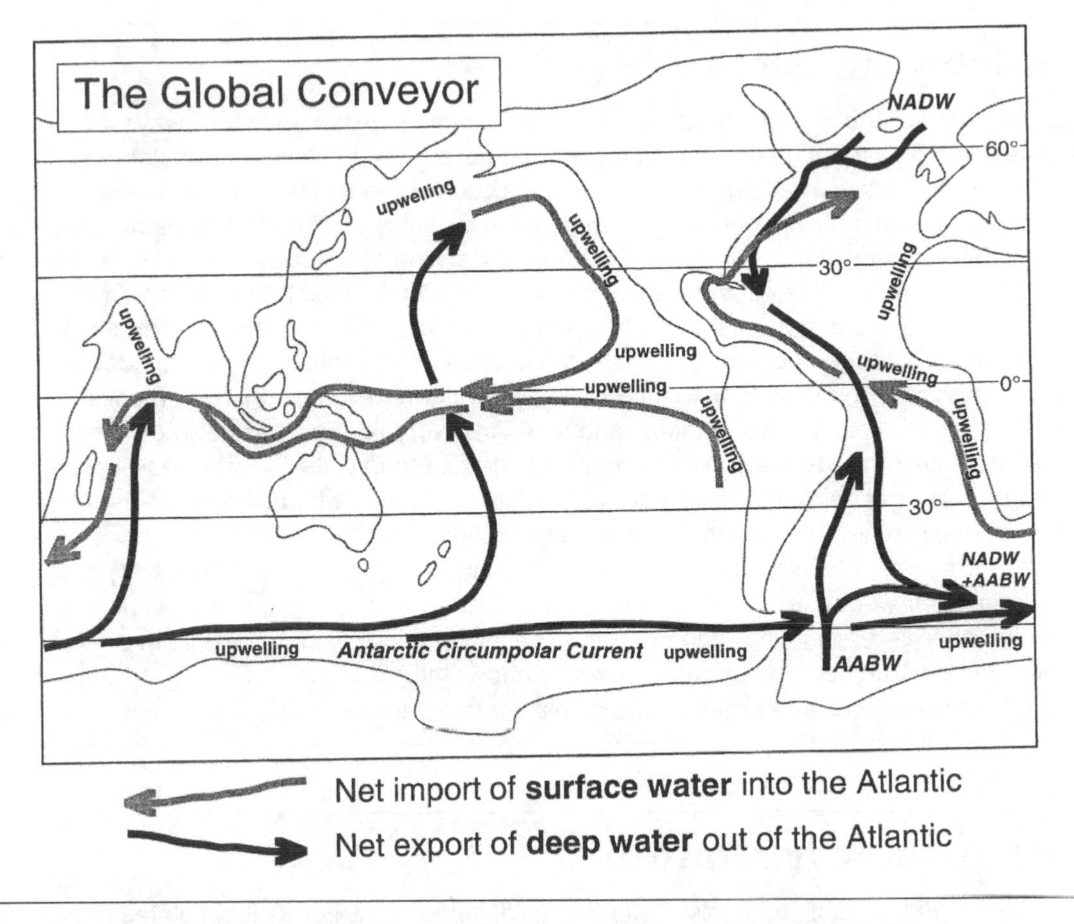

Fig 3.34 The surface ocean currents of the world are connected to the thermohaline circulation system by the upwelling and downwelling that occurs at various locations in the ocean.

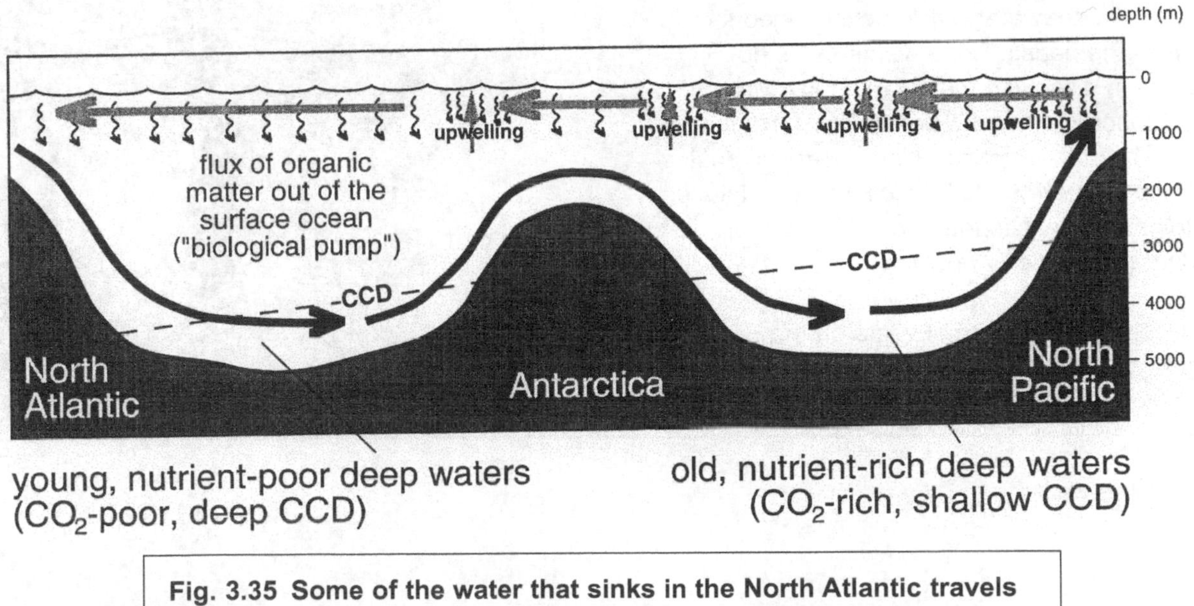

Fig. 3.35 Some of the water that sinks in the North Atlantic travels the conveyor and rises in the North Pacific up to 1000 years later.

A Chemistry Refresher

Throughout our study of the ocean we will be dealing with chemistry in a variety of ways, and it will be helpful to review some of the fundamental principles that govern the behavior of substances at the Earth's surface. The material world is made up of 92 naturally-occurring chemical elements. These rarely exist by themselves, but they combine with one another to produce a variety of chemical compounds. Water is one such compound. Each chemical element has a nucleus consisting of a specified number of protons (the atomic number) and neutrons (protons + neutrons together = atomic mass). The protons have a positive electrical charge, and this charge is balanced by an equal number of negatively-charged electrons that are depicted as orbiting about the nucleus. Chemical elements can often achieve a greater stability by sharing these electrons in some way, forming a chemical compound. Water is an example of a covalent bond, where the electrons are truly shared by the elements and creating a very strong bond between them. It takes a lot of energy to break these bonds, which is why making hydrogen from water is not a realistic alternative to fossil fuels for our own needs. Another type of bond is the ionic bond, whereby one element actually donates an electron to another to give them both a more stable configuration. Sodium (Na) will bond with chlorine (Cl) by transferring an electron, so that sodium has a positive charge (a sodium ion – Na^+) and chlorine has a negative charge (a chloride ion – Cl^-). The compound NaCl, which is common salt, is held together in its solid form by the charge difference on the two ions. These bonds are relatively weak, and the ions can be removed and attached to other ions or charged compounds. Salt dissolves easily in water because the Na^+ and Cl^- ions are attracted to the charges on the dipolar water molecule.

Hydrothermal Circulation

In addition to rivers and volcanic aerosols, dissolved solids enter seawater as it circulates through the fractured oceanic crust of active spreading centers. Cold, deep waters are drawn into the crust, superheated by the magma reservoir below the ridge, and then expelled as hot fluids in or near the central rift valley of active spreading ridge segments. These superheated fluids are commonly rich in particulate materials and dissolved ions yielding smoke-like discharges called **"black smokers"** or **"white smokers"**. This hydrothermal circulation vents fluids of a different composition than the original seawater. For example, seawater Mg^{2+} is exchanged for Ca^{2+} from the basalt. Some vents expel hot fluids rich in dissolved metals (e.g., Fe, Mn, Cu, Zn, Co) leached from the basalt. Ionic exchange between hydrothermal fluids and oceanic crust is responsible for the metalliferous ions precipitated in authigenic deposits found on the seafloor, including **manganese nodules**.

For videos of hydrothermal vents on the seafloor, go to:http://www.whoi.edu/sbl/liteSite.do?litesiteid=188738articled=28271

Name ______________________________

First three letters of last name

Investigation 3.1 **Polar and Nonpolar Liquids**

1). Look at the structure of the molecules the two substances, methanol and hexane, both of which are liquids at room temperature. Are either of these polar liquids? On what basis are you making your decision?

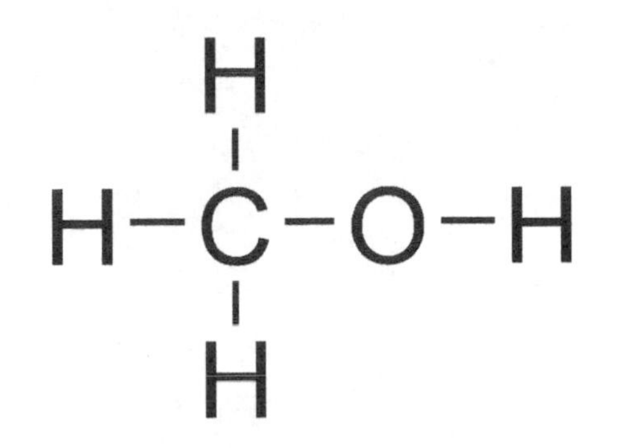

Methanol has three hydrogen (H) atoms attached to a central carbon (C) atom. A hydroxyl group (OH) is attached to the C in the fourth position.

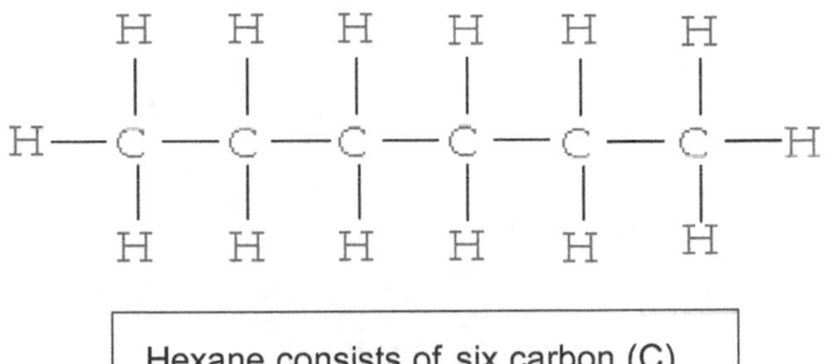

Hexane consists of six carbon (C) and hydrogen (H) atoms arranged in a straight chain.

2). Now let's do a simple thought experiment. If you fill three chemistry burettes with liquid: One contains water, another is filled with methanol, and the third has the liquid hexane. When the stopcock is opened to let the liquids flow out, a charged rod will be brought close to the stream. What will you anticipate the results will be?

3). Your instructor may be able to demonstrate this, or you may be able to try it in a laboratory. After the experiment is finished, explain the reasons for the differences in the behavior of the three liquids.

Name ______________________________

First three letters of last name

Investigation 3.2 Temperature and Heat Capacity

Your instructor will set up an experiment or demonstration for you to observe. There is a flask of methanol and a flask of water each with a temperature-measuring device inserted into it. A heat lamp will be turned on, and you should carefully note the change in temperature for each beaker.

Time Interval	Methanol Temperature	Water Temperature

Your instructor will turn off the heat lamp. Now record the temperature of each over the span of several minutes.

Time Interval	Methanol Temperature	Water Temperature

Plot the results on the graph on the back of this page.

1). What differences do you note between the response the methanol and that of the water to the heating and cooling?

2). Which of the two substances has the higher heat capacity?

3). What conclusions can you draw from this experiment about how the temperature at the surface of the Earth might be regulated?

Name ______________________________

First three letters of last name

Investigation 3.4 Seawater Chemistry

1). a. Using the data in Table 3.3 (page 115), list the five most common dissolved ions in seawater in the table below. Rank them in order from the most common at the top to the least common at the bottom.

b. In the second column, list the five most common ions in rivers. Use the same ranking as above.

	Seawater	River Water
1		
2		
3		
4		
5		

2). How can you explain the difference in the importance of the ions sodium (Na^+) and (Cl^-) in seawater as compared to river water?

3). Why do you think the bicarbonate (HCO_3^-) ion is so far down the list of ion abundance in seawater?

Name ____________________________

First three letters of last name

Investigation 3.5 Residence Time of Salts

The total mass of water plus salt in the ocean = 14,200 x 10^{20} g. From the concentration data in the first column, determine the mass of Na^+ and Ca^{2+} in the ocean. Then determine the residence time for these two dissolved components.

Substance	Concentration ‰	Mass in Ocean g	Input Rate g/yr	Residence Time yr
H_2O	965	13,700 x 10^{20}	3.8 x 10^{20}	
Na^+	10.5		2.1 x 10^{14}	
Ca^{2+}	0.4		4.9 x 10^{14}	

How can you explain the difference in the residence time for the two dissolved components of Na^+ and Ca^{2+}?

Name ______________________________

First three letters of last name

Investigation 3.6 Seawater Density

1). Suppose you had exactly 1 liter (1000 cm^3) of pure water (salinity = 0‰) at a temperature of 10°C. What would the mass (in grams) of this water be? If you lowered the temperature to 5°C, what would the mass of the 1 liter of water be? Refer to table 3.6 (page 120) for useful information.

2). What is the mass of 1 liter of sea water (salinity = 35‰) at a temperature of 20°C?

3). Design an experiment that would allow you to measure the change in the density of water as temperature changes.

Name ______________________________

First three letters of last name

Investigation 3.8 Solar Angle and Radiation

1). What is the latitude of the town where you are at the present time?

2). What time(s) of year will you have exactly 12 hours of sunlight during the day?

3). What is the sun's angle above the horizon at noon on June 21st? Use the figure on the next page to help in your calculations.

4). What is the sun's angle above the horizon at noon on December 21st?

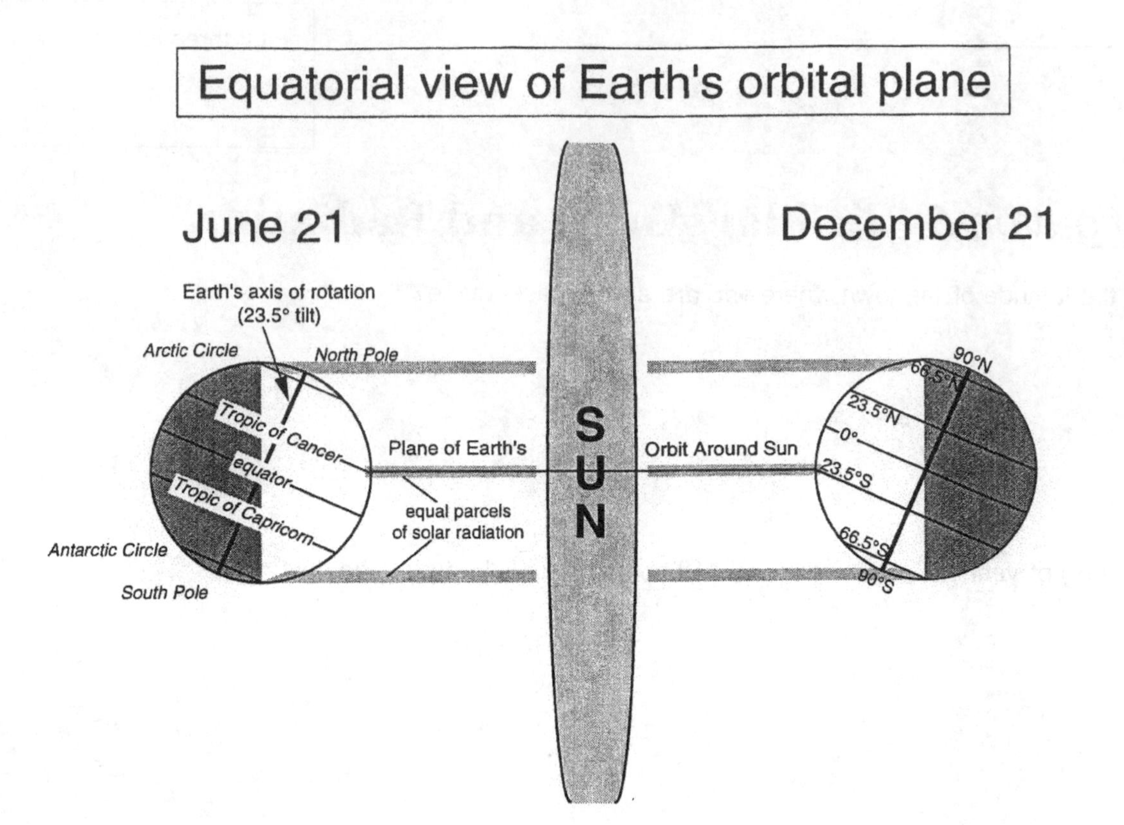
Equatorial view of Earth's orbital plane
June 21
December 21
Earth's axis of rotation
(23.5° tilt)
Arctic Circle
North Pole
Tropic of Cancer
equator
Tropic of Capricorn
Antarctic Circle
South Pole
Plane of Earth's
Orbit Around Sun
equal parcels
of solar radiation
SUN
90°N
66.5°N
23.5°N
0°
23.5°S
66.5°S
90°S

Name ______________________________

First three letters of last name

Investigation 3.13 Ocean Currents

1). In what direction do the Equatorial Currents flow? Why do they flow in this direction?

2). Look at the figure below (Note: you will need to refer to the full-color version found on the inside back cover of the book). If you are in the middle of the Sargasso Sea, will you be at higher or lower elevation than at the coastline in the New York area? Can you estimate from the illustration what your elevation difference will be?

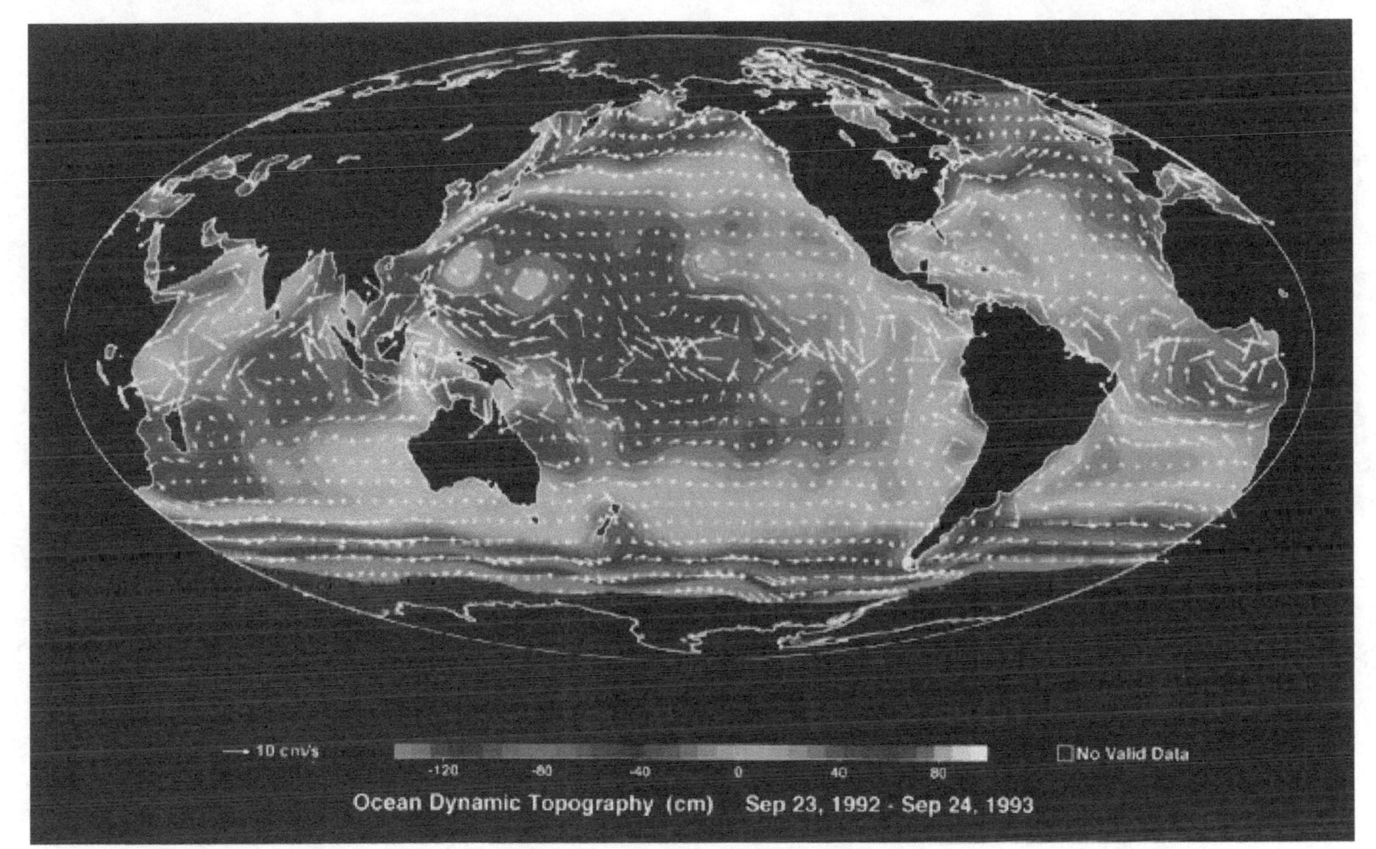

You can view the color image at http://sealevel.jpl.nasa.gov/gallery/science/gifs/P44076.jpg and on the inside back cover of this book.

3). Where in the ocean does the highest elevation occur? Explain the pattern that you see.

PART 4

Life in the Sea

Most of us think immediately of marine biology when the science of the ocean is mentioned. In particular, we are very aware of the larger animals of the marine realm, such as whales, sharks, seals, and similar creatures that are frequently the center of television documentaries or newspaper articles. However, the realm of marine life is much more than this. The ocean teems with life on an incredible scale, from microscopic organisms that produce a good part of the Earth's oxygen to the largest mammals on the planet, the baleen whales. However, life in the ocean is not evenly distributed throughout its breadth and depth, but it is concentrated in particular zones governed by the availability of sunlight and nutrients. All marine organisms are tied together in a complex web of life sustained by the sun and governed by the recycling of energy and nutrients. We humans are also a part of the marine food chain, and we have had a tremendous impact on the ecology of the ocean that will require the development of real management plans to help sustain the ocean system as we know it.

In the chapter you will learn:

- The basic principles that govern the ways we study marine life
- How life is distributed in the ocean, and the influences that determine this distribution
- The influence of nutrients, salinity, and the change of the seasons upon marine organisms
- The characteristics of different marine ecosystems, ranging from coastal environments to the deep sea
- How organisms interact with one another, and the role of humans in the oceanic food chain

■4.1 Studying Marine Organisms

The scientific study of marine life has a few primary goals: we want to understand how marine organisms survive, what their habits and habitats are, and how these creatures may have originated or evolved. The first step in reaching these goals is to develop a systematic way to see how different organisms are related. A classification scheme helps to see these relationships and biologists have developed a number of different ways of classifying organisms.

> *We will examine the process of photosynthesis in greater detail in section 4.4, and the various marine habitats will come under review in section 4.2.*

1. **Classification by nutrition**: organisms can be divided into two broad groups.
   a. **Autotrophic** organisms are those that can make their own food, usually by the process of **photosynthesis**. Examples include the unicellular diatoms, coccolithophorids, and dinoflagellates, as well as multicellular algae (seaweed) and coastal vascular plants.
   b. **Heterotrophic** organisms are those that survive on other organisms or their by-products as a food source. In the ocean, there are several modes of nutrition used by heterotrophic organisms.
      i. **Grazers** float in the water and feed upon microscopic autotrophic organisms that surround them. These are usually unicellular or very small planktonic organisms. *(examples: foraminifera, copepods).*
      ii. **Predators** constitute the larger members of the ocean community that feed upon smaller animals *(jellyfish, tuna, sharks, toothed whales are all examples).*
      iii. **Filter feeders** (also called **suspension feeders**) are able to capture and strain organic particles or small organisms suspended in the water column, or pump large volumes of sea water through their bodies and extract organic material that the water contains. *(examples: clams, mussels, scallops, oysters, corals, barnacles, anemones, krill, baleen whales).*
      iv. **Scavengers** are organisms that subsist primarily on the decaying remains of other creatures. *(sea stars, sea urchins, and many crabs are scavengers).*
      v. **Deposit feeders** are animals that crawl on or through the bottom sediments of the ocean and extract bits of food *(examples: many marine worms and snails).*

2. **Classification by habitat**: organisms can live either in the water column itself **(pelagic)** or on the sea floor **(benthic)**.

3. **Classification by mobility**:
   a. **Motile** organisms can move about, either as free swimmers (**nekton**), floaters (**plankton**) or on the bottom (**benthon**).
   b. **Sessile** organisms have no ability to move about.

4. Classification by **taxonomy**. This is the most familiar way of classifying life that arranges organisms according their cellular type (**prokaryote**, **eukaryote**), body plan and development, nutrition, and how the various body parts function.

In a view of life dating back to the mid-1800's, biologists identified three Kingdoms: plants, animals, and bacteria. It turns out that the tree of life is much more complicated than this, with plants and animals constituting only a fraction of life on Earth. Today, most biologists recognize 5 or 6 Kingdoms of life that are grouped into 3 Domains (**Archaea**, **Bacteria**, **Eukarya**) (Fig. 4.1). Our goal is to become familiar with life in the sea, but in order to do this we must familiarize ourselves with the characteristics that distinguish the different groups of organisms from one another (fig. 4.2).

> *Investigation 4.1 explores the basis for the classification and study of marine organisms.*

Kingdom MONERA* (bacteria, archaea)

- most are TINY CELLS (~1 micron) which lack a membrane-bounded nucleus and contain 'naked' DNA (= PROKARYOTIC CELLS)
- HETEROTROPHIC bacteria (consumers and decomposers)
- AUTOTROPHIC bacteria (photosynthetic cyanobacteria and chemosynthetic bacteria)

*some biologists prefer to split this group into two Kingdoms (and two Domains), BACTERIA ("true bacteria") and ARCHAEA ("old bacteria"); ARCHAEA are distinguished by unique aspects of their biochemistry, and many forms tolerate extreme conditions (very high temperatures, high salinity, acidic and/or anoxic waters)

Kingdom PROTOCTISTA (algae, protists, slime molds)

- cells which have a membrane-bounded NUCLEUS, and usually contain internal organelles such as mitochondria, plastids, and golgi bodies (= EUKARYOTIC CELLS; advanced cells evolved via bacterial symbiosis)
- not bacteria, not fungi, not plant, not animal
- most are larger than bacteria
- diverse in structure and feeding (AUTOTROPHIC and HETEROTROPHIC forms)
- many are UNICELLULAR (single-celled organisms called PROTISTS) including <u>all PHYTOPLANKTON in the ocean</u> and other microscopic protozoans ("microzooplankton")
- MULTICELLULAR forms include green, brown, and red ALGAE ("seaweeds")

Kingdom FUNGI (yeasts, molds, mushrooms)

- all have NUCLEATED CELLS
- develop from SPORES which are resistant to drying
- mostly TERRESTRIAL (living on land in moist air)
- require food in the form of organic compounds (like animals) but digest food outside rather than inside their bodies by releasing enzymes onto their food and decomposing it (SAPROTROPHIC)

Kingdom PLANTAE (plants)

- develop from an EMBRYO surrounded by tissue of female parent
- all are MULTICELLULAR and each nucleated cell is covered by a cell wall composed of cellulose
- most conduct PHOTOSYNTHESIS: produce oxygen and use green pigment chlorophyll to make their own food by reducing carbon dioxide (AUTOTROPHIC)
- marine varieties include salt marsh grasses, turtle and eel grasses, mangrove trees

Kingdom ANIMALIA (animals)

- develop from a type of embryo called a BLASTULA (multicellular hollow sphere) formed when an egg is fertilized by a sperm
- all are MULTICELLULAR with nucleated cells
- require food in the form of organic compounds (HETEROTROPHIC), other organisms or the remains of other organisms
- includes invertebrates and vertebrates; sponges to squid, and tiny zooplankton crustaceans to huge cetaceans (whales) and humans

Fig. 4.1 A taxonomic classification scheme that organizes life into five kingdoms.

The green sea turtle is a marine reptile that belongs to the Phylum Chordata along with fish and marine mammals.

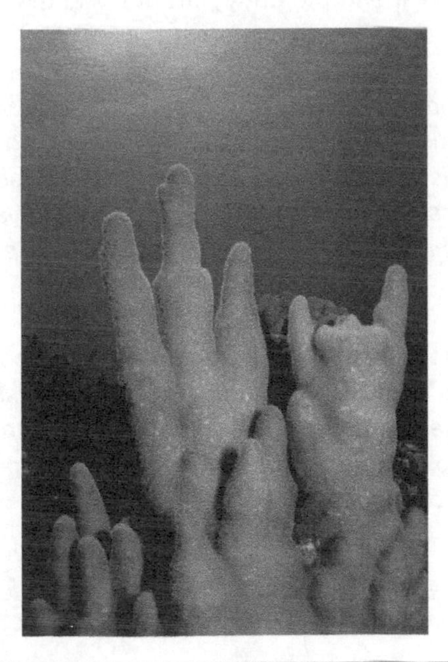

Corals are marine invertebrates that belong to the Phylum Cnidaria.

Kingdom ANIMALIA

Major groups (PHYLA) of marine invertebrate and vertebrate animals

Invertebrates

PORIFERA ***(sponges)***
- primitive suspension feeders with digestive cavity; intertidal to abyss

CNIDARIA ***(corals, jellyfish, sea anemones, comb jellies)***
- radial symmetry, possess stinging cells; corals build $CaCO_3$ skeleton

PLATYHELMINTHES ***(flat worms)***
- bilateral symmetry, primitive central nervous system

NEMOTODA ***(round worms)***
- flow-through digestive system

ANNELIDA ***(segmented worms)***
- includes tube worms and feather duster worms

MOLLUSCA ***(chitons, snails, clams, oysters, mussels, squid, octopi)***
- bilateral symmetry; flow-through digestive tract; well-developed nervous system
- most have internal or external shell of calcium carbonate ($CaCO_3$)

ARTHROPODA ***(crabs, shrimp, lobsters, barnacles, krill, copepods)***
- appendages with joints; organism grows by molting
- exoskeleton of tough chitin (N-rich carbohydrate), some strengthened with $CaCO_3$

ECHINODERMATA ***(sea stars, sea urchins, sea cucumbers)***
- pentameral symmetry; water-vascular system; tube feet for locomotion and feeding
- some with external shell of calcium carbonate ($CaCO_3$)

CHORDATA ***(tunicates, salps)***
- possess stiffened nodocord

Vertebrates

CHORDATA

VERTEBRATA (Subphylum)
- cartilaginous fishes ***(sharks, skates, rays)***
- bony fishes ***(tuna, halibut, sea horse, eel)***
- amphibians *(no marine representatives)*
- reptiles ***(turtles, crocodiles, sea snakes, marine iguanas)***
- birds ***(gulls, albatrosses, petrels, penguins)***
- mammals ***(whales, seals, otters, manatees)***

Fig. 4.2 The detailed classification scheme of the Animal Kingdom, all of which are represented in the marine environment.

■4.2 The Distribution of Life in the Ocean

Although life is found everywhere in the ocean, it is not distributed evenly. The availability of sunlight and the amount of nutrients in the water ultimately determine where life is concentrated. To help us understand this distribution, oceanographers subdivide the ocean into various zones (Fig. 4.3). The **pelagic environment** refers to the water column (from the surface to the bottom); the **benthic environment** refers to the seafloor (from a salt marsh or beach to the deepest trench). There are many more species of animals that live in the benthic zone (~98% of all animal species) than in the pelagic zone(~2%) because of the greater variety of habitats available for exploitation and specialization on the seabed compared with the water column (see sections 4.8 to 4.11).

Plankton includes all organisms that drift with the ocean currents. These are *"passive floaters"*. In general, they can be divided into several different groups:

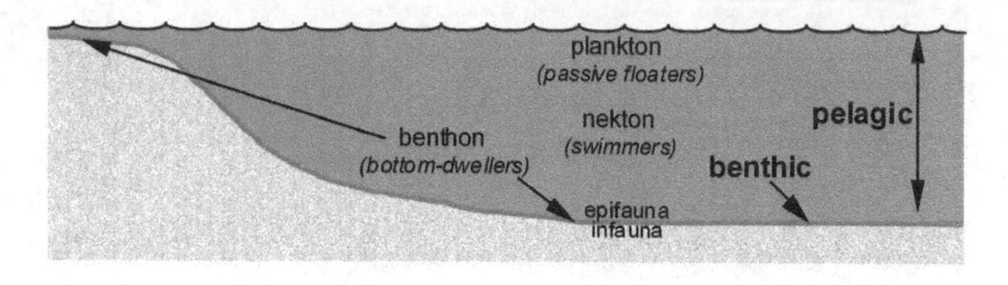

Fig. 4.3 The pelagic zone refers to the water of the ocean; the benthic zone is the seafloor. Organisms residing in these zones are classified according to their life style.

The **phytoplankton** are microscopic, unicellular (single-celled), photosynthetic algae such as *diatoms, dinoflagellates,and coccolithophorids* (Fig. 4.4).

The **zooplankton** includes some multicellular animals (*copepods, krill, ctenophores, jellies, salps, arrow worms)* and microscopic, single-celled protists *(flagellates, ciliates, foraminifera, radiolaria*).

The **bacterioplankton** includes heterotrophic and photosynthetic forms of bacteria (*cyanobacteria*).

The **meroplankton** are the larval stages of some familiar marine animals *(clams, crabs, barnacles, lobster, corals, sponges and many, many others)*. The young of these creatures spend the early part of life in the plankton.

Nekton are all organisms capable of moving independent of ocean currents. These are the *"free swimmers"* familiar to most people (Fig. 4.5) and include squid, chambered nautilus, fish (*pelagic fish such as herring, anchovy, mackerel, tuna, marlin, shark, rays, tropical reef fish, flying fish, salmon, eel, and "ground fish" such as cod and haddock*), marine mammals (*seals, manatees, toothed whales such as dolphin and sperm whale, baleen whales such as the Humpback, Right, Fin, Gray, and Minke whales*), marine reptiles (*sea turtles, sea crocodiles*).

Benthon are all organisms that live on the seafloor (**epifauna**) or buried within sediments (**infauna**). These are animals that are *"bottom-dwellers"* (Fig. 4.6). This group includes most marine invertebrates (*clams, mussels, oysters, scallops, limpets, snails, barnacles, lobsters, shrimp, crabs, sea urchins, starfish, brittle stars, sea cucumbers, corals, anemones, sponges, worms*) as well as attached plants (*sea grasses*) and benthic algae (*kelp and other seaweeds*) and even some bottom-dwelling fish (*flounder, sole*).

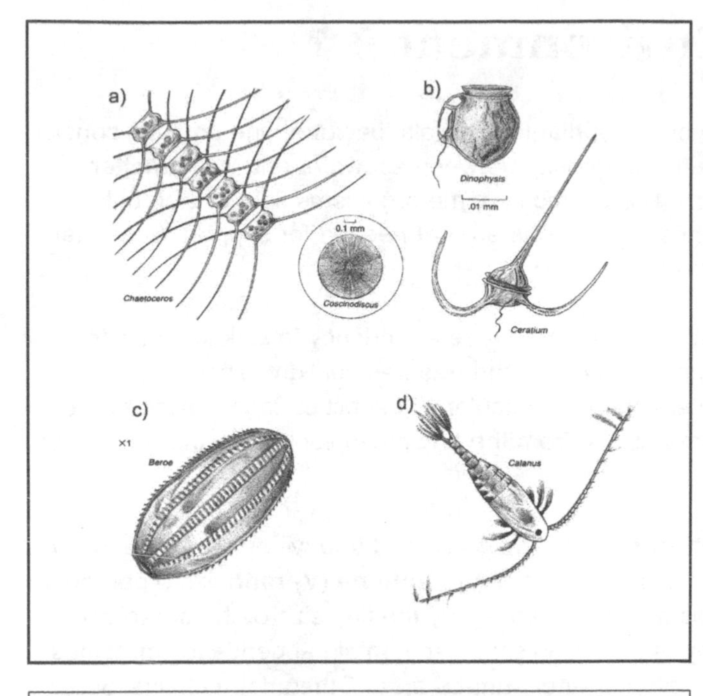

Fig. 4.4 Examples of organisms that belong to the plankton. a) Two diatoms (phytoplankton); b) Two dinoflagellates (phytoplankton) c) a comb jelly (zooplankton); d) a copepod (zooplankton).

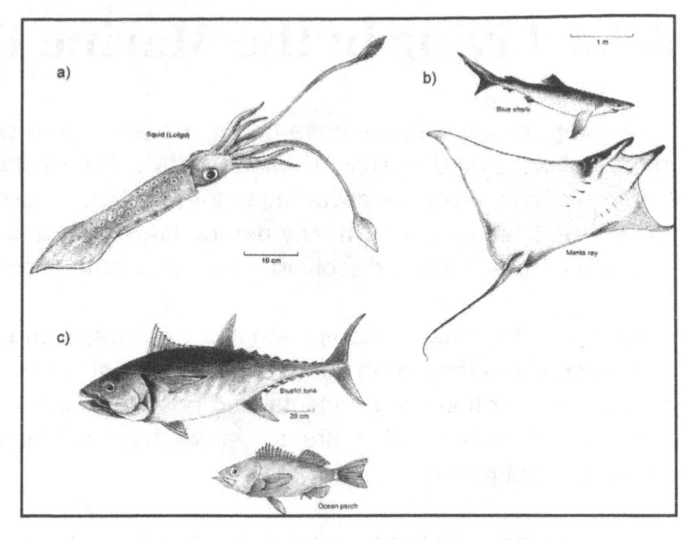

Fig. 4.5 Some organisms that are part of the nekton community.

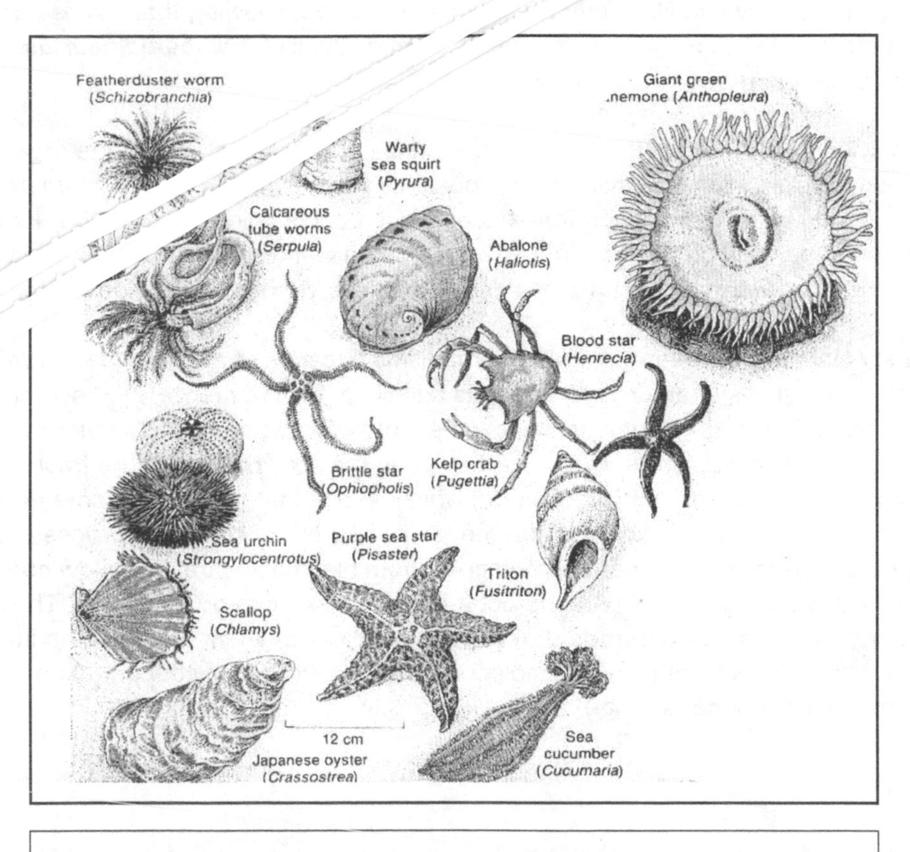

Fig. 4.6 Examples of organisms that belong to the benthon.

■4.3 Living in the Marine Environment

Seawater and living tissue have nearly the same density because plants, animals, bacteria, and protists, consist mostly of water and dissolved solids ("salts"). The similarities in density between seawater and living matter confer several important advantages for marine organisms. For example, some organisms float or sink only slowly because they have nearly neutral buoyancy, and heavy skeletons are not needed for support. Seawater also contains abundant dissolved gases and mineral nutrients.

Although organisms are composed mostly of water, most organisms will have a tendency to sink in seawater. However, life in the ocean, as on land, is dependent on photosynthesis and requires sunlight. Therefore, adaptations for flotation or maintaining position in the water column, particularly in sunlit surface waters where photosynthesis is possible, are crucial for many marine organisms, from the tiny phytoplankton to the herbivores to the biggest predators.

In order to maintain their positions in the water column, marine organisms have had to develop various adaptive strategies. The plankton, or passive floaters, have a large **surface area (A) to volume (V) ratio** like a parachute, which helps them maintain their position in the water. This ratio is enhanced by the tiny size of the organisms, since the smaller the size, the greater the A/V ratio. Many of the organisms also contain appendages or spines, whereas other organisms have flat shapes that provide them a greater surface area. Others form chains, which accomplishes the same purpose. Some organisms also produce **oil droplets** within protoplasm that gives them greater buoyancy since oil has a lower density than water.

The nekton (swimmers) have also evolved numerous ways to help them stay in their preferred depth range in the ocean. Fast predators, such as sharks, use active swimming and expend energy to overcome gravity. They are often assisted by having oil in their flesh that gives them greater buoyancy. Most fish also have swim bladders to regulate buoyancy which they can fill or empty with carbon dioxide, allowing them to rise or sink in the water column. Many nektonic invertebrates such as the cephalopod molluscs (*chambered nautilus, squid, cuttlefish*) have similar gas containers to regulate buoyancy.

The temperature, and hence the **viscosity**, of water has an important impact on marine organisms, particularly floating organisms such as plankton and swimming organisms such as fish, marine mammals, and reptiles. Cold water is more viscous than warm water; therefore it is easier to float in cold water, but harder to swim. For the plankton, the problem of maintaining position in the water column is more difficult in the sunlit surface waters of low to mid-latitudes because warm waters are less dense and less viscous than colder waters.

Seawater poses a special problem for many marine organisms because of a difference in **ionic concentration** (salinity) between the body fluids of an organism and its salt water environment. This becomes particularly problematic for organisms that migrate seasonally to waters of the world ocean with different salinities, or for **anadromous fish** such as salmon, which mature in the ocean but spawn in the same fresh water streams where they were born. Cell walls are **semipermeable,** which means that they allow some molecules to pass through and screen others out. Molecules can move into and out of cells by a process called **diffusion** (Fig. 4.7). Diffusion is the passive movement of molecules from high concentration to low concentration; no energy is exerted (watch what happens when you put a tea bag into a cup of hot water). The diffusion of water molecules into or out of a cell is called **osmosis**. If there is a salinity gradient between the inside and outside of the cell, an **osmotic pressure** will cause water molecules to move from high concentration of water (low salinity) to low concentration of water (higher salinity).

The osmotic pressure experienced by many salt-water fish and marine mammals is caused by cells and tissue having an ionic concentration less than the seawater they live in. This condition is called **hypotonic** and these organisms have evolved strategies to overcome the loss of water (dehydration) from their cells (Fig. 4.6). The opposite problem is faced by fresh water fish because their cells have a higher ionic concentration than their environment. This condition is referred to as **hypertonic**. Sharks, rays, and many marine invertebrates experience little osmotic pressure because their body fluids have an ionic concentration, which is very close to that of the seawater they live in. This condition is called **isotonic**.

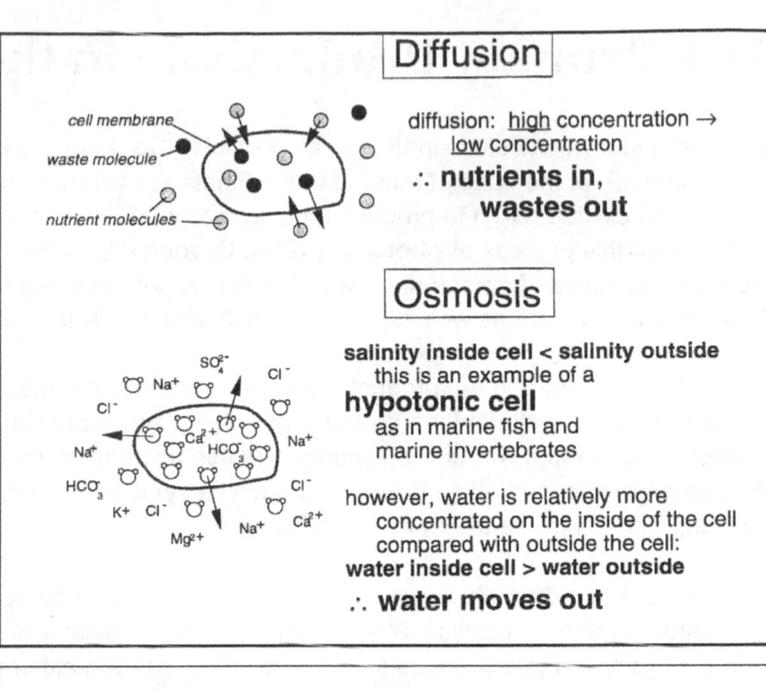

Fig. 4.7 The processes of diffusion and osmosis regulate the amount of water and salts that are present inside a cell.

Many marine organisms are sensitive to relatively small changes in the physical characteristics of their environment. **Salinity** can significantly impact the distribution of some marine organisms because of osmotic pressures. **Stenohaline** organisms tolerate only a narrow range of salinity. For example, many organisms are not able to tolerate the high salinities (>40‰) of some subtropical lagoons, or the reduced salinities (<30‰) of coastal waters or estuaries. **Euryhaline** organisms can tolerate a wider range of salinities. For example, many organisms that live along the coasts of the mid-latitudes must be able to tolerate daily and seasonal swings in salinity due to the tidal fluctuations, evaporation, precipitation, and river runoff from the land.

Table 4.1 Examples of environments with narrow and broad ranges of salinity and temperature.

Organisms are adapted to the conditions of the environment in which they live:	*Tropical Coral Reefs*	*Mid-Latitude Intertidal Zone*
salinity	~34°/oo-37°/oo	~0°/oo-40°/oo
temperature	~18°-29°C (~65°- 84°F)	~0°-25°C (~32°-77°F)
organism tolerances	stenohaline, stenothermal *(narrow range)*	euryhaline, eurythermal *(broad range)*

Temperature also has a significant impact on the distribution of marine organisms. For example, rates of diffusion, osmosis, and metabolism are temperature-dependent. The higher the temperature the higher the rate of molecular movement into or out of cells, and the higher the rate of biological activity including growth rates, motility, and life span. Temperature also controls the concentration of dissolved gasses in water including CO_2 for photosynthesis and O_2 for animal respiration. The higher the temperature, the less dissolved gas water can hold. **Stenothermal** organisms can tolerate only a narrow range of temperatures and **eurythermal** organisms can tolerate a wider range. Coral reefs and mid-latitude intertidal communities are two examples of shallow water communities representing the end-members of stenohaline-stenothermal and euryhaline-eurythermal organisms, respectively (Table 4.1).

Investigation 4.2 explores how different organisms adapt to the range of marine environments

■4.4 Primary Productivity in the Ocean

How is all the diversity of life in the ocean possible? Consider the nature of the food chains and food webs on land: plants are at the base of most of them. Plants are **primary producers**: they reduce inorganic carbon derived from carbon dioxide (CO_2) to produce organic compounds that can be used as food. The sun provides the source of energy for this process of **photosynthesis**. Oxygen (O_2) is released as a by-product of photosynthesis. Plants depend on supplies of carbon dioxide (CO_2), water, nutrients (especially nitrates and phosphates, but also trace elements such as iron, as well as vitamins), and sunlight. This creation of food is **primary productivity**.

The vast majority of primary productivity in the oceans is the result of photosynthesis, and much of this is by microscopic single-celled algae collectively called **phytoplankton** (autotrophic protists). Other important primary producers include **cyanobacteria** (photosynthetic bacteria) in near-surface waters of the world ocean, as well as multicellular benthic algae (seaweeds such as kelp) and vascular plants (such as salt marsh, eel, and turtle grasses, and mangrove trees) in coastal waters.

Not all primary productivity is driven by sunlight. Bacteria at hydrothermal vents and hydrocarbon seeps on the seafloor produce organic molecules by utilizing chemical reactions, rather than sunlight, as the energy source. Organisms that are able to produce their own food either by photosynthesis or chemical processes (chemosynthesis) are known as **autotrophs**.

In contrast to plants, animals cannot synthesize their own food and hence are **heterotrophs** dependent on primary productivity, either by feeding directly on autotrophs in the case of **herbivores** (grazers and filter feeders), or by feeding indirectly through predation by **carnivores**, or by scavenging dead organisms. The organic matter produced by autotrophs is stored chemical energy in the form of carbohydrates, proteins, and fats. For example, you might eat a candy bar for a quick shot of energy, or load up on "carbs", which are easily broken down to sugars and provide energy for a busy day of work or play.

Primary productivity by photosynthesis requires two essential ingredients, solar energy and inorganic nutrients. If both are not readily available, productivity will be limited. The **photic zone** is the depth in the ocean to which photosynthesis is possible: approximately 20 m (~66 ft.) in coastal waters and rarely exceeding 200 m (~660 ft.) in the tropical ocean (see section 3.6). The **euphotic zone** is the upper part of the photic zone that receives enough light to support a net gain in photosynthetic production. The **oxygen compensation depth** defines the base of the euphotic zone; below this depth, the consumption of O_2 by respiration exceeds production of organic matter and O_2 by photosynthesis.

Photosynthesis can be summarized by the following reaction:

$$6CO_2 + 6H_2O + \text{inorganic nutrients} + \text{solar energy} \rightarrow C_6H_{12}O_6 + 6O_2$$

carbon dioxide (6CO₂) · water (6H₂O) · glucose (simple sugar) ($C_6H_{12}O_6$) · oxygen ($6O_2$)

the opposite of this reaction is ***respiration*** *(what animals do)*

The availability of solar energy varies across latitude and it varies by season, particularly in the mid- to high latitudes because of the differences in the angle of solar incidence (Fig. 4.8). The magnitude of surface water heating (hence the degree of thermocline development) and the depth of the photic zone depend on the angle of solar incidence; the higher the sun is in the sky, the warmer the surface waters become and the deeper sunlight will penetrate into the ocean. The availability of nutrients in the surface waters of the world ocean varies greatly. Coastal waters generally have abundant nutrients, which are derived from the weathering of the land and soils, and

We will examine the seasonal changes in primary productivity more completely in section 4.6.

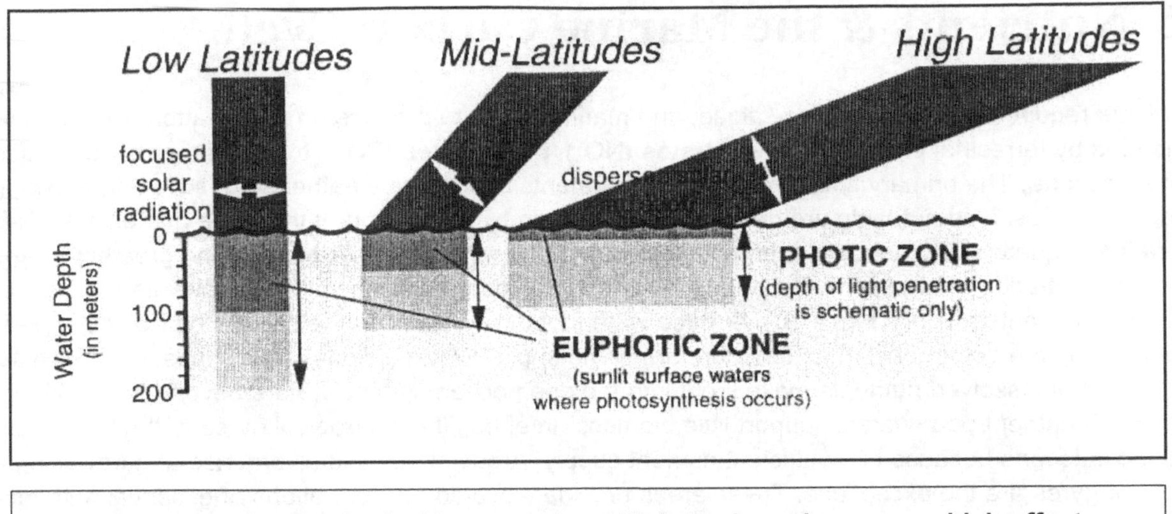

Fig. 4.8 The angle of solar incidence varies with latitude and season, which affects the depth of the photic and euphotic zones in different parts of the ocean.

delivered to the ocean by river runoff. By contrast, the open ocean is far-removed from riverine influences. Rather, nutrient availability in the open ocean is significantly influenced by the density structure of the upper water column. For example, in the tropics, nutrients are concentrated in the deep waters below the euphotic zone and below the thermocline (Fig. 4.9). The presence or absence of a seasonal thermocline in the temperate belt is important because it may limit the availability of nutrients for part of the year. You can think of the thermocline as a "density doorway"; when closed (year-round or seasonal thermocline) nutrient availability to the euphotic zone is limited, when open (weak or absent thermocline) nutrient diffusion to the euphotic zone is not limited. The weak thermal and density stratification of polar waters does not prohibit the upward diffusion of nutrients at any time of the year. However, the low sun angle and large seasonal changes in number of daylight hours controls the timing of productivity in the high latitudes.

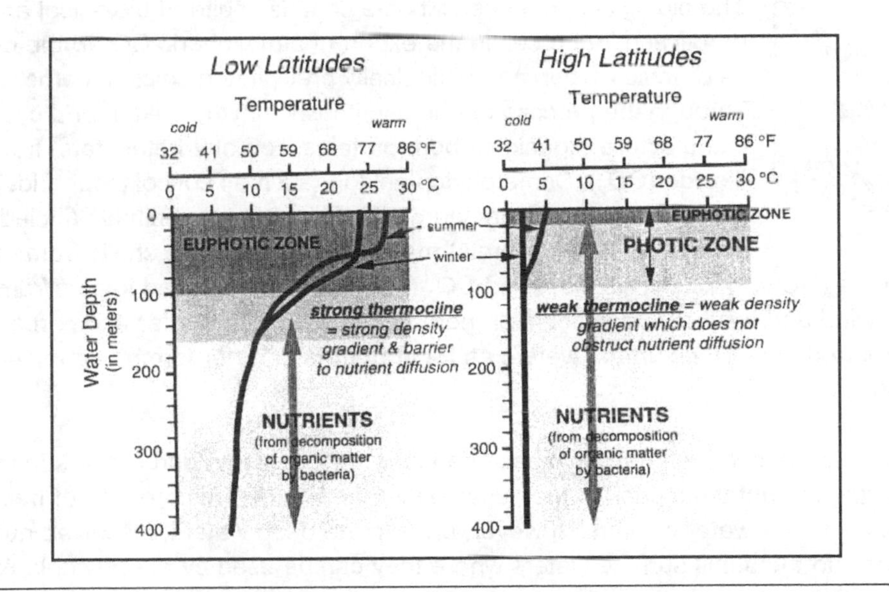

Fig. 4.9 The thermocline is an effective barrier to the diffusion and vertical advection of nutrients between nutrient-rich and the sunlit surface waters.

Investigation 4.3 shows a principal way that primary productivity in the ocean can be measured.

■4.5 Nutrients & the Marine Carbon Cycle

The nutrients required by phytoplankton, algae, and marine plants to produce organic matter are the same as those needed by terrestrial plants, namely, **nitrates** (NO_3), **phosphates** (PO_4), **trace elements** such as iron (Fe), and **vitamins**. The primary source of dissolved nutrients is from the weathering of soils and rocks on the land. These dissolved nutrients are delivered to the ocean by river runoff. If there are nutrients available and there is adequate solar radiation, then primary productivity will be high. Therefore, the greatest **biomass** (greatest concentration of organisms) is along the continental margins, especially coastal waters, close to the source of nutrients (rivers) (Fig. 4.10). Surface waters of the continental shelves are typically stripped of their nutrients by the autotrophs, although there are some important exceptions. As a consequence, limited concentrations of dissolved nutrients make it out into the open ocean surface waters beyond the continental margins. Such nutrient-poor waters support little biomass. In effect, the subtropical gyres of the world ocean are biological deserts because of insufficient nutrient supply. Areas of oceanic divergence and upwelling at the edges of the gyres are the exceptions. These areas provide elevated concentrations of essential nutrients along relatively narrow bands of surface waters.

Marine life is concentrated in sunlit surface waters where photosynthesis occurs; however, vast areas of the surface ocean (e.g., subtropical gyres) are depleted in the nutrients required for photosynthesis due to the presence of a pycnocline (thermocline). The rain of organic matter from surface waters **(biological pump),** as well as the influx of terrestrial organic material from the continents, provide food for pelagic and benthic organisms that live below the euphotic zone. Therefore, greater concentrations of pelagic and benthic organisms occur beneath areas of higher primary productivity and terrestrial organic carbon input, such as along the continental margins, compared with the water column and seafloor beneath the subtropical gyres.

You can review the basic principles of upwelling and its relationship to ocean circulation that are outlined in section 3.18 and 3.19.

The structure of the ocean water column—thermocline and pycnocline—is discussed in section 3.7.

The biological pump describes a complex suite of biological and biochemical processes that result in the export of atmospheric CO_2 to the deep ocean as organic carbon and biologically precipitated calcium carbonate ($CaCO_3$). Through the process of photosynthesis, phytoplankton and cyanobacteria manufacture organic carbon (proteins, carbohydrates, fats) from inorganic carbon dioxide (CO_2). Some phytoplankton (such as coccolithophorids), other protists (foraminifera), and many groups of invertebrate animals (including molluscs, echinoderms, and corals) manufacture carbonate shells from dissolved calcium (Ca^{2+}) and bicarbonate (HCO_3^-) ions. This dissolved CO_2 (and HCO_3^-) is derived in part from the atmosphere due to the action of wind and waves. A significant proportion of the organic matter and carbonate created in the euphotic zone is exported out of the surface waters as **fecal pellets** or other forms of particulate organic matter called **marine snow**.

Once organic matter is produced, heterotrophic bacteria in the water column and at the seafloor break it down again, thereby recycling the nutrients back to their usable inorganic form. This process of **bacterial degradation** releases nutrients back to the water column. However, once in the deep waters, dissolved nutrients do not easily diffuse upward into the sunlit surface waters where they can be used by the phytoplankton because of the stratified nature of the water column in the low to mid-latitudes. The nutrients become "trapped" in the deep waters below the pycnocline (thermocline), except where upwelling occurs. In this way, deep waters are a sink, or a storehouse, for nutrients. Upwelling provides a mechanism to deliver nutrients, the raw ingredients of primary productivity, back to the sunlit surface waters.

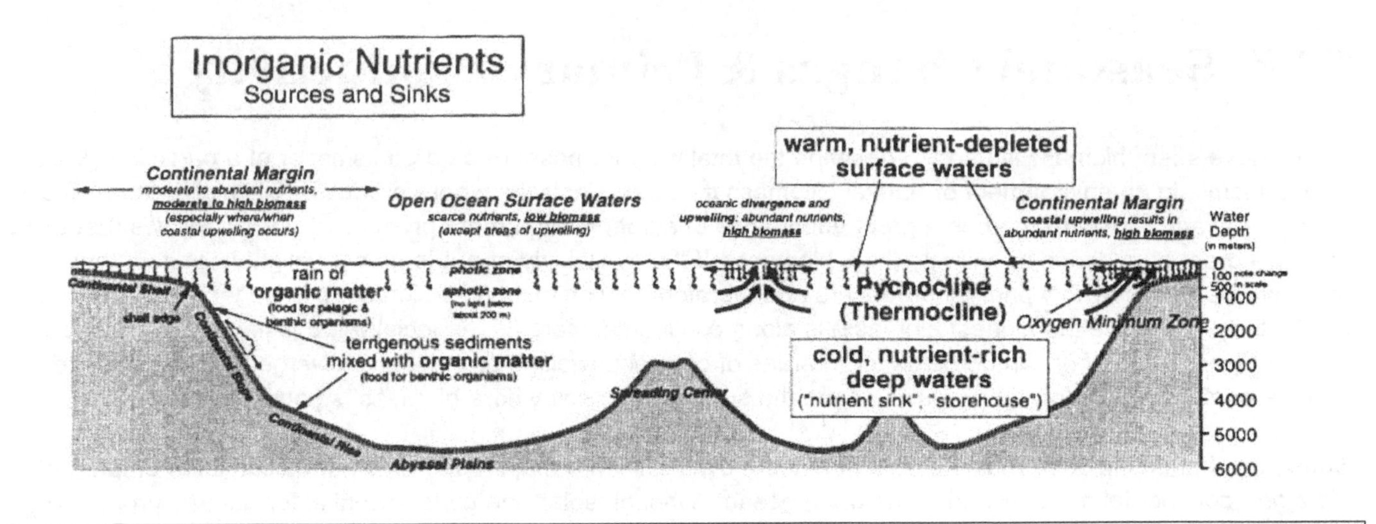

Fig. 4.10 Life in the sea requires nutrients, which are transported from the continents by rivers and then recycled through the food chain throughout the ocean.

In addition to bacterial degradation, organic matter from the sunlit surface waters will begin to oxidize and decompose as it rains down through the water column. **Oxidation** causes oxygen depletion at depth and the formation of **oxygen minimum zones**, especially along continental margins where surface productivity is high. The oxygen minimum zone (<4 ml/l, milliliters of dissolved oxygen per liter of seawater) is generally restricted to the middle part of the water column (~300–1300 m) because deep waters below the pycnocline are very cold and oxygen-rich (Fig. 4.11). The biological pump is an important component of the **carbon cycle**, whereby carbon in a variety of forms is used by organisms and then recycled back to its inorganic form to be used again. For example, some of the organic matter produced in the euphotic zone is buried in marine sediments, but much of it is eventually consumed by heterotrophic organisms or decomposed by bacteria, both of which liberate CO_2 as a by-product of respiration and decomposition. Much of the dissolved CO_2 will eventually find its way back to the surface ocean in areas of upwelling where it can interact with the atmosphere once again. Above the level of the **carbonate compensation depth** (CCD), carbonate shells are deposited on the seafloor as calcareous ooze. Below the CCD, the carbonate shells are dissolved, and Ca^{2+} and HCO_3^- are returned to the water column.

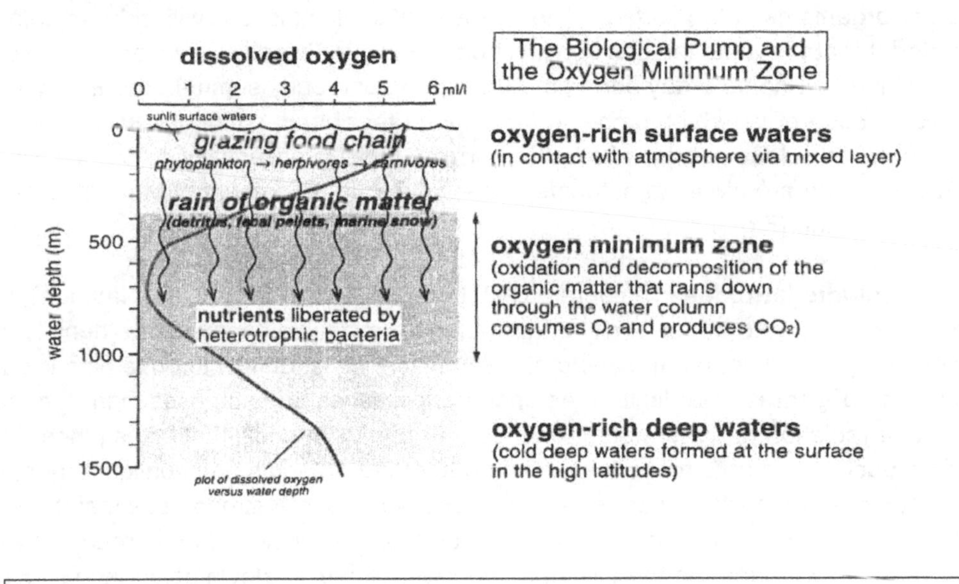

Fig. 4.11 Oxygen in sea water is highest near the surface where it is produced as a by-product of photosynthesis. Below the photic zone, oxygen in consumed and declines to low levels. Thermohaline circulation keeps oxygen levels higher close to the sea floor.

■4.6 Seasonal Changes & Primary Productivity

As we have seen, biomass is used to describe the total weight (mass) of all organisms, or of a particular group of organisms, in an environment or habitat. Biomass tracks productivity: where productivity is high, biomass is high. For example, where there is a great abundance of autotrophs (primary producers), then it follows that there will be a great abundance of animals (high biomass). If the availability of nutrients or sunlight is limited, then there will be relatively few primary producers and therefore few animals (low biomass). In general, the highest productivity (therefore the highest biomass) is along continental margins, especially in coastal waters near rivers, the principal source of ocean nutrients, or in areas of coastal upwelling and oceanic divergence. Areas of the surface ocean with the lowest productivity are the subtropical gyres where biomass is generally low.

Seasonal changes in solar radiation and in nutrient availability are major controls on the distribution of marine life along continental margins and in the open ocean. Although solar energy is essential for primary productivity (photosynthesis) in the surface ocean, the amount of solar radiation contributes to the presence or absence of a strong thermocline (which is the same as a strong pycnocline or "density doorway"). The balance between the intensity of solar radiation and the temperature or density structure of the upper water column varies across latitude and results in some surprising patterns in productivity (Fig. 4.12).

We will take a detailed look at the coral reef environment and how it maintains high productivity in section 4.11.

In the **high latitudes** (Polar Belt, > 60° N or S latitude) there are abundant nutrients in the surface water because a very weak thermocline (or pycnocline) allows deep water masses (such as NADW) to rise to the surface (upwelling). In other words, the "density doorway" is open and the dissolved gases and nutrients that have accumulated in these deep waters over a long period of time are now available to the organisms at the surface. The intensity of sunlight is low, with a large solar footprint that prevents the sea surface from getting too warm. However, because the sun shines 24 hours a day during the late spring and early summer, there is a short-lived episode of very high productivity. On the other hand, during the winter months when the sun does not rise above the horizon, there is essentially no productivity. Overall, there are plenty of nutrients year-round, but the amount of productivity is limited by the availability of solar radiation (Fig. 4.12).

In the **middle latitudes** (Temperate Belt, between 30° and 60° N or S latitude), the seasonal variability is very pronounced. In the winter plenty of nutrients are available because the "density doorway" is open owing to the lack of a pycnocline, but the angle of solar incidence is too low to drive high productivity. The productivity at this time of year is solar-limited. As spring approaches, the sun rises higher in the sky, increasing the amount of solar radiation and therefore the amount of photosynthesis that takes place. The result is a **"spring bloom"** of productivity as autotrophs take advantage of the nutrients and sunlight that are available. However, during the summer the surface waters become quite warm and a strong seasonal thermocline develops that cuts off the nutrient supply from below. The "density doorway" is closed and productivity is nutrient-limited and therefore relatively low. In autumn the seasonal thermocline breaks down as surface waters begin to cool, which allows nutrients to "leak" into the photic zone. The "density doorway" is now partially opened, and there is still enough solar energy to cause a second pulse of productivity, or **"fall bloom."**

In the low latitudes (Tropical Belt between 0° and 30° N or S latitude) there is always enough solar radiation, but as a consequence of the warm surface waters and strong thermocline the nutrient supply is cut-off from below ("density doorway" is closed tight); productivity is nutrient-limited year-round, except where there is upwelling (see section 4.10). Overall, the tropical oceans have surprisingly low productivity. **Coral reefs** are an exception because highly efficient ecosystem-level recycling of nutrients supports high productivity, despite very low concentrations of dissolved nutrients in the warm, clear waters.

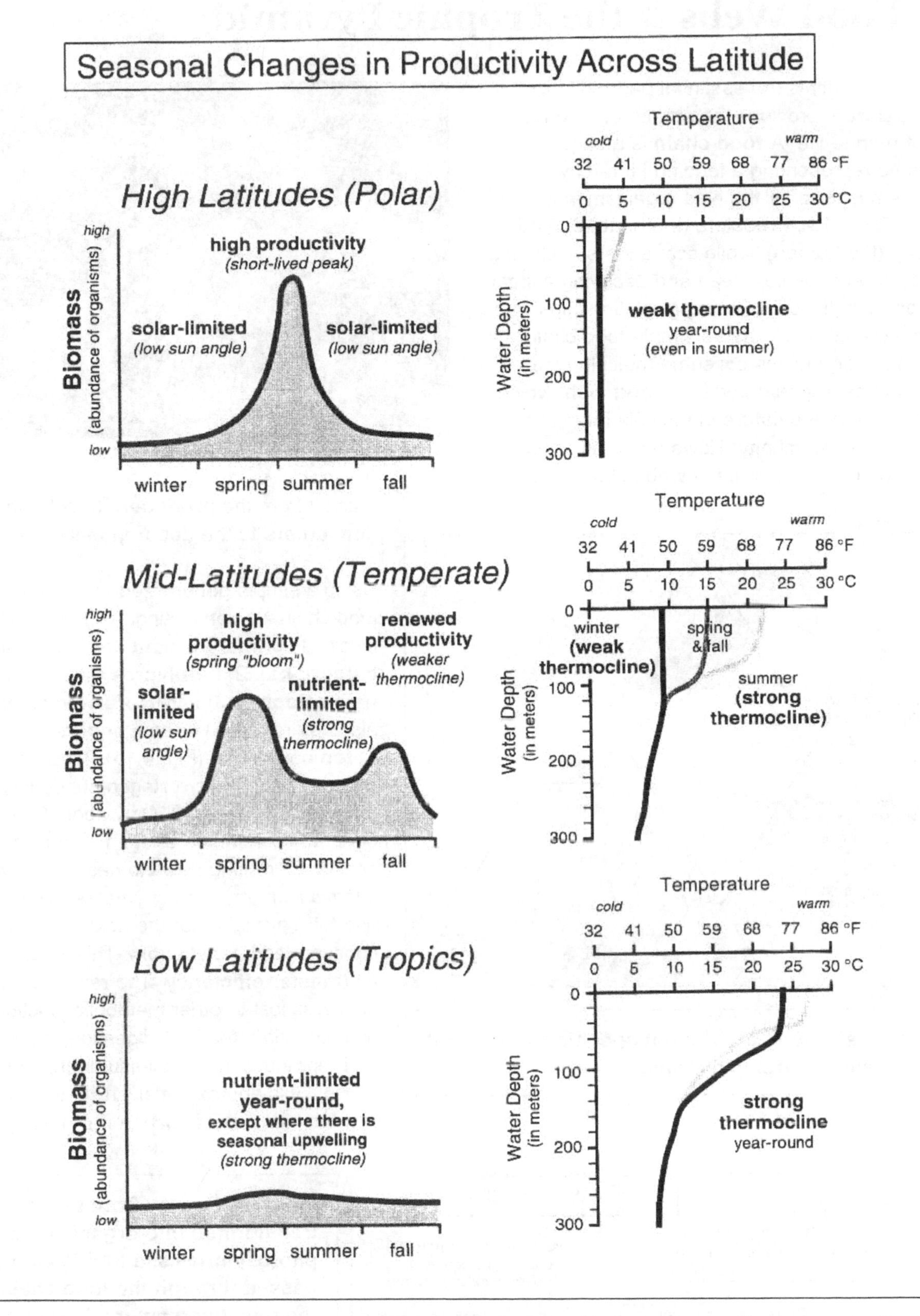

Fig. 4.12 Primary productivity undergoes seasonal changes in response to the amount of sunlight and the abundance of nutrients in the surface ocean, most of which are provided by upwelling from deeper waters.

■4.7 Food Webs & the Trophic Pyramid

Primary productivity is the essential part of life in the ocean, since it provides the source of food for the rest of marine life. A **food chain** is a sequence of organisms representing a feeding hierarchy; one organism is food for the next organism in the sequence (Fig. 4.13). Predators (the hunters) feed on live prey (the hunted), while scavengers (including deposit feeders) consume dead and decaying animal or plant remains. In reality, feeding relationships are much more complex than a simple food chain because many organisms consume multiple types of prey. This is best represented by a **food web**, which describes the intricate nature of multiple interacting food chains in a community. However, in all cases, the flow of energy in a food chain or web is the same: it is passed from the **producers** (autotrophs) to the **consumers** to the **decomposers** (Fig. 4.14).

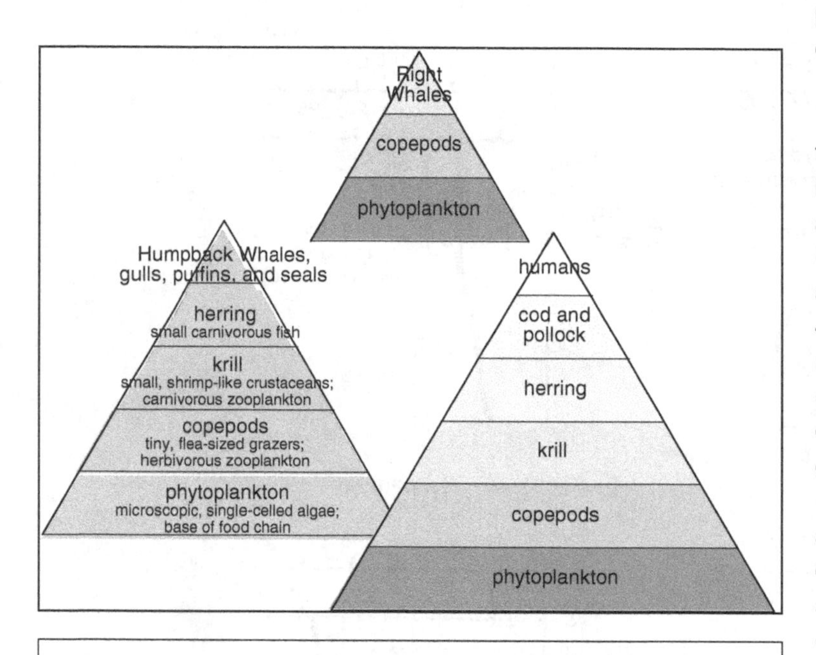

Fig. 4.13 Illustrations of different specific marine food chains shown as trophic pyramids.

Using a simple generalized example of a food chain we can distinguish four trophic levels: 1) **primary producers** (phytoplankton, **autotrophs**), 2) **herbivores** (grazers, **heterotrophs**), 3) **carnivores** (predators, also heterotrophs) or **scavengers**, and 4) **top carnivore**. (Fig. 4.15). **Trophic levels** represent successive stages of nourishment (energy consumption). Only about 6 to 14% of energy consumed at each trophic level goes into creating new biomass (i.e., *stored chemical energy*: carbohydrates, proteins, and fats) available for the next trophic level to consume and benefit from. This is referred to as **transfer efficiency**. The remainder of the energy is lost to other metabolic functions such as respiration, feeding, digestion, locomotion, and reproduction. If we assume that this transfer efficiency is approximately 10%, then it follows that the biomass of each trophic level differs

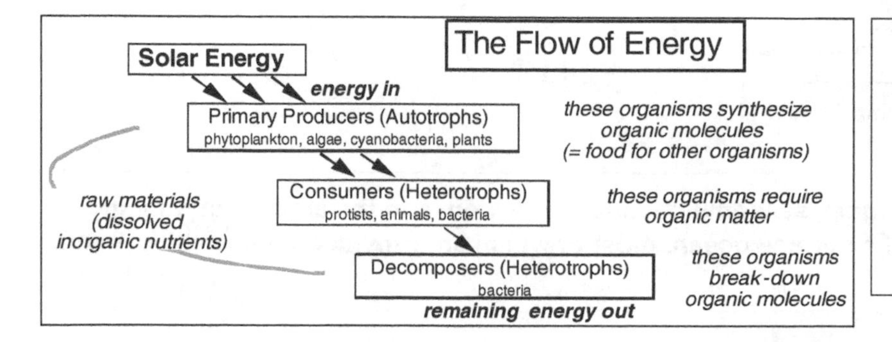

Fig. 4.14 Energy from the sun is transformed into organic matter by photosynthesis, and this energy is passed through the food chain until the remaining energy is returned as nutrients released by bacterial decomposition.

by a factor of 10: ten times as much phytoplankton biomass as grazers, and ten times as much grazer biomass as the first-level predators, etc. Therefore, in a stable ecosystem, a much larger biomass must be available to support (feed) the next trophic level. This hierarchy of decreasing biomass from the base of the food chain to the top of the food chain represents a **trophic pyramid** (Fig. 4.16).

An **ecosystem** includes all the organisms in a particular environment; from the primary producers to the top carnivores, as well as the diverse communities of bacteria, algae, protists, and fungi that play vital roles in food webs and the recycling of carbon and nutrients. **Ecology** is the study of organisms and their interactions with their environment and each other.

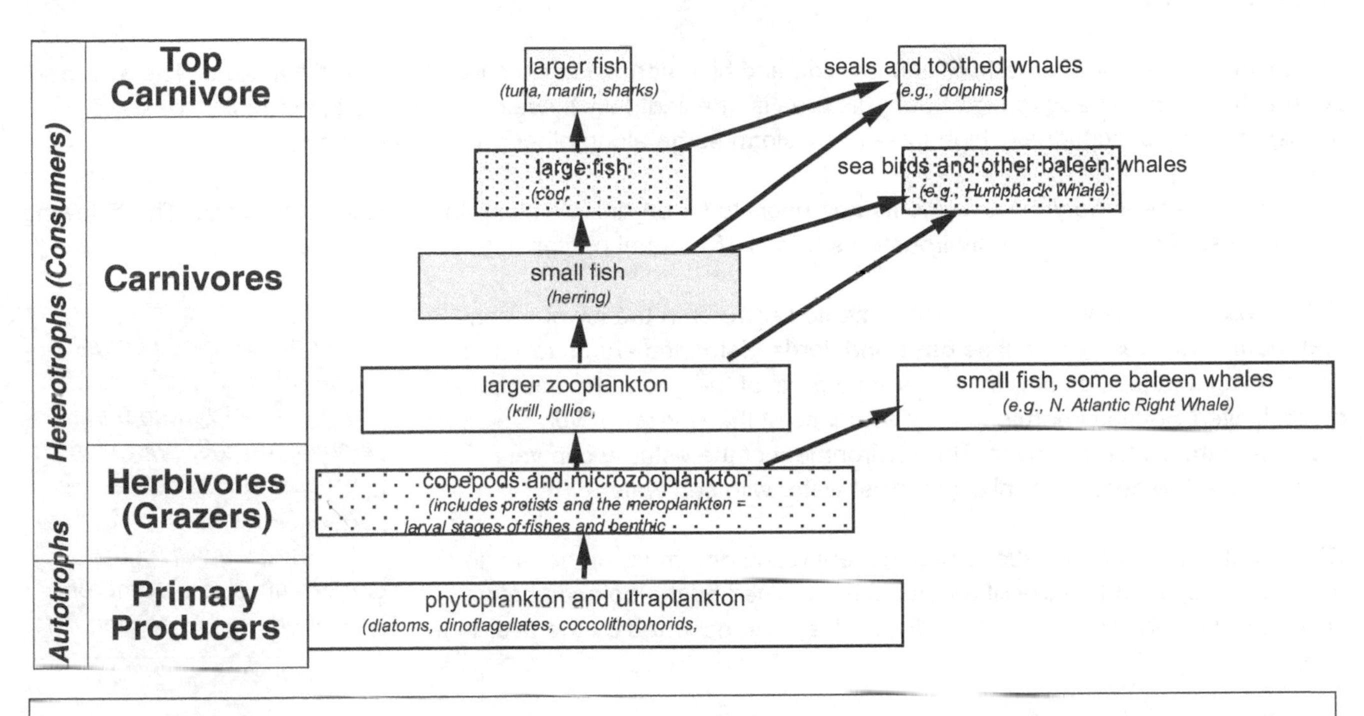

Fig. 4.15 The different trophic levels in a marine food chain and examples of organisms at each level.

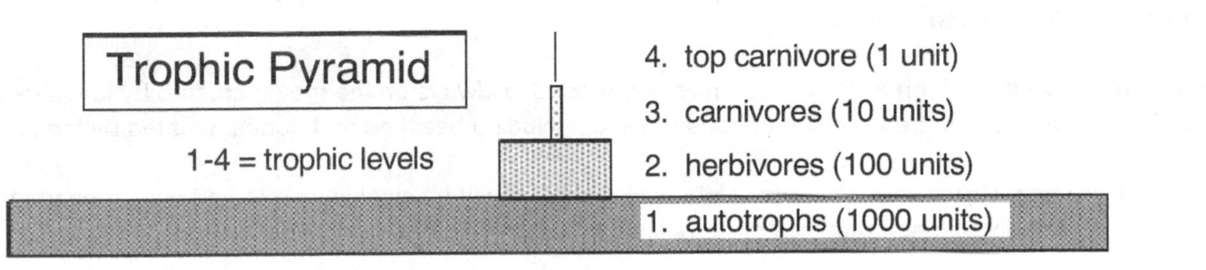

Fig. 4.16 Trophic level refers to the position of an organism in the local food chain. In general, each level of a food chain requires a mass of organisms in the level beneath it to be ten times as large in order to sustain it.

Investigation 4.4 explores the relationships in the marine food chain in greater detail.

■4.8 Coastal Ecosystems: Highly Productive But Vulnerable

As we have seen from our studies of ocean circulation, coastal habitats are especially rich in life because of the abundance of nutrients that stimulates vigorous productivity. The primary producers in coastal ecosystems include representatives of three kingdoms of life: 1) autotrophic bacteria (MONERA), 2) single-celled protists and multi-cellular algae (PROTOCTISTA), and 3) true vascular plants (PLANTAE). **Detritus** is also an important food source in coastal waters; it consists of dead and decaying algae and/or grasses covered with heterotrophic bacteria (Fig. 4.17).

The **littoral zone** is the area between low tide and high tide. It is also called the **intertidal zone**. The **supratidal zone** is the area just above high tide. This area is affected daily by salt water spray along rocky coasts, or occasionally by exceptionally high tides or by storm surge along other parts of the coast.

There are a wide variety of ecosystems and habitats for organisms along the coasts of the world. The following is a brief list of major coastal environments (Fig. 4.18): Aerial photos might be nice here:

Estuaries are areas where freshwater meets seawater in the lower reaches and mouths of rivers, as well as bays and fjords. Estuaries are usually formed when rising sea level floods the lowermost parts of the river. The east coast of the United States is dominated by estuaries of the Hudson River, Delaware River, and the Potomac River. The environment of the estuary can vary according to the degree of mixing of freshwater with sea water.

River deltas are accumulations of sediment (sand and mud) at the mouth of a river. The size and shape of a delta is determined by the balance between wave energy and the volume of sediment that is transported by the river to the ocean.

The physical and chemical characteristics of estuaries are explored more fully in section 5.8. Shoreline processes along beaches are investigated in section 5.7, and we will learn more about the coral reef environment in section 4.11.

Tidal mud flats are intertidal areas choked with mud; found along low energy shorelines and estuaries. **Salt marshes** are tidal mud flats vegetated by salt-tolerant grasses; found along low energy shorelines and estuaries. **Mangrove swamps** are intertidal areas vegetated by mangrove trees; found along low energy shorelines and estuaries of the tropics and subtropics.

Beaches and dunes are high energy shorelines where sand is always on the move; created by longshore drift. **Barrier islands and spits** are low-lying ribbons of sand, including beaches and dunes; created by longshore drift.

Coral reefs are rigid structures of calcium carbonate ($CaCO_3$) built by colonial corals and calcareous algae that support biologically diverse communities of organisms in the photic zone of tropical waters.

Lagoons are shallow bodies of water separated from the open ocean by a barrier island/spit, or reef.

Coastal habitats are some of the richest environments known on Earth. High biological productivity supports large and often diverse communities of organisms. Two types of biological "oases" can be distinguished by the level of nutrients. Salt marshes, estuaries, bays, and mangrove swamps can be considered as "fertile oases" because of the abundant nutrients that support these ecosystems. Coral reefs, on the other hand, can be considered as "fragile oases" because they are adapted to scarce nutrients and are easily perturbed by nutrient loading, environmental degradation, and increased runoff from the land. All of these habitats are important because they support coastal and oceanic food webs, including nurseries for many species of fish, and they provide productive habitats along flyways for migratory birds, supply food and support livelihoods for humans, and they stimulate ecotourism. Loss of these precious resources through environmental degradation and development will cause untold damage to commercial fisheries and to marine ecosystems in general.

Coastal Habitats

Littoral Zone
= Intertidal Zone

Inner Subneritic Zone
within the photic zone,
attached benthic algae and plants

HIGH TIDE
LOW TIDE

salt marsh grasses
food source and protection

seaweeds (kelp and other algae)
and grasses (turtle grass, eel grass)
food source and protection

Base of Food Chain in Coastal Waters:

1. phytoplankton (PROTOCTISTS: **planktic diatoms & dinoflagellates**)
2. benthic microscopic autotrophs (PROTOCTISTS: **benthic diatoms**)
3. benthic algae (PROTOCTISTS: **brown & green algae = seaweed**) & grasses (PLANTS: **salt marsh grass**)
4. **detritus** = dead and decaying algae and grasses covered with bacteria (MONERA)

Fig. 4.17 Coastal habitats can be subdivided into three distinct zones that have different environmental characteristics and support different communities of organisms. Primary productivity is high with different organisms at the base of the foods chain.

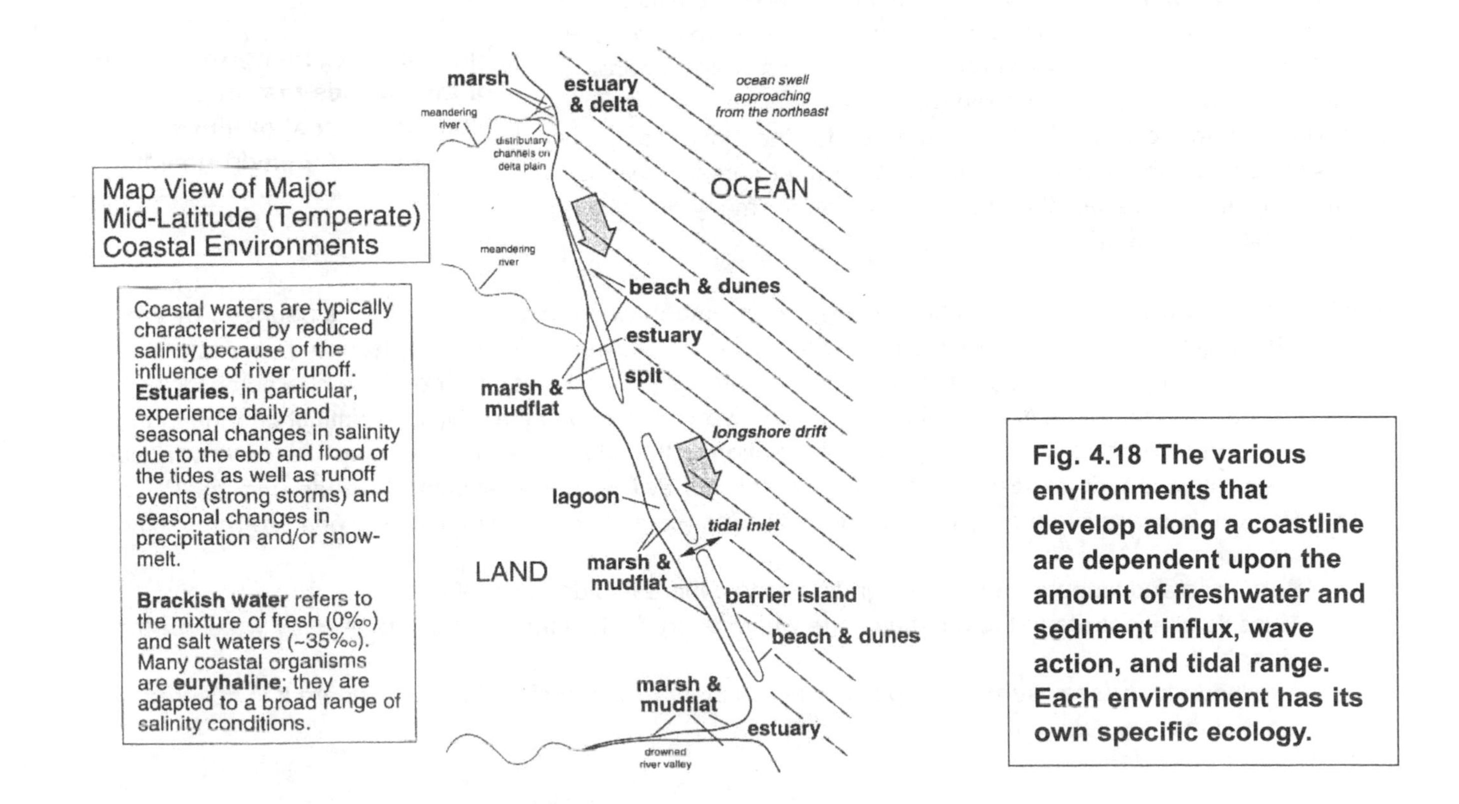

Map View of Major Mid-Latitude (Temperate) Coastal Environments

Coastal waters are typically characterized by reduced salinity because of the influence of river runoff. **Estuaries**, in particular, experience daily and seasonal changes in salinity due to the ebb and flood of the tides as well as runoff events (strong storms) and seasonal changes in precipitation and/or snow-melt.

Brackish water refers to the mixture of fresh (0‰) and salt waters (~35‰). Many coastal organisms are **euryhaline**; they are adapted to a broad range of salinity conditions.

Fig. 4.18 The various environments that develop along a coastline are dependent upon the amount of freshwater and sediment influx, wave action, and tidal range. Each environment has its own specific ecology.

■4.9 Benthic Life Along the Coast

The various environments that we designated in the previous section can be divided into two broad categories based upon the amount wave energy they receive. **Low-energy** environments are usually protected from the direct action of wind waves, although tidal changes are a very important influence. The tides help in the distribution of nutrients and oxygen, and can also cleanse waste materials from the environment. The sediment that accumulates in these locations is dominated by fine-grained silt, clay and organic matter, and the salinity of the water can vary over short distances. Oxygen can be in short supply at or below the sediment surface. The organisms that live here must be tolerant of these conditions. High-energy shorelines, on the other hand, often receive the direct force of waves from the open ocean. Although salinity and oxygen are readily available, organisms must adapt to the constant pounding of the surf.

Fig. 4.19 Salt marshes are dominated by vast expanses of sea grasses that provide a habitat for many other organisms.

Salt Marshes and Mud Flats are low energy "fertile oases" where abundant nutrients permit vital communities to thrive. One of the characteristics of the salt marsh is the presence of abundant sea grasses, such as eel grass and turtle grass, some of the few representatives of the Plant Kingdom that exist in the marine environment (Fig. 4.19). These grasses are the base of a rich food web, and also provide physical protection for an array of animals that lives among them. Many of the animals that thrive here remain buried (**infauna**) and survive by deposit feeding or filter feeding.

Fig. 4.20 Red mangroves are one of the species that traps mud along tropical shorelines helping to stabilize the environment.

Mangrove Swamps are a specific variety of low-energy coastal environment that is restricted to the tropical latitudes. Mangroves are trees that have adapted to life in brackish and saline water. There are two types of mangrove. The red mangrove has multiple "legs" that allow the tide to wash through and around it; the black mangrove sends out shoots above the water line that allow it to obtain oxygen more easily. In both cases, these provide shelter for many different kinds of epifauna and infauna (Fig. 4.20).

Rocky Shores are an example of a high energy environment, where exposed bedrock is pounded by the surf. Many of the animals that live here are attached to rocks and seaweed. They are **epifauna** that have developed mechanisms to hang on to their positions despite the often rough conditions. One of the characteristics of the rocky shore environment is an easily recognizable vertical zonation that shows a distinct change in the abundance and diversity of various organisms in relation to the tidal range. These organisms have very specific tolerances to atmospheric exposure depending on where they live. Some examples include (Fig. 4.21):

- *Periwinkle snails* live mostly in the supratidal zone (spray zone) above high tide and are rarely covered by water;
- Barnacles and limpets prefer the high tide zone, where it is dry most of day.
- Mussels concentrate in the mid-tide zone where is dry for half the day and covered by water for the other half.
- Attached algae *(seaweed), anemones, and sea stars* live in the low tide zone where it is covered by water most of the day.

Beaches are examples of a high energy environment that is dominated by soft and mobile sediment. Although different groups of organisms prefer supratidal or littoral areas, the zonation of the different organisms is not as easily recognizable. However, because of the soft bottom conditions, there are numerous infaunal organisms (Fig. 4.22) such as: *clams, echinoderms (like sand dollars), crabs, and various worms. There are also various* examples of epifaunal organisms such as *snails (gastropods), crabs, and sea stars.*

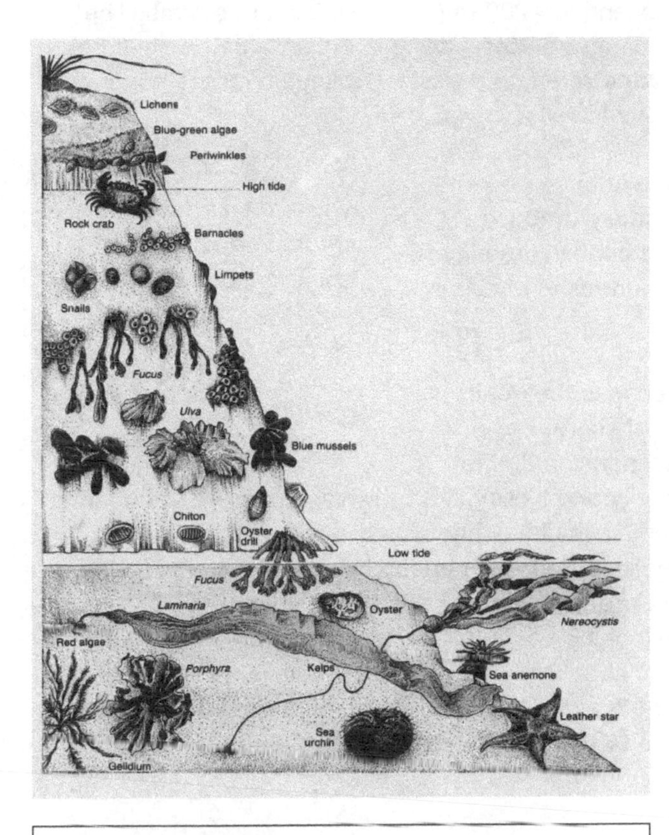

Fig. 4.21 Rocky shore environments are highly zoned with respect to high and low tides, and are dominated by epifaunal organisms.

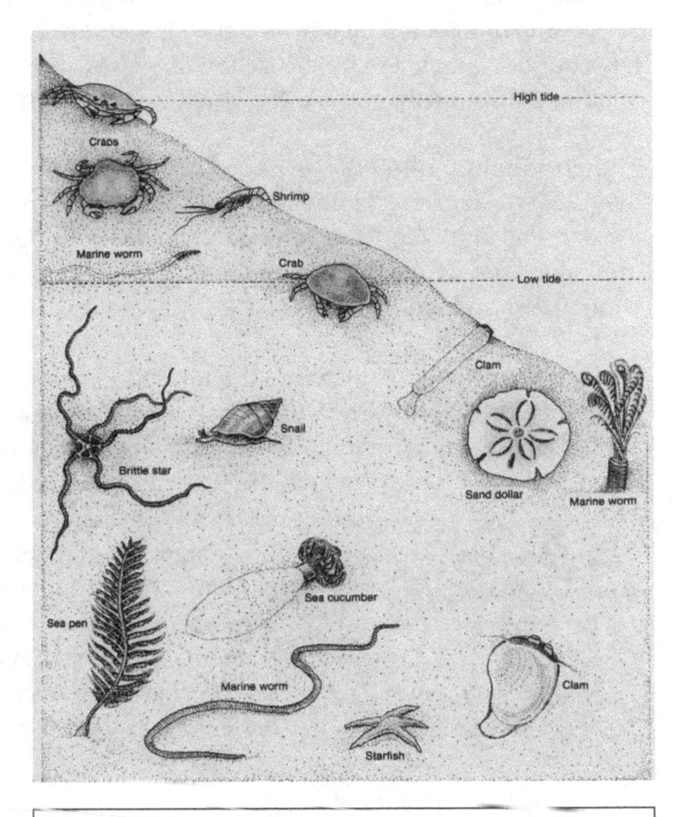

Fig. 4.22 Sandy shores show much less prominent biological zonation and contain more infauna.

Investigation 4.5 takes a closer look at various ecological relationships in coastal environments.

■4.10 Continental Shelf Ecosystems

As we move farther offshore, the factor of wave energy changes as water depth increases. Under fair weather conditions, the influence of wave motion may extend from 5 to 15 m (~16-49 ft.) depending upon the length of the waves. This is the normal or fair weather **wave base**. Because of larger waves, wave base during storms typically reaches to depths of 20-30 m (~66-99 ft.), but can extend to >200 m (657 ft.) in severe storms. The seafloor is unaffected by waves below the storm wave base. The **sublittoral zone** is the area of the shelf below low tide that is affected by the action of waves. The **neritic zone** refers to the water column over the continental shelf and **subneritic zone** is the seafloor of the continental shelf itself (Fig. 4.23).

The **continental shelf** is a dynamic oceanographic environment because of the relatively shallow depths and the seasonal changes in primary productivity, water mass characteristics, and storminess. Both pelagic and benthic organisms are influenced by these daily or seasonal changes, which includes the effects of tidal mixing and storm waves.

Waves affect the bottom to a water depth equivalent to half their wavelength. This is discussed in detail in section 5.1 and 5.2.

Benthic plant life is restricted to the inner part of the shelf because the depth of the euphotic zone is typically much shallower than further offshore. For example, river runoff and sediment turbidity (sediments in suspension due to wave and tidal energy) clouds the water thereby reducing clarity and turning it a brownish color. An abundance of dissolved river-borne nutrients stimulates photosynthesis and the resulting phytoplankton biomass further limits light penetration in coastal waters. These waters may appear seasonally greenish in color due to the abundance of chlorophyll pigment in the phytoplankton. Tidal mixing and storms reintroduce nutrients back into the euphotic zone thereby helping to sustain high productivity on the shelf. The euphotic zone may be less than 20 m (66 ft.) in turbid coastal waters and as deep as ~150 m (492 ft.) in the "blue" waters of the tropical open ocean.

As we initially learned in section 4.4, the euphotic zone is the part of the upper water column where there is a net gain in productivity.

The continental shelf is home to a great diversity of both benthic and pelagic organisms. Like the immediate coastal environments, the benthic communities are different dependent upon the materials that cover the seafloor (Fig. 4.23). On rocky bottoms, there is an abundance of attached benthic algae (e.g., *kelp*) on the inner shelf where sunlight can reach the seafloor. Among the animals, epifaunal varieties dominate including *lobsters, echinoids (sea urchins), oysters, and snails* (Fig. 4.24). When the shelf is covered by soft sediment, marine grasses rather than benthic algae occur on the inner shelf where sunlight reaches the sea floor. Both infaunal and epifaunal animals can be found including *clams, scallops, worms, sea stars, horseshoe crabs, echinoids (sand dollars), snails, and shrimp* (Fig. 4.24).

Pelagic life on the shelf is also quite varied owing to the abundance of nutrients that can be supplied either by runoff from rivers or by coastal upwelling (Fig. 4.25). These nutrients provide the essential ingredients to support a large population of autotrophic organisms at the base of food chain, especially *diatoms and dinoflagellates.* These are fed upon by zooplankton grazers, such as *foraminifera and copepods.* Invertebrate carnivores that are common in the neritic environment are *squid, jellyfish, and arrow worms.* The continental shelf environment is often a breeding ground for a wide variety of fish species, and is therefore prime target for commercial fisheries. Seasonal changes in productivity result in corresponding changes in pelagic and ground fish stocks: Some of the common pelagic fishes include *anchovy, herring, and mackerel.* There are also numerous species of ground fish that spend a great deal of their time on or near the bottom. Numbered among these are numerous food fishes such as *cod, haddock, hake, flounder and sole.* Where productivity is high, seasonal migratory visitors may include species of toothed whales (*dolphin and killer whales*) and baleen whales (*Humpback, Gray, Right, Fin, Blue*).

Fig. 4.23 The continental shelf environment is a dynamic place where freshwater mixes with sea water to varying degrees, water depth changes, and the conditions for productivity are thereby affected.

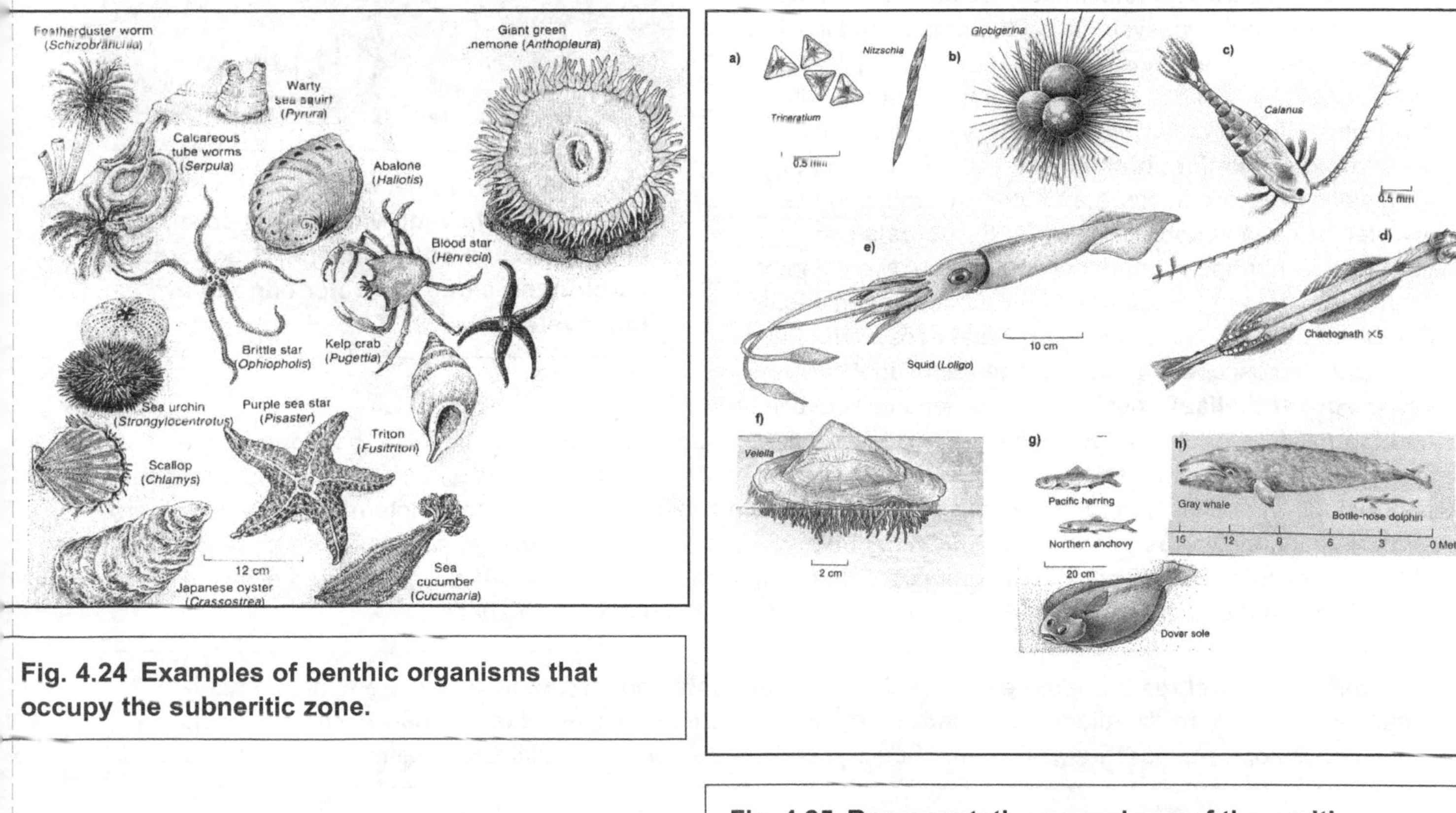

Fig. 4.24 Examples of benthic organisms that occupy the subneritic zone.

Fig. 4.25 Representative organisms of the neritic zone: a) diatoms, b) foraminiferan, c) copepod, d) arrow worm, e) squid, f) jellyfish, g) bony fish, h) whales. Note the different scale bars for the various pictures.

Investigation 4.6 provides a further look at life in the intertidal zone.

■4.11 Coral Reef Ecosystems: the Rainforests of the Sea

Coral reefs are very important components of coastal ecosystems. They consist of wave-resistant, rigid structures of calcium carbonate ($CaCO_3$) built by colonial corals and calcareous algae that support biologically diverse communities of organisms in the tropical photic zone (Fig. 4.26). Coral reefs develop in warm (>18°C or >65°F), clear waters of normal to slightly elevated salinity. Water clarity is due to the river runoff, and scarce dissolved nutrients. Coral reefs and their associated environments develop on shallow platforms fringing continents and volcanic islands in the tropics where river input is minimal. Reef growth maintains its position relative to the sea surface even if sea level changes over time. Charles Darwin demonstrated this process in his observations of coral reefs from the Pacific Ocean. He theorized that **atolls** (rings of coral reefs enclosing shallow lagoons) formed when volcanic islands subsided below sea level and coral reef growth continued upward into the photic zone (Fig. 4.27).

Fig. 4.26 a) A typical coral reef community showing varieties of coral, fish, and calcareous algae. b) Staghorn coral found along the outer edge of a reef system.

Coral reefs, like tropical rainforests, are among the most biologically diverse ecosystems on the planet, and like the rainforests, coral reefs are highly productive despite the limited availability of nutrients. Both of these ecosystems are highly efficient at recycling nutrients and capitalizing on **symbiotic relationships** at all levels of the intricate food webs, from the bacteria and other microbes to the invertebrate and vertebrate animals. **Symbiosis** is a term to describe the intimate co-existence of two different organisms, or the dependence of one organism on another. Symbioses are common in the coral reef ecosystem. For example, microscopic symbiotic algae (dinoflagellate protists called **zooxanthellae**) exist in the tissue and cells of corals and foraminifera (protists), respectively. The algae and their host organisms both benefit. The algae receive protection from predators and the metabolic waste products of the hosts serve as a nutrient supply in a nutrient-poor world. The corals and foraminifera benefit because the zooxanthellae provide an internal source of oxygen for respiration as well as a food supply provided by photosynthesis. The symbionts also assist in the precipitation of their calcium carbonate colonies and shells. Other examples of symbiotic relationships in the reef include the clown fish and the anemone, cleaner fish and moray eel, and remora fish and shark.

Indo-Pacific coral reefs are more diverse than **Atlantic reefs** and calcareous algae are a minor frame-builder of Atlantic reefs. Atlantic reefs lack many of the invertebrate species of the Indo-Pacific, including numerous coral species, the giant clam *Tridacna*, and the diverse communities of molluscs and crustacea.

In general, a coral reef is characterized by a high-energy **reef core** (or reef terrace) composed of the frame-building corals, as well as calcareous algae, which encrust and bind the reef structure. At its seaward edge, the reef grows up to sea level where the stony structure provides turbulence and vigorous mixing. A low energy **back reef** and shallow **lagoon** may contain small **patch reefs** (Fig. 4.28). Variable conditions of water depth, turbulence, light level, and nature of the substrate across the reef profile create a great variety of "ecospaces" (**niches**) for organisms to occupy.

BENTHIC LIFE IN THE CORAL REEF

corals, sponges, calcareous algae, foraminifera (protists), anemones (& clownfish), bryozoans, crown-of-thorns seastars, sea urchins, nudibranchs, barnacles, crabs, sea urchins, featherduster worms, sea fans, brittle stars, soft corals, tunicates, giant clams, cowry snails, shrimp.

PELAGIC LIFE IN THE CORAL REEF

moray eel, angelfish, scorpion fish, bumphead parrot fish, butterfly fish, puffer fish, trigger fish, grouper, sharks, rays, sea nettles.

> Under environmental stresses, linked in part with elevated sea surface temperatures (**SSTs**), corals and foraminifera will expel their zooxanthellae. In the colonial corals this process is called **coral bleaching** because the normally greenish or brownish color of the living coral animals turns a ghostly white. If the SSTs return to normal within a matter of months, the corals and foraminifera will regain their zooxanthellae and recover fully. But if elevated SSTs persist for several years, massive coral die-off can occur and the health of the reef ecosystem will be compromised. **Global warming** is but one threat to coral reef ecosystems; sediments associated with clear-cutting of tropical forests, chemical pollutants, nutrient loading, illegal fishing practices (e.g., use of cyanide and explosives), and even ecotourism are also threatening reef ecosystems around the world.

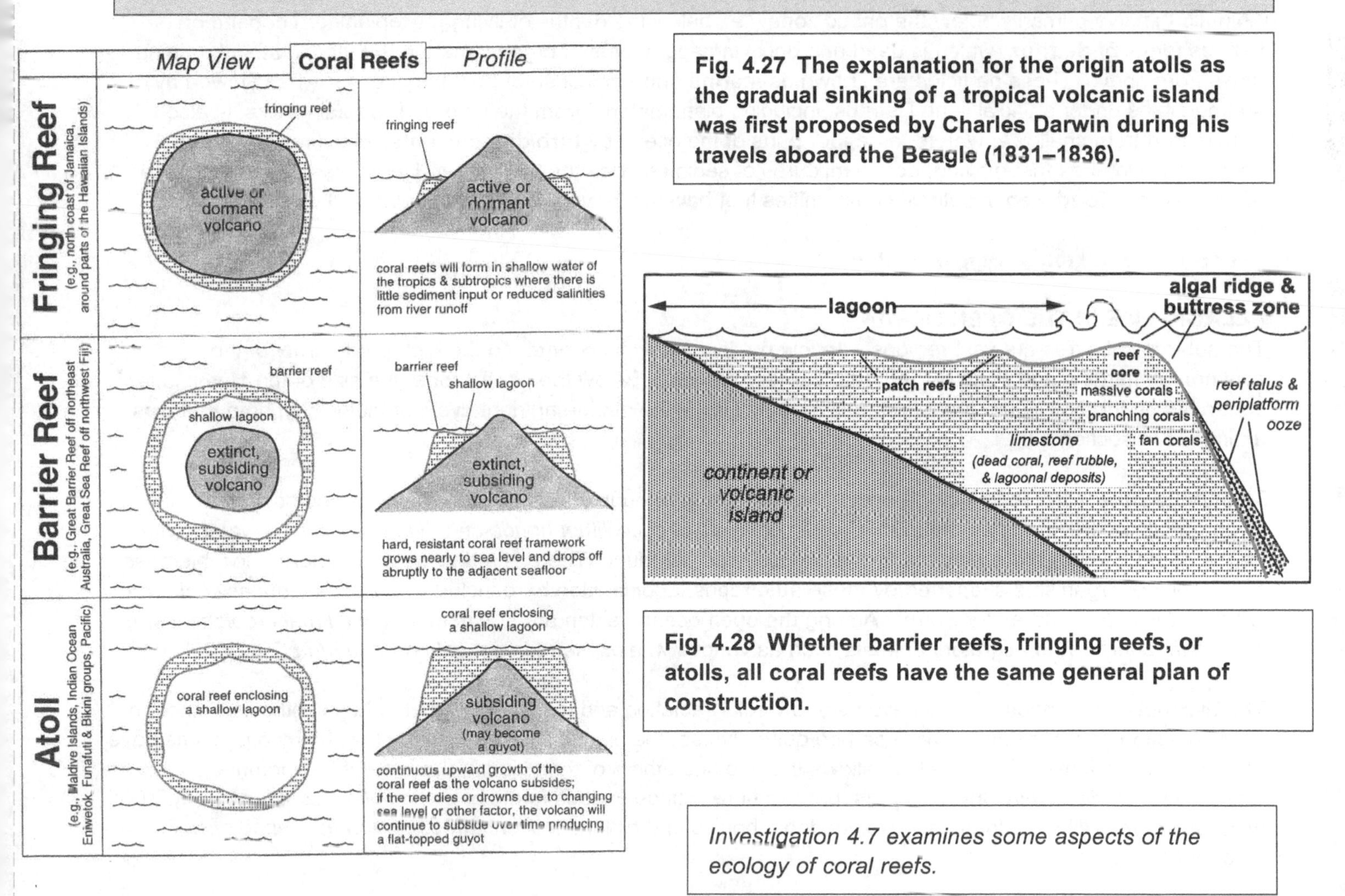

Fig. 4.27 The explanation for the origin atolls as the gradual sinking of a tropical volcanic island was first proposed by Charles Darwin during his travels aboard the Beagle (1831–1836).

Fig. 4.28 Whether barrier reefs, fringing reefs, or atolls, all coral reefs have the same general plan of construction.

Investigation 4.7 examines some aspects of the ecology of coral reefs.

■4.12 Open Ocean ("Blue Water") Ecosystems

Although we have previously referred to the open ocean as a "biological desert," this is really an exaggeration. To be sure, the open ocean has a much lower productivity than coastal environments, but there is still quite a bit of vitality to this region (Fig. 4.29). The distribution of life in the open ocean is controlled primarily by the availability of an energy source (solar radiation or chemical energy) and nutrients. The greatest concentration of primary producers is in sunlit waters. Therefore, many animals live close to their food source in the upper water column. This feeding relationship can be generalized by the grazing food web in photic zone communities:

phytoplankton → zooplankton (grazers & predators) → nekton (fish) → bigger nekton

You can review the basics of food webs and food chains in section 4.7.

Primary productivity supported by an external supply of nutrients, such as river-borne nutrients in coastal waters or upwelled nutrients in open ocean divergences, is new production. The nutrient-poor surface waters of the open ocean in the subtropical gyres are characterized by regenerated production, which refers to productivity sustained by an internal supply of recycled nutrients released by bacterial degradation within the photic zone. This food web contains diverse communities of bacteria, including autotrophic cyanobacteria, and single-celled protoctist consumers. These "blue water" ecosystems (no turbidity, scarce nutrients, low phytoplankton biomass = clear blue water) cannot sustain large communities of animal zooplankton and fish due to the scarce nutrient supply, but heterotrophic bacteria play an important role in recycling the limited nutrients available.

Animals that live primarily below the photic zone (i.e., below the depths of living phytoplankton) depend on various forms of **detritus**, which is dead and decaying aggregates of organic matter and fecal material, raining down from above. These particles are known as **marine snow** because of how they appear when viewed by submersibles under artificial light. Detritus, including plant material from the land and coastal waters, is also transported from shallower waters to deeper parts of the ocean by **turbidity currents**, which roll down the continental slope as fast-moving, dense mixtures of sediment, detritus, and water. Detritus serves as the base of the **detritus food web** in pelagic communities that have either very low light **(dysphotic)** or no light at all (**aphotic**):

detritus → nekton → bigger nekton

PELAGIC LIFE IN THE OPEN OCEAN

The subtropical gyres are vast regions with low nutrient levels, in contrast to the high productivity of the continental margins and the divergent (equatorial) upwelling. Below the photic zone, the size of the biomass is controlled by the downward flux of organic matter. This is the marine nutrient cycle or biological pump that was examined in section 4.5.

The photic zone is the region in the ocean where there is enough solar radiation to power photosynthesis. In low nutrient waters, the base of the food chain consists of *coccolithophorids* and *cyanobacteria*; in waters with higher nutrient levels more *diatoms* and *dinoflagellates* are found. There is a diverse, but generally low biomass community of organisms supported by these autotrophs. Zooplankton here include *copepods, euphasiid shrimp, jellyfish*, *tunicates*, and *arrow worms*, Among the open-ocean nekton are s*quid, marlin mahi mahi (dolphin fish), flying fish, sharks*, and migratory animals such as various *whales, sea turtles, salmon and tuna* (Fig. 4.30).

The dysphotic and aphotic zones have very low solar radiation and, consequently, no photosynthesis. Although the population of sea creatures here can be quite diverse, the biomass is usually very low. Many organisms have some kind of bioluminescence, which allows them to find others of their kind in the low-light environment, or to lure prey into their vicinity. Invertebrates that live here include various forms of *comb jellies, squid, and jellyfish.* Fish forms typically have large jaws, expandable bodies and bioluminescent lures: *lantern fish, angler fish, hatchet fish, gulper*.

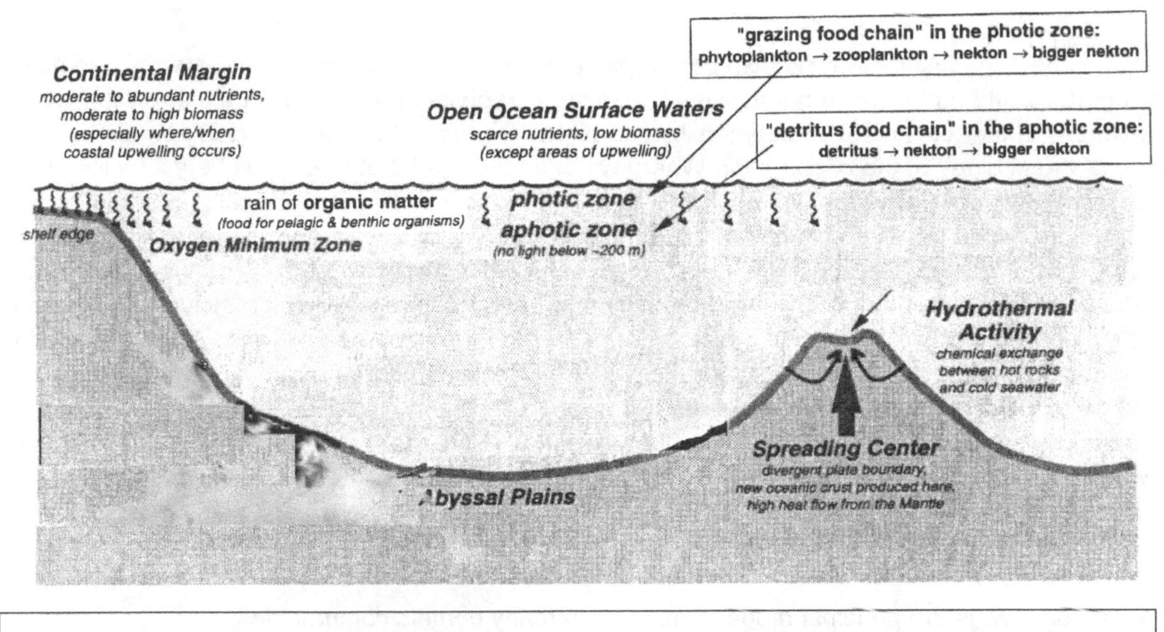

Fig. 4.29 Photosynthetic plankton and cyanobacteria, limited only by the availability of nutrients and solar radiation, support life at all levels in the pelagic zone of the open ocean via the rain of organic matter into deeper waters.

Fig. 4.30 Examples of pelagic organisms that live in the open ocean: a) diatoms b) coccoliths c) foraminifera d) ctenophores e) squid f) epipelagic fishes g) meso- and bathypelagic fishes h) sharks i) dolphins j) large whales.

■4.13 Benthic Life in the Deep-Sea

The bottom of the ocean is the least known part of planet Earth. The great depths and eternal darkness of this large area of the world have limited our abilities to explore and observe the conditions that exist. Nevertheless, recent advances in the technology of submersibles and remotely operated vehicles (ROV) have transformed our knowledge of the ecology of the ocean floor. Where we once believed that there was very little life at all on the deep ocean floor, we now know that life has occupied almost every available niche, and in some localized spots, can be extremely abundant. The **suboceanic province** is that part of the seafloor beyond the continental shelf (Fig. 4.31). No light reaches the seafloor in this region, so photosynthetic autotrophs cannot exist. Temperatures are very low, rarely greater than 4°C, yet the diversity of organisms is relatively high including microorganisms such as single-celled protists. The limiting factor for maintaining the deep-sea biomass is the availability of food, which consists of bacteria, other microorganisms, other animals, and the rain of detritus from surface waters. Some of the marine snow that filters down from the photic zone reaches the sea floor in the deep parts of the ocean. The supply of this food may be highly seasonal, related to the productivity in the overlying sunlit surface waters. Near the continental margins, turbidity currents that cascade down the continental slope and rise can also supply organic detritus to deeper parts of the adjacent abyssal plains, helping to nourish benthic communities in these areas.

The detritus food web is the principal mode of nutrition in many benthic communities:

detritus → scavengers and deposit feeders → nekton

Echinoderms (*sea stars, sea urchins, sea cucumbers*) are more common in this environment than molluscs (*clams, snails*).

Both low biomass and high biomass communities can exist in the suboceanic province.

Low biomass communities are typically found on the abyssal plains where food is scarce but there is a very high diversity of animals, protists, and bacteria (Fig. 4.32). The environment is stable over long (geologic) time scales and the organisms have specialized by partitioning the limited resources available to them.

High biomass communities are more localized in the suboceanic environment (Fig. 4.33). They are often found under areas of high surface-water productivity such as in regions of equatorial upwelling where there is abundant food derived from the rain of organic matter falling through the water column. Of particular interest are the "chemosynthetic oases," which are isolated, short-lived communities that have chemosynthetic bacteria (= autotrophs) at the base of the food chain. Examples of these include the **hydrothermal vent communities** that are found around the vents of hot water discharging around spreading centers. In addition high biomass communities can be found around hydrocarbon seeps where methane (CH_4) and other natural gases are emerging from the sea floor. These can be used as a food source by some microorganisms. Lastly, an accumulation of the carcasses of large animals, such as whales, are the base of a food web that includes decomposers and scavengers.

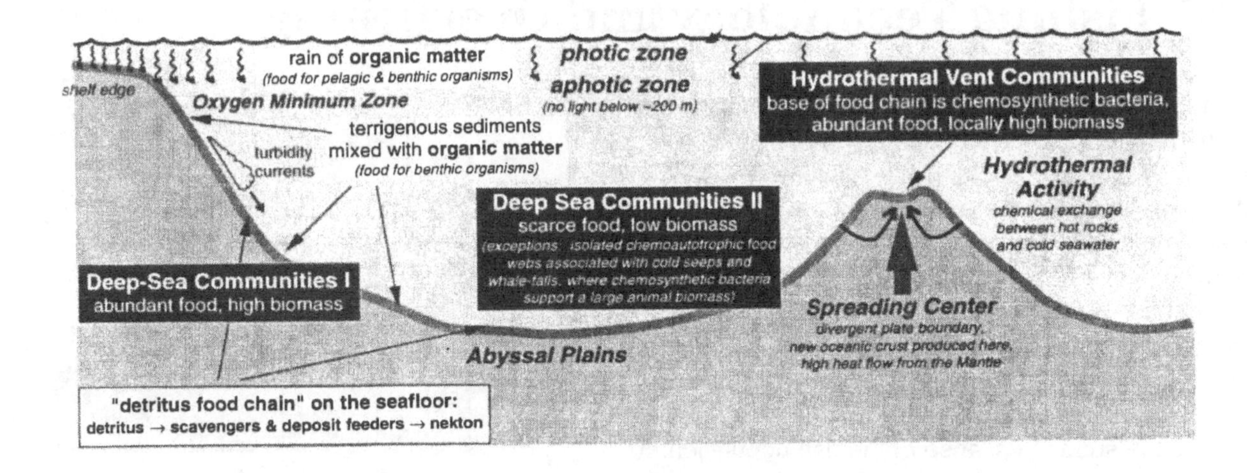

Fig. 4.31 Benthic communities of the deep sea can establish themselves wherever a sufficient supply of food is available.

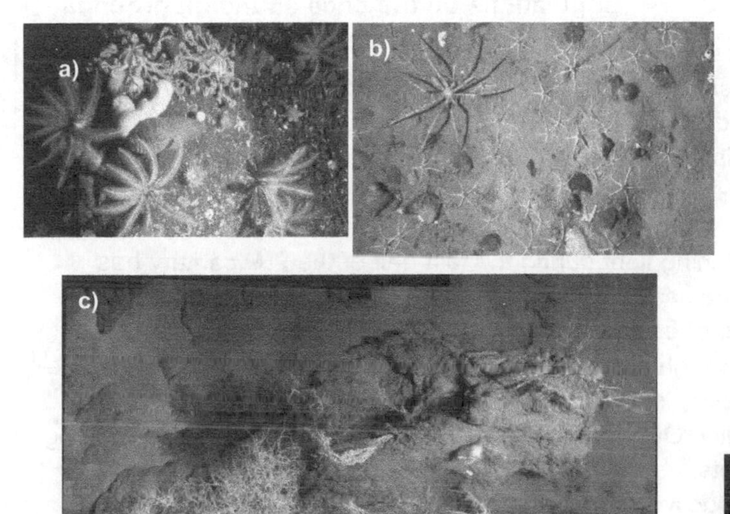

Fig. 4.32 Examples of life on the deep sea floor in low-biomass communities. a) feather stars, basket stars, and sea cucumbers; b) brittle stars; c) deep-water corals.

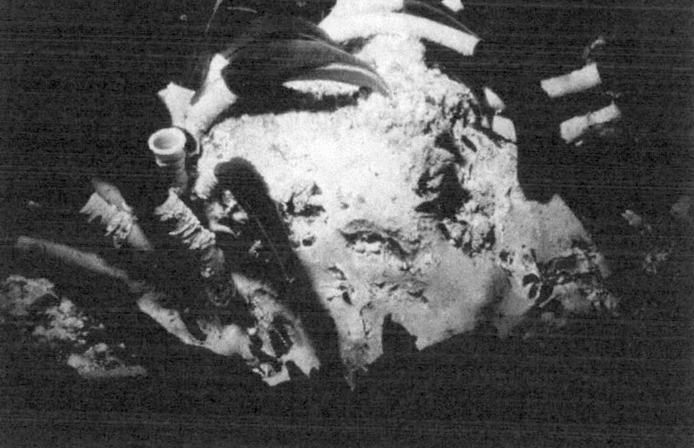

Fig. 4.33 Hydrothermal vents are prime sites for high-biomass communities on the deep-sea floor. Tube worms containing symbiotic chemosynthetic bacteria are common organisms in vent communities.

■4.14 Fishing Technology and Overfishing

For many years, it looked as if the fish in the ocean were an inexhaustible resource, but as fishing technology advanced over the 20th century with ruthless efficiency and the demand for fish as a food resource has increased, many popular fish species are showing signs of an alarming decline (Fig. 4.34). Most fisheries managers believe that fish stocks have an equilibrium level between the reproduction rates of the species and the amount that can be safely harvested by fishing operations. This level is the **maximum sustainable yield**, which, if exceeded, can lead to the sudden collapse of the fish population. It now appears as if we have reached or exceeded this level in most of our most sought-after food fishes. The official levels of world fish harvest appear to have stabilized over the past several years (Fig. 4.35). However, many fisheries experts believe that the People's Republic of China has been exaggerating their annual catch for internal political reasons. When more realistic numbers are applied to the Chinese data, fish yields for the past decade have been declining, and many important food fishes are being harvested well below their peak levels, which were mostly in the 1960's and 1970's.

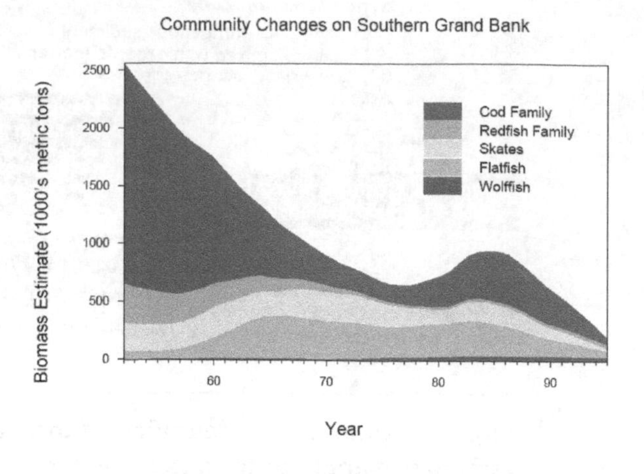

Fig. 4.34 The collapse of the fish populations on the once abundant grounds of the Grand Banks off the coast of eastern Canada is an illustration of the effects of overfishing.

It's not for want of trying. The industrialization of the fishing fleet during the last half of the 20th century has exponentially increased our ability to strain fish from the sea. This has been a large part of the overfishing problem, since the huge factory ships and the process of **bottom trawling** inflict a measurable toll on the marine environment. Bottom trawling uses large nets weighted at one end. These are then dragged behind the ship to snare cod, sole, shrimp, and other bottom-dwelling species (Fig. 4.36). Unfortunately, these nets also cause a great deal of damage to the benthic community. Oysters, corals, sponges, and sea urchins are among the organisms that are inadvertently killed by these nets. Repeated trawling over the same area can turn a productive environment into a virtual desert (Fig. 4.37) and disrupt one or more of the critical food webs that helps the commercially valuable fish to thrive.

The intensive fishing that is now commonplace globally has also caused an increase in the amount of **bycatch**. These are fish and other marine organisms that are brought up in the nets, but have little commercial value. They are simply thrown back into the sea, but the vast majority of animals hauled aboard ship are already dead or severely injured. These are not only fish, but octopus, sharks, dolphin, and sea turtles are among the victims (Fig. 4.38). Trawling for shrimp often produces a large amount of bycatch.

We will look more closely at the promise of aquaculture for increasing seafood production in section 4.15.

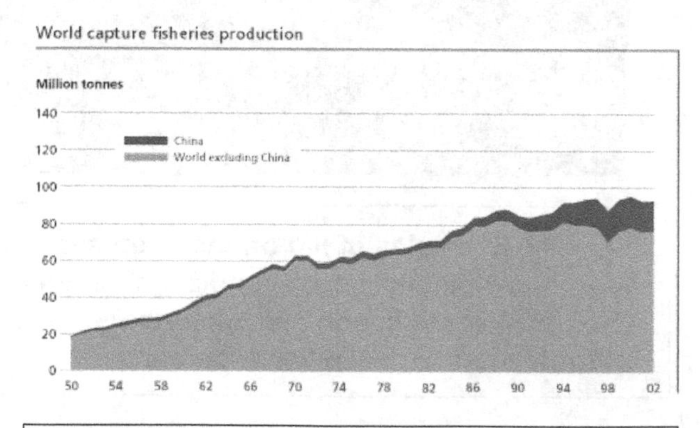

Fig. 4.35 Fish capture from the oceans has leveled off during the past 10 years, despite more intensive fishing efforts, leading many to believe that fishing has reached its limit.

The demand for fish as food is likely to remain high as the Earth's human population increases and knowledge of the healthful aspects of seafood become more widespread. There are solutions to the problem of overfishing. Although none are particularly easy to implement and have their own environmental or economic costs:

- Re-design of bottom trawl nets to minimize damage to the sea-floor environment.
- Stricter monitoring and regulation of fishing practices by governments and international bodies to keep fishing rates below the maximum sustainable yield.
- Further research into the habitats and behavior of desirable marine organisms.
- Increased use of aquaculture for food production.

The key word for all of these is "sustainability" so that the ocean ecosystem can continue to renew itself and serve as a valuable resource into the future.

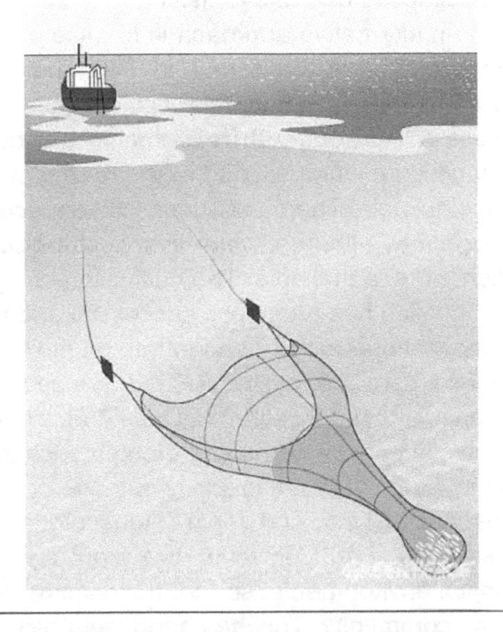

Fig. 4.36 In bottom trawling, large nets are dragged along the seafloor in order to catch schools of groundfish, such as cod or flounder.

Fig. 4.37 Bottom trawling has the unfortunate side effect of destroying the entire benthic ecosystem, as seen in these before (top) and after (bottom) photographs.

Fig. 4.38 Many unwanted fish and animals are caught in the large nets of commercial fisheries, including this sea turtle shown here. This dead bycatch is thrown overboard.

Investigation 4.8 examines the problem of overfishing and potential solutions.

■4.15 Fisheries and Aquaculture

Fig. 4.39 Aquaculture has successfully cultivated many kinds of commercial fish and shellfish, such as at this abalone farm shown in this photo.

Increasing the yield of food from the sea is a goal that is being examined as one means to help address the chronic food shortages that affect a large part of the Earth's human population. Although one approach to this is to fish the ocean more intensively, many fish and other marine animals that are common food sources are under extreme pressure, and the stocks of many of these common fish (cod, haddock, halibut) have collapsed due to overfishing (see section 4.14). An alternative approach is to raise marine animals and plants on "farms" in the same way that we do for crops and domestic animals, a process called **aquaculture**, sometimes known as mariculture when applied to the raising of marine animals. The most successful aquaculture has occurred with freshwater fish, such as carp, catfish, trout, and tilapia. The cultivation of marine finfish has been less successful and most commercial operations concentrate on mollusks, such as mussels or oysters (Fig. 4.39), and arthropods, primarily shrimp (Table 4.2). With these latter organisms, it is relatively easy to raise them in pens in coastal environments and then process them for shipment worldwide. The aquaculture industry has been growing in recent years, especially in those countries where seafood is a central part of the local diet, such as in Southeast Asia, China, and Japan. Aquaculture now accounts for about 17% of the world's fish harvest from the ocean (Fig. 4.40). However, the practice is not without its own environmental costs. Most aquaculture occurs in coastal environments, so that the construction of seafood farms can damage the ecology and productivity of the natural community. This has been identified as a particular problem in southeastern Asia, where intensive shrimp aquaculture has destroyed large areas of native mangrove swamps, an exceedingly productive and diverse coastal habitat. If the farmed fish are fed by catching smaller fish from the ocean, this can cause the population of the fished species to collapse, since small fish are usually younger and not sexually mature. In addition, there is often a significant amount of bycatch, which are marine organisms not sought after, but that are trapped in the nets. The ecology of these creatures can be severely damaged as well. Farmed fish are kept in pens with large numbers of their own kind, and there waste products can often build up to unsafe levels. Cleaning these pens releases the wastes into the surrounding water, which can be harmful to other animals. In addition, the antibiotics and other additives are often a part of the farmed fish's diet, and these can also contribute to the pollution of the coastal area where the aquaculture is taking place. Aquaculture may hold the key for providing more seafood to satisfy the growing demand from the human population, but both national and international regulations must be implemented and enforced to make sure that they don't do more harm than good.

Table 4.2 Worldwide Aquaculture Production in 2002.

Species	*Harvest (Metric Tonnes)*	*Value (Million $)*
Freshwater Fish	21,938,000	21,343
Mollusks (Oysters, Mussels)	11,784,000	10,582
Aquatic Plants (Seaweed)	11,784,000	6,189
Anadromous Fish (Salmon)	2,530,000	6,465
Crustaceans (Shrimp)	2,131,000	10,839
Marine Fish	1,200,000	4,144
Misc. Aquatic Animals	155,000	496

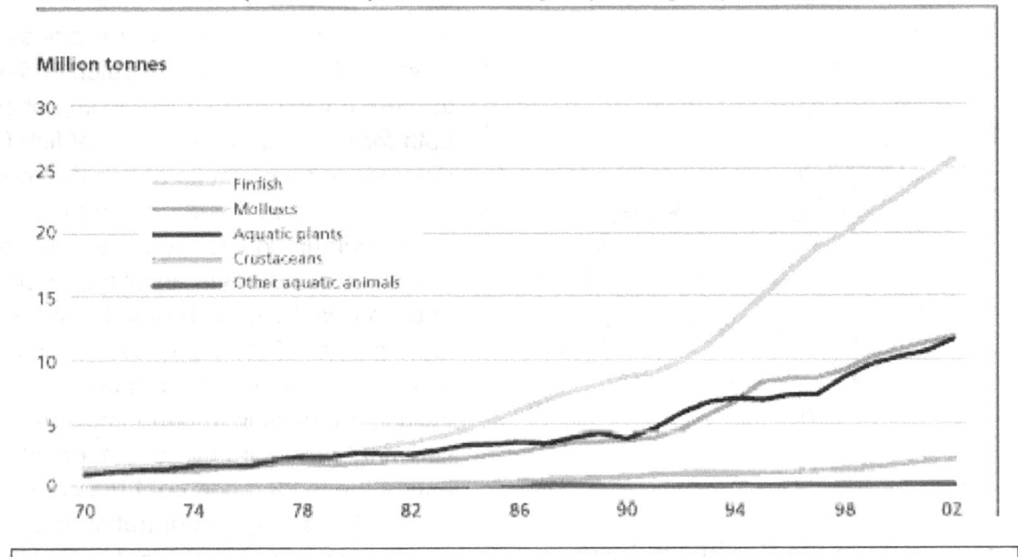

Fig. 4.40 Aquaculture of marine organisms has increased substantially in the past several years. It now provides almost 30% of the world supply of seafood.

Notes:

Name ______________________________

First three letters of last name

Investigation 4.1 **Marine Organisms**

1). List 10 organisms that live in the marine environment.

1. ______________________________
2. ______________________________
3. ______________________________
4. ______________________________
5. ______________________________
6. ______________________________
7. ______________________________
8. ______________________________
9. ______________________________
10. ______________________________

2). Now sort your list of organisms into logical groups by any system of your choosing. Explain what criteria you used to assign them to different groups.

Group ________ Group ________	Group ________ Group ________

Add other groups as needed. Describe your criteria for organizing the organisms into groups:

3). Pick an organism from your list. Describe it according to its **nutrition, habitat, mobility**, and, if you can, its **taxonomy**.

Organism: ____________________

Nutrition:

Habitat:

Mobility:

Taxonomy:

Name ______________________________

First three letters of last name

Investigation 4.4 The Food Chain

1). Describe the concept of a food chain or food web in a phrase or sentence that does not use the words "food," "chain" or "web."

2). Arrange the following organisms into a likely food web and estimate the trophic level that each occupies:

Cod	Herring	Dolphins
Krill	Radiolarians	Squid
Tuna	Diatoms	Baleen whales

3). Where does the energy come from that drives the food chain in the open ocean?

4). How many kg of phytoplankton (primary producers) does it take to grow 1 kg of fish assuming that:

a. this fish is at the fifth trophic level in the "grazing food chain," and

b. there is a 10% transfer efficiency between trophic levels.

5). Hydrothermal vents have a diverse and abundant community of organisms in a benthic environment where no sunlight penetrates. What is at the base of the food chain in these communities?

Name ______________________________

First three letters of last name

Investigation 4.5 Coastal Ecology

1). What makes coastal environments “fertile”?

2). What is the importance of “seaweed” (= algae) in coastal waters?

3). What are copepods and krill?

4). Give two examples of coastal food chains.

5). How many tons of phytoplankton are needed to feed one Cod during its lifetime?

6). Why are salt marshes important?

7). What are some examples of human impacts on the coastal environment?

Name ____________________________

First three letters of last name

Investigation 4.6 **The Intertidal Zone**

1). What conditions make the intertidal zone a good place for marine organisms to live?

2). What conditions make the intertidal zone a very difficult place to live?

3). Many organisms develop peculiar ways to adapt to their environment. Organisms in the surf zone need ways to firmly attach themselves to the sea floor so they will not be washed out to sea by the waves. How do these organisms accomplish this?

a. sea palms

b. sea urchins

c. barnacles

d. sea stars

4). What large marine animals live in the intertidal zone?

5). What are some of the difficulties that organisms encounter during times of low tide?

6). How do mussels and clams eat? What problems may arise from this type of feeding?

Name ______________________________

First three letters of last name

Investigation 4.7 Coral Reef Ecology

1). Where are coral reefs located?

2). What conditions are necessary for coral reefs to thrive?

3). Describe the main characteristics of the coral animal and name some biological relatives.

4). What characteristics do sea stars, sea urchins and sea cucumbers have in common?

5). What are some of the threats that are facing coral reef communities?

Name ______________________

First three letters of last name

Investigation 4.8 **Overfishing**

1). Describe how the act of fishing became an environmental problem.

2). Does overfishing have economic impacts? Provide at least two examples.

3). Who has jurisdiction over fish resources on the high seas? What difficulties are caused by this?

4). Propose some reasonable solutions to the problem of overfishing.

Name ______________________________

First three letters of last name

Investigation 4.9 Environment of the Gulf Stream

The Gulf Stream is a **western boundary** current that originates in the equatorial Atlantic, flows up the eastern coast of North America and crosses the North Atlantic towards Ireland and England. The water returns to the equatorial region by way of the Canary Current along the western coast of Africa.

1). What causes the Gulf Stream to flow?

2). What are the major physical characteristics of the Gulf Stream? What distinguishes it from the surrounding water?

3). Is productivity high or low within the Gulf Stream? Why?

4). Where is the Sargasso Sea? How did it get that name, and why is it there?

5). What are meanders in the Gulf Stream, and how do they form?

6). How does the Gulf Stream affect the ocean ecology off the coasts of the northeastern United States and eastern Canada?

7). How does the Gulf Stream affect the climate of Europe?

Name ______________________________

First three letters of last name

Investigation 4.10 **Marine Mammals**

1). What are the distinguishing characteristics of marine mammals?

2). Devise a classification scheme for a group of marine mammals using habitat, mobility, nutrition, and taxonomy.

3). How did these creatures evolve?

PART 5
Waves, Tides, and the Coastal Environment

As we saw previously, the abundance of life in the coastal region is extremely high, and the health of the coastal waters is needed to maintain a sustainable ecology throughout the ocean. At the same time, people love to live along the shore, and this inevitably causes a conflict between preserving the environment and developing it in a manner for the convenience and well-being of the human inhabitants. Coastlines are among the most dynamic regions of our planet, where the action of waves, tides, and storms can change the shape of the shoreline drastically. As the world population continues to grow, we must apply our knowledge to our use of coastal and marine resources so that we can minimize the negative effects that humans have on the ocean and adapt to the environmental changes that are occurring on a global basis.

In the following sections you will learn:

- The processes that form waves and tides
- Possible ways we can tap into the massive energy of the ocean
- The variety of environments that are found along the coastline
- The dynamics of beaches, estuaries, and salt marshes
- How storms and rising sea level affect coastal areas
- The causes and effects of marine pollution

■5.1 Deep-Water Waves: Energy on the Move

A large wave moves away from a ship after crashing on the deck.

As we have learned earlier, surface ocean currents are moving masses of water that are propelled along by the energy from winds. Most of us are more familiar with the other kind of "moving water" that we call waves. The quotation marks here serve notice that the way water moves in waves is not what you might think! **Waves** represent the transmission of energy, not mass, along the interface between fluids of differing density; for example, between the surface of the ocean and the atmosphere. In other words, the waves may move forward, but the water within those ways actually doesn't travel very far. The water molecules stay in the same place and orbit in circles as the waves pass by.

Wind waves on the ocean surface are produced by the day-to-day changes in weather, particularly storms (in contrast to the prevailing winds, which impart momentum to the upper water masses and drive ocean currents). Waves start when the friction of the wind blowing across the sea surface forms small ripples (ripples that are <1 cm and called **capillary waves**). The frictional forces of the wind blowing over the water cause these ripples to become higher until they achieve equilibrium between the force of the wind, which causes the water to mound up, and the force of gravity, which pulls the water back down to the sea surface (Fig. 5.1). These **equilibrium or gravity waves** can have a height-to-length ratio up to 1/7. That is, the height (H) of the wave can be no greater than 1/7 of the wavelength (L) or else they become unstable, forming whitecaps or breakers (Fig. 5.2). In deep-water waves, the water molecules move in an orbital (circular) motion within the water column (Fig. 5.3). As the wave crest passes a point, the water moves upward, tracing part a circular path as it does so; it completes the circle as the trough of the wave passes by, and the cycle is repeated as the next wave arrives. You may have experienced this yourself as you floated on your back in the ocean or a lake as waves passed around you. You were not pushed in the direction of the waves, but rather experienced a gentle bobbing motion as each wave progressed. This orbital motion of the surface water is transmitted to the underlying water column, but with a loss of efficiency with depth. The water travels in ever-smaller circles until the effects of the wind energy disappear at a depth of one-half the wavelength (L/2).

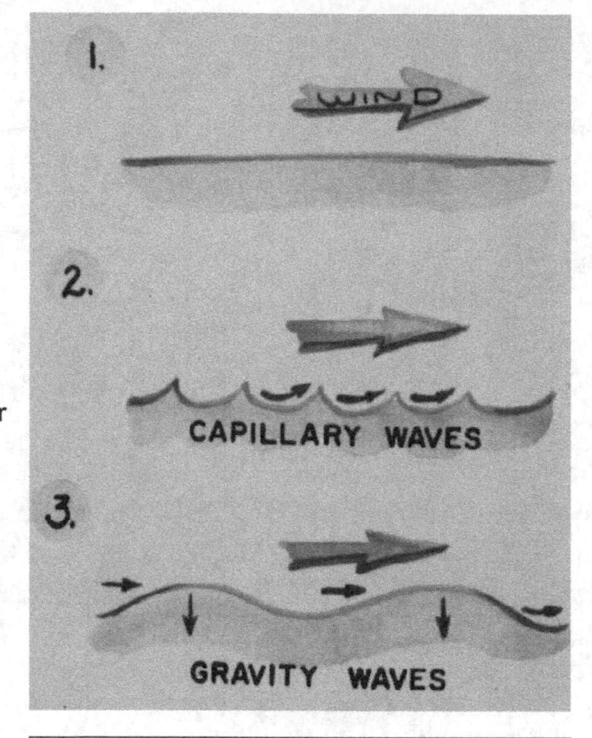

Fig. 5.1 The formation of wind waves. 1) Wind blows across the ocean surface. 2) Ripples form in response to the friction of the wind. 3) Waves reach equilibrium between the force of friction building them up and the force of gravity attempting to restore them.

Deep-water waves move at a velocity (also called **celerity**) that is a function of the wavelength (Fig. 5.3). so if you know the size of the wave, you can calculate how fast it is moving.

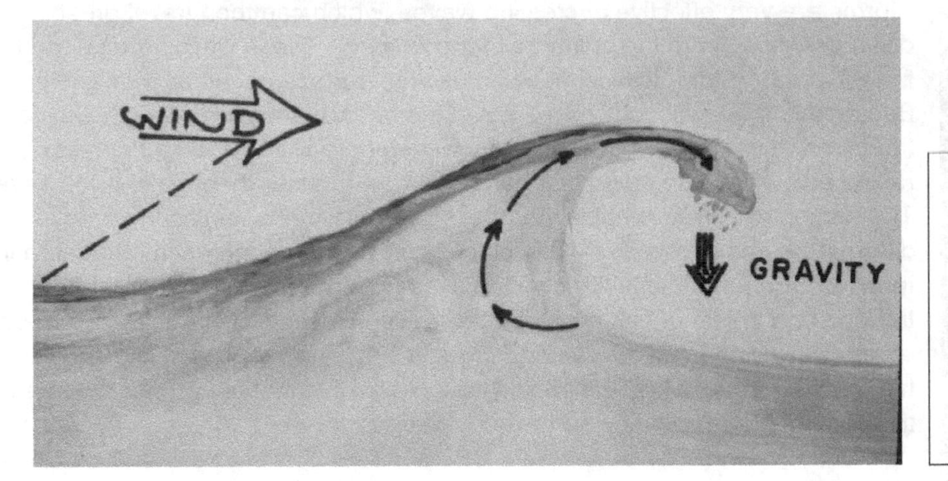

Fig. 5.2 When the height of the wave (H) is greater than 1/7 of its wavelength, the wave will break, forming whitecaps on the open ocean.

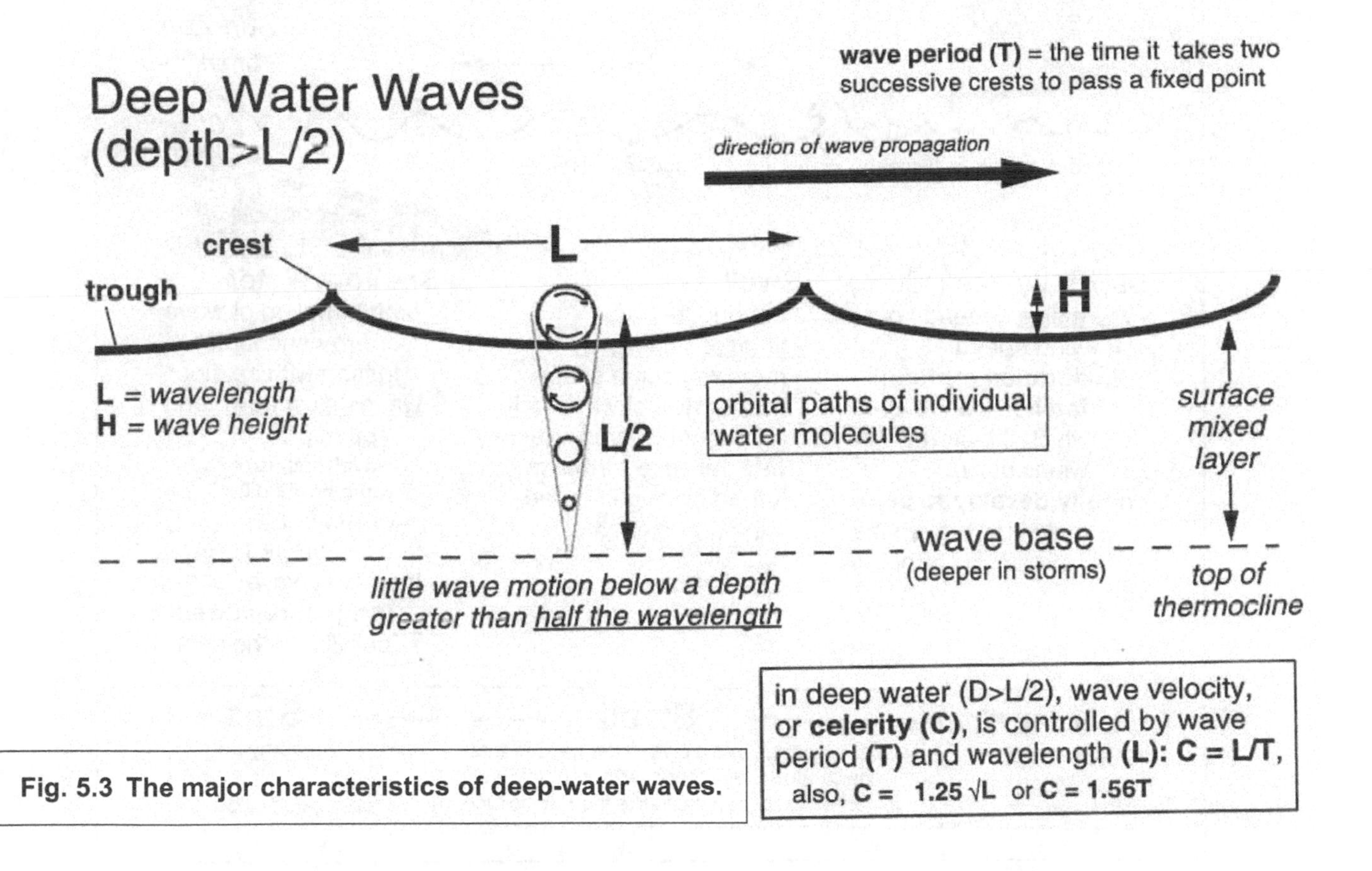

Fig. 5.3 The major characteristics of deep-water waves.

Investigation 5.1 examines the characteristics of deep-water waves in more detail.

■5.2 Waves in Shallow Water

Storms are very effective at creating waves, which can then travel great distances away from the storm that formed them. These waves are generated far out at sea. Storm waves move across the surface ocean as **swell** (Fig. 5.4). Because long-wavelength waves travel faster than short wavelength waves the trains of waves become sorted by wavelength with the longer waves racing away from the storm that generated them faster than the shorter waves. The sorting of waves is called **dispersion**. Wave trains originating from different storms in other far away places can pass through each other creating **interference patterns** in the swell. Waves become more irregular as the troughs and crests of each contributing wave train add to or subtract from each others waveform (constructive or destructive interference). Occasionally a very tall wave is produced by the additive effect of wave crests from multiple wave trains creating a rare and short-lived **rogue wave**.

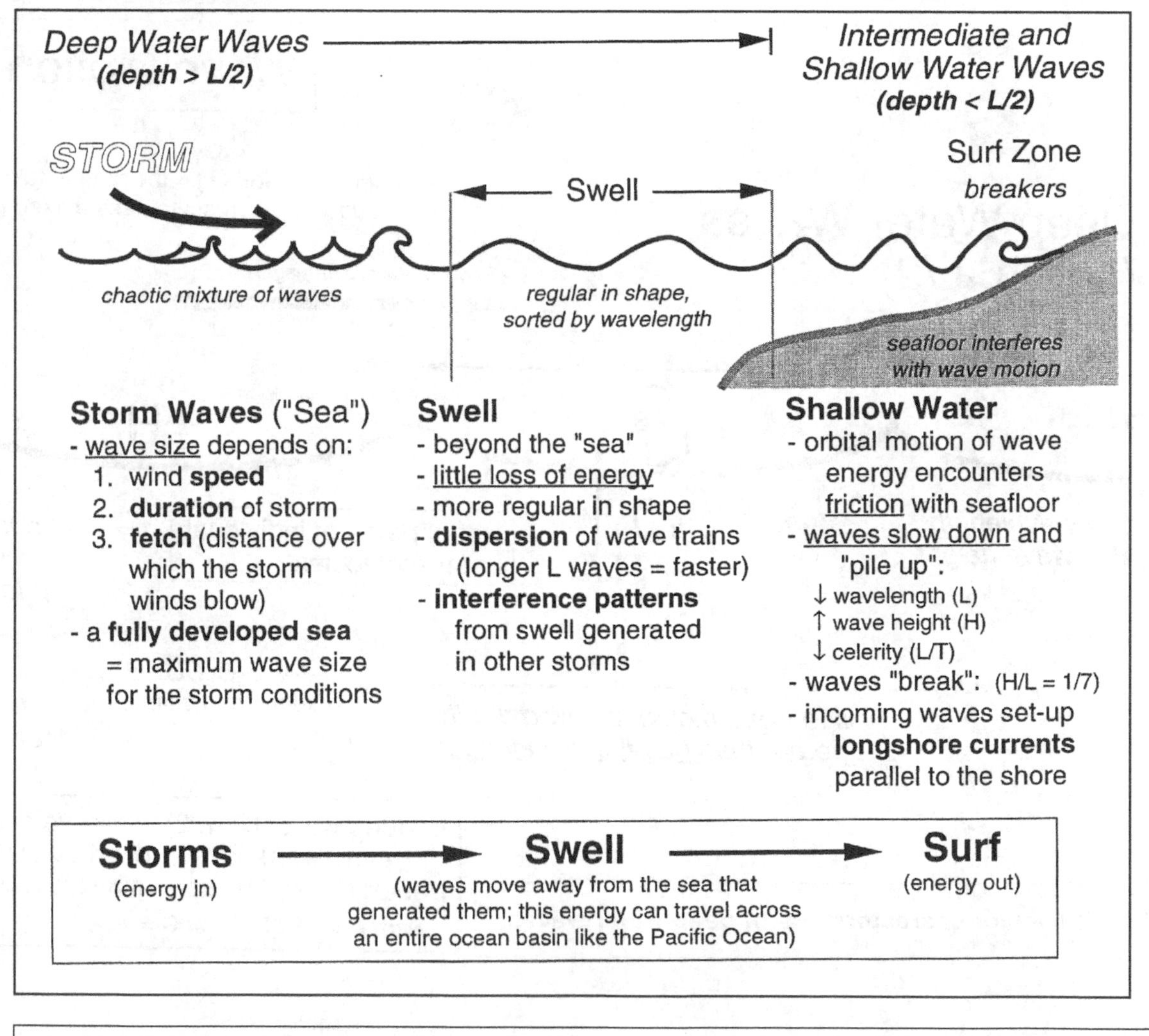

Fig. 5.4 Storms generate waves in all sizes that separate by size as they move away from the storm area, eventually reaching the coastline as breaking waves.

Waves also occur below the ocean surface. **Internal waves** move along the interface of subsurface waters of differing density such as along the pycnocline (thermocline).

Waves eventually lose their energy in the surf zone (Fig. 5.5). As waves encounter shallower water, their kinetic energy is transferred to the ocean floor when the orbital motion of the water in the waves "touches bottom." This results in intermediate waves when the water depth is less than half the wavelength of the waves (<L/2) and shallow-water waves when the water depth is less than one-twentieth of the wavelength (<L/20). The seafloor impedes the wave motion and causes the waves to slow down and sediment is put into motion. The celerity (velocity) of intermediate- and shallow-water waves is controlled only by the depth of the water beneath the wave. The orbital motion of the water flattens out into an elliptical shape as the height (H) increases and wavelength (L) decreases. When H/L > 1/7, then the waves will break and the water will stream ashore (Fig. 5.5). Finally, as the waves run up the beach the water is moving horizontally, reversing its direction as the wave recedes (giving rise to the undertow we experience when standing in ankle deep surf). This wave energy in coastal waters sets up **longshore currents** and moves sand around as **longshore drift** of sediment.

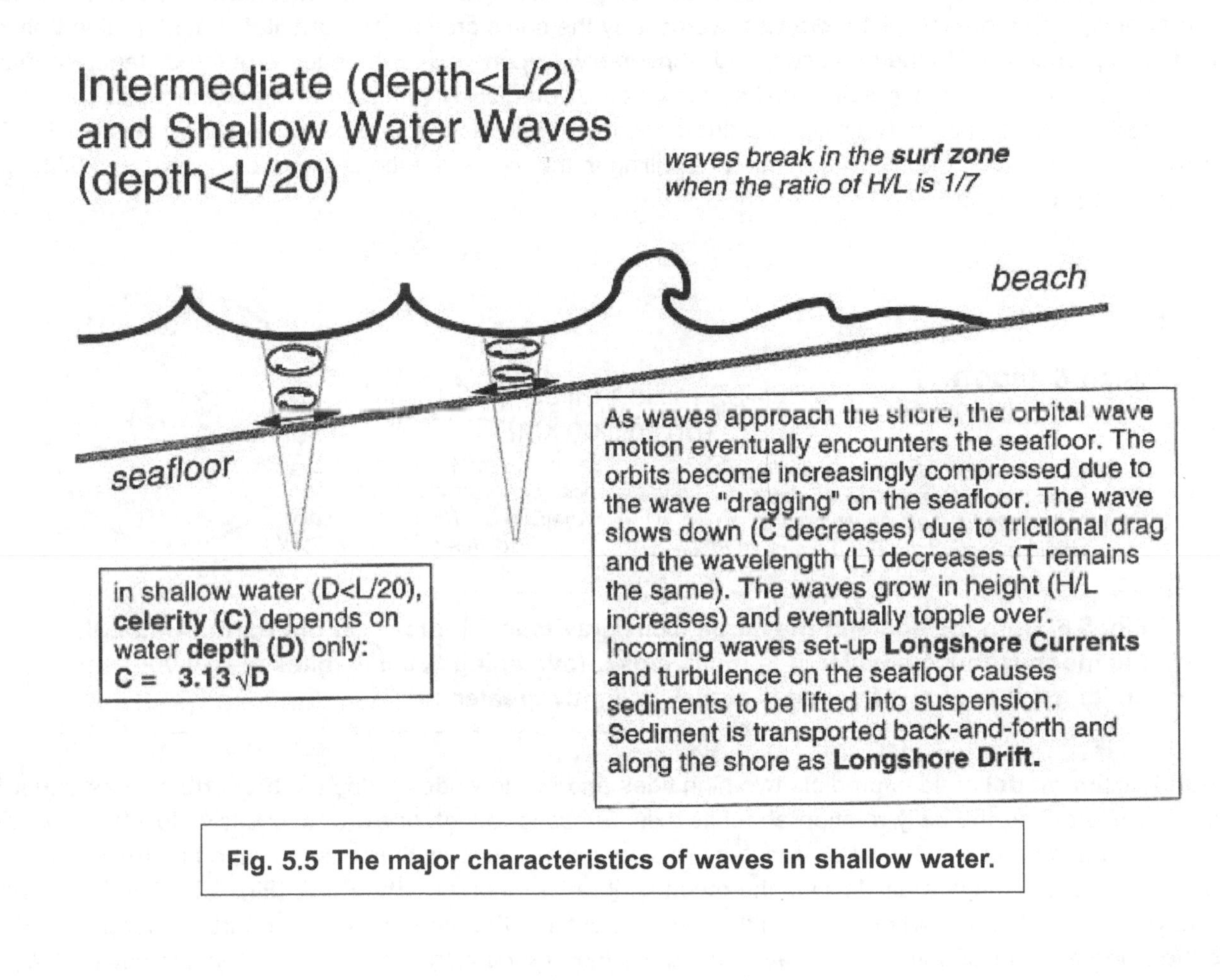

Fig. 5.5 The major characteristics of waves in shallow water.

You can learn more about the movement of waves in Investigation 5.1.

■5.3 Tides: Earth's Attraction to the Moon & Sun

In addition to the familiar wind waves, the ocean experiences another kind of wave, although we don't usually recognize it as a wave. The ocean tides, which are produced by the gravitational attraction of the Moon and the Sun, are in reality long-wavelength, shallow-water waves. Let's see how this works. The Earth is held in orbit around the sun by the force of gravity, and, in a similar fashion, the moon orbits the Earth (Fig. 5.6). Although we usually think that the Moon revolves around the Earth, the large size of the Moon makes the Earth-Moon system a "double planet" that revolves about a common center of mass. This produces **two tidal bulges** on the surface of the ocean: one bulge is drawn toward the moon and a second (same size) develops on the opposite side of the Earth resulting from the centrifugal force of the rotating Earth-Moon system (fig. 5.7). Like two skaters facing each other, holding hands, and rotating in a circle, the force necessary to grasp hands and stay together is equal to the centrifugal force that is trying to send them flying backwards onto their backsides.

The Sun also gets into the act as well. As the Earth races around the sun in its annual orbit, the side that faces the sun at any given moment will be drawn towards it by the sun's gravity. The gravitational attraction between two bodies is proportional to their masses, and is inversely proportional to the square of the distance (radius^2) between them. In other words, gravitational attraction drops off quickly with increasing distance. Despite its much smaller mass, the Moon has about twice the tide-generating force as the Sun because it is so close to Earth (fig. 5.6). At certain times, the moon and sun are pulling in the same direction, and this makes the tidal bulges on the Earth more pronounced.

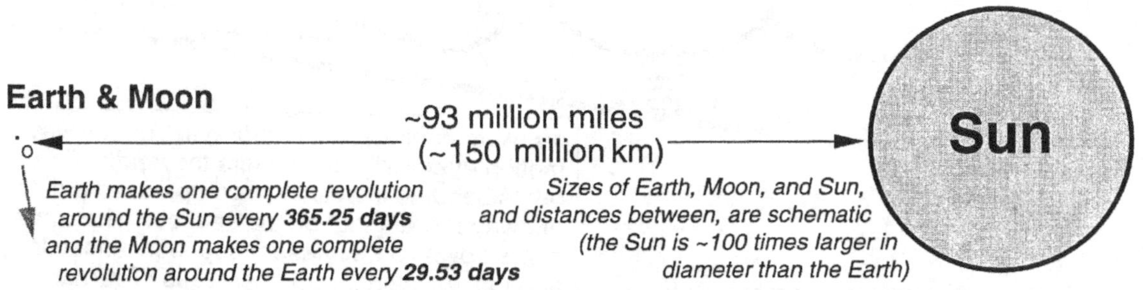

Earth & Moon

~93 million miles
(~150 million km)

Sun

*Earth makes one complete revolution around the Sun every **365.25 days** and the Moon makes one complete revolution around the Earth every **29.53 days***

Sizes of Earth, Moon, and Sun, and distances between, are schematic (the Sun is ~100 times larger in diameter than the Earth)

Fig. 5.6 Both the sun and the moon exert gravitational forces on the Earth. Although the moon is much smaller, it is much closer (averaging 230,000 miles or 370,000 km) so its gravitational influence is actually slightly greater.

The **equilibrium model** of tides predicts two high tides and two low tides a day as the Earth passes under the two tidal bulges during the daily rotation about its axis. Successive high tides (or successive low tides) would be separated by an interval of 12 hour 25 minutes. This seemingly unusual timing is explained by the movement of the tidal bulge, which generally follows the moon as it revolves around the Earth (Fig. 5.7). The Earth will rotate one full revolution in 24 hours, but in that amount of time, the moon has moved further along in its orbit. It takes the Earth another 50 minutes to "catch up" to the moon's location and the tidal bulge directly underneath it (Fig. 5.8). However, tide-generating forces are very complex, and actual tides can diverge widely from the predictions based upon the equilibrium model.

all diagrams below represent polar views looking down on the Earth's axis of rotation (North Pole) and the plane of the Moon's orbit around Earth; the Sun is to the right

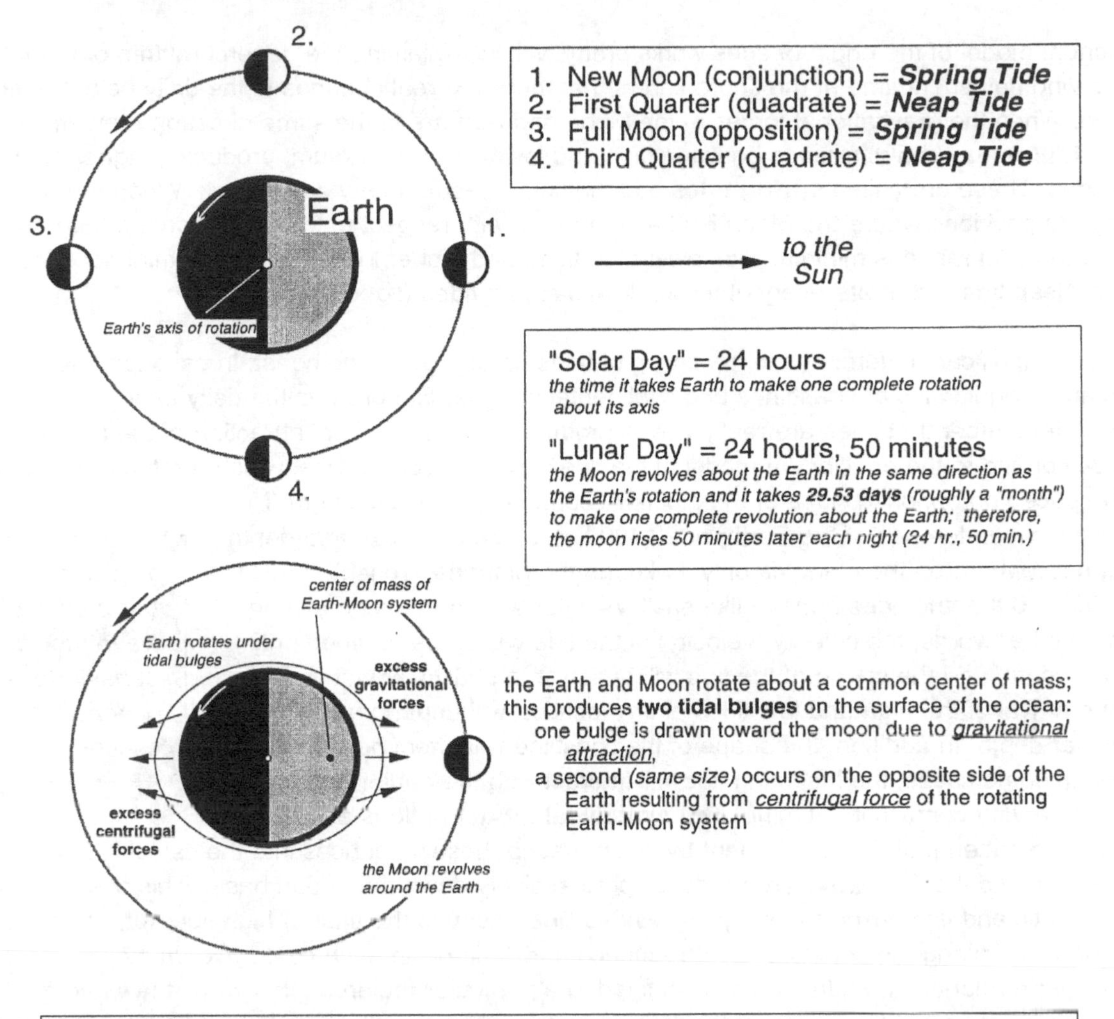

Fig. 5.7 Tidal bulges form in response to the gravitational attraction of the sun and the moon, and their direction and intensity changes as the Earth rotates on its axis and the moon revolves around the Earth.

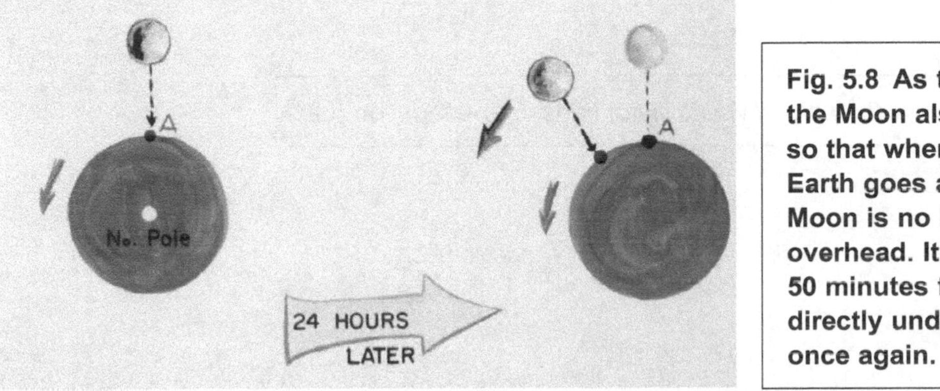

Fig. 5.8 As the Earth rotates, the Moon also orbits the Earth, so that when point "A" on the Earth goes around once, the Moon is no longer directly overhead. It takes an additional 50 minutes for point "A" to be directly underneath the Moon once again.

■5.4 The Changing Tidal Cycle

The equilibrium model of the origin of tides works pretty well in explaining the general rhythm of the tidal cycle. Yet anyone who has spent time at the shore knows that there are real changes in the daily height of tides at any one location. When the gravitational forces of the Moon and Sun are in the same direction (new moon and full moon), the **tidal range** (the difference between high and low tide) is maximum, producing higher high tides and lower low tides. These are called **spring tides** and they occur about every other week. When the Moon and Sun are in quadrate positions where the Moon is at a right angle with respect to the Sun (first and third quarter of the moon), then tidal range is minimal with lower high tides and higher low tides. These minimal tides are called **neap tides**. Neap tides alternate every other week with spring tides (fig. 5.9).

There are also significant differences in the timing of tides up and down the coast. In essence, the presence of continents and irregularities of coastlines and continental margins complicates the daily movement of the two tidal bulges. Remember that tides are really waves produced by gravitational attraction of the Moon and Sun on the Earth. According to the equilibrium model of the tides, the two tidal bulges, which are the crests of the wave, are evenly spaced on opposite sides of the globe. Accordingly, the wavelength (L) is one-half of the circumference of the Earth, or 22,400 km. Since the maximum depth of the ocean anywhere on the planet is only 11 km (in the Mariana Trench), the D/L ratio is 1/2000, so that the tides behave like shallow-water waves at every point in the ocean. In other words, the celerity (velocity) of the tide will be determined only by the water depth, and the speed of the tide will be lower in shallower water. The timing of the arrival of the high and low tides at any location will depend heavily on the local water depth. In addition, the shape of the coastline will affect how soon the tide arrives. In some cases, the incoming tide will interact with the earlier outgoing tide producing a very complicated timing. The **dynamical model** of tides accounts for the observed patterns of tidal movement by incorporating these influences into the calculations. In some ocean basins, the tidal bulge (wave crest) moves progressively down the ocean basin. This scenario occurs in the South Atlantic and is referred to as a **progressive tide** because the time of high tide, for example, gradually migrates northward along the coasts of South America and Africa with each tidal cycle. In other ocean basins, such as the North Atlantic, the tidal bulge is confined to a particular region. In this case, the wave rotates around a node in the central part of the basin where there is no tidal influence. This node is called the **amphidromic point** and the pattern of tidal bulge movement is called a **rotary standing wave** because of the progression of each high tide around the coastline of the North Atlantic in a counter-clockwise pattern (the rotation is clockwise in the Southern Hemisphere) (fig. 5.10).

You can review the basic principles of wave motion and the behavior of shallow-water waves in sections 5.1 and 5.2.

The east coast of the U.S. has a twice-daily tide, called a **semidiurnal tide**, with a tidal period of 12 hours, 25 minutes. This is the tidal cycle most like the equilibrium model. Some coasts, like those around the Gulf of Mexico, experience a once daily tidal cycle, called a **diurnal tide**. A diurnal tide has a tidal period of 24 hours, 50 minutes. The most common type is a **mixed tide** with either one or two tidal cycles a day as exemplified by the west coast of the U.S. (fig. 5.11).

You can explore the natural variability of tides in Investigation 5.2.

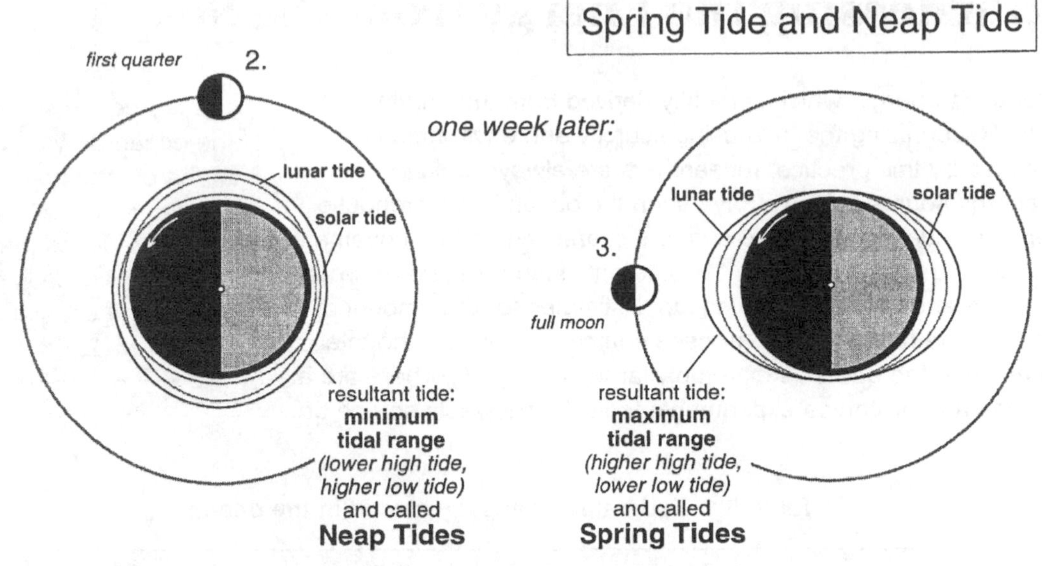

two Spring Tides and two neap Tides per month

Fig. 5.9 Spring tides occur when the gravitational forces of the moon and the sun act in the same direction. Neap tides take place when the gravitational forces of the moon and sun are at right angles.

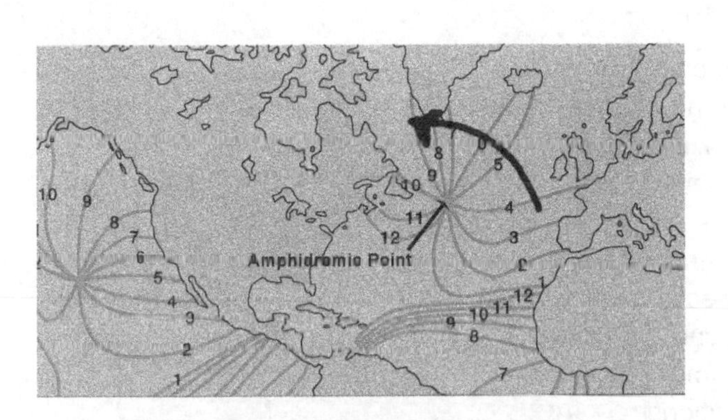

Fig. 5.10 The high tides in the North Atlantic and North Pacific move counterclockwise as the day progresses. Here positions of the high tide are indicated on an hourly basis. The tides in the South Atlantic move progressively northward.

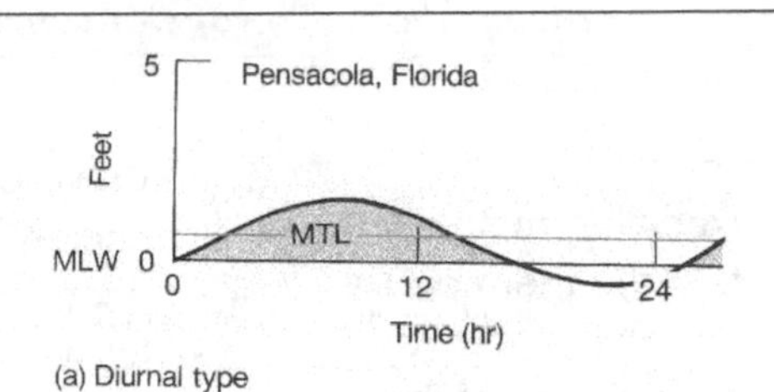

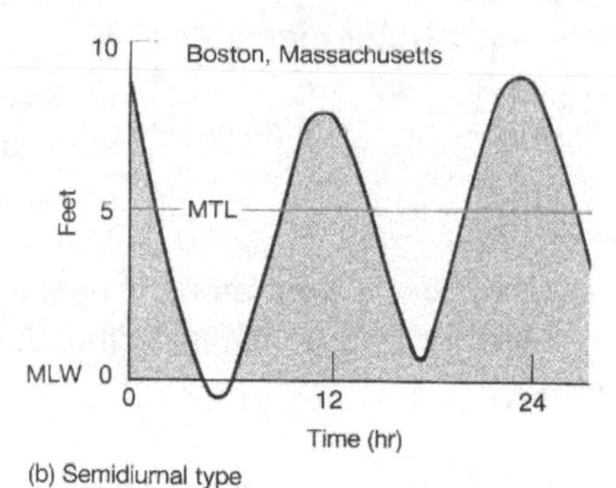

San Diego, California

Feet

MTL

MLLW 0

Time (hr)

(c) Mixed type

Fig. 5.11 The interaction of the coastlines with tidal forces produces three types of tidal cycles.

5.5 Harnessing the Energy from the Sea

Our world requires energy, which is mostly derived from the burning of fossil fuels. Recognizing the increasing scarcity and environmental problems caused by this practice, researchers are always looking for alternative energy sources. As we have seen the ocean is a storehouse of energy originally derived from the sun, but expressed as the movement of waves, tides, and currents, and in the differential temperature between the warm surface and the cold deep ocean. Estimates for the amount of energy that it can be harnessed from these sources varies, but the total energy contained in the ocean is extremely large (Table 5.1). There are a number of ideas and prototype experiments tap this renewable source of energy.

We learned in section 2.16 how the ocean provides almost half of the oil and natural gas that we use today. We will also look at the problems that burning fossil fuels is causing for the ocean and coastal regions in section 5.12.

Table 5.1 Estimates of energy stored in the ocean.

Energy Source	Annual Power Potential (million megawatts)
Ocean Thermal Energy	100,000
Wave Energy	10
Tidal Energy	5
Present World Power Consumption	*15*

Recall from section 3.7 that the thermocline separates the warm mixed layer of the surface ocean from the vast deep water that is extremely cold.

Wave energy is appealing since it occurs in all coastal areas of the ocean and many different designs for wave-energy generators have been proposed, although none have gotten past the design stage (Fig. 5.12). The practical aspects of designing generators that can survive the salt-water environment under a variety of wave conditions will require a great deal of development. In addition, the power output from each generator will be small, so that a method of linking them together and transmitting the electricity to the shore will be needed.

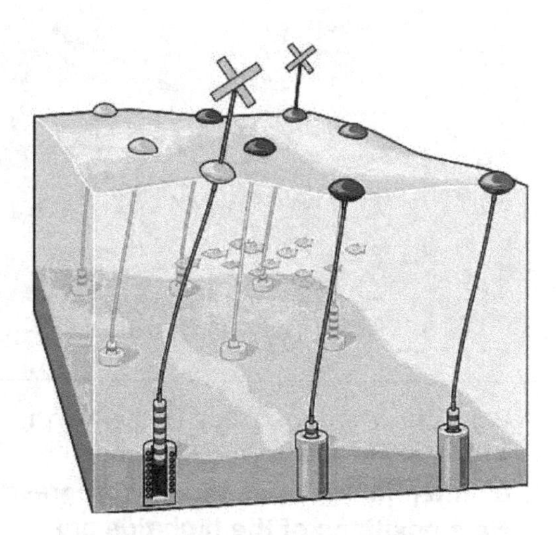

Fig. 5.12 These point absorbers are one model for harnessing energy from waves. In this design, the floats rise and fall with the waves. As they do, they drive pistons, which, in turn, can be used to generate electricity either though electromechanical or hydraulic energy conversion.

Tidal power holds a bit more promise for short-term energy needs, since a functional prototype tidal power station has actually been built on the coast of France. As the tide starts to come in, gates are closed in a large dam that has been built across the estuary. At high tide, these gates are opened, and the water flowing through them is used to drive turbines and produce electricity (Fig. 5.13). The gates are closed again, trapping the water at high tide behind the dam. At low tide, re-opening the gates allows water to rush through again and generate additional electricity. Tidal power stations will only generate electricity four times a day (for semi-diurnal tides), and for practical reasons, there needs to be a very high tidal range, on the order of five meters, to drive the turbines. This limits the location of potential power stations, and the negative environmental effects of constricting estuaries and bays with large dams may be severe.

One novel idea of extracting energy from the sea exploits the large temperature difference between the surface mixed layer and deep water. An experimental power plant called OTEC (for Ocean Thermal Energy Conversion) has already been built. It operates on a principle similar to that of a refrigerator or air conditioner. Warm water from the surface ocean helps vaporize a fluid, which turns an electric generator. This vapor is cooled and liquefied by cold ocean water pumped from below the thermocline, and the process continues as a cycle (Fig. 5.14). The efficiency of the OTEC plant is very low, about 2%, which is much less than that of a typical fossil-fuel power plant (about 85%). Moreover, OTEC can only be used in the tropics, where the surface water is warm all year round. In all these cases, it will be many decades, or possibly centuries, before they become practical alternatives to fossil fuels.

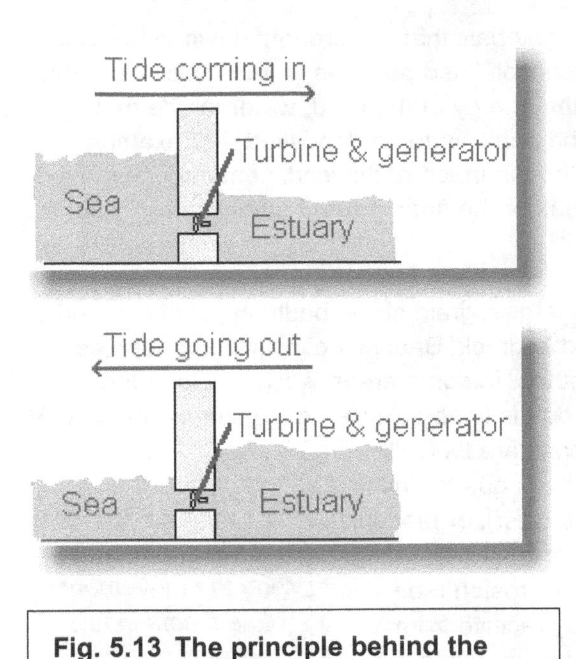

Fig. 5.13 The principle behind the operation of tidal power stations.

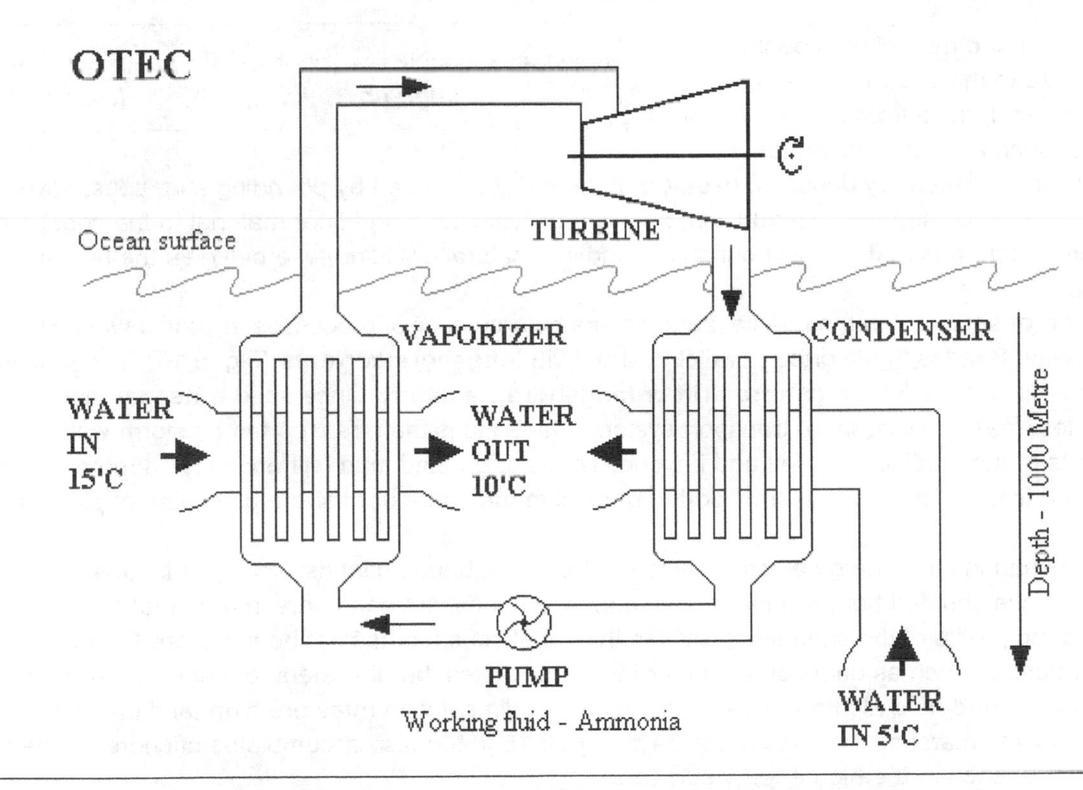

Fig. 5.14 The principle behind the Ocean Thermal Energy Conversion (OTEC) system. Warm tropical ocean water circulates through the evaporator at left, while cold, deep ocean water is drawn through the condenser at right. As ammonia is pumped through the warm chamber, it expands and drives a turbine. The vapor is cooled in the condenser and the process continues.

■5.6 Sediment in the Coastal Zone

The coastal zone constitutes the initial "dumping ground" for all the materials that are brought down to the sea by rivers, wind, or ice. These materials include a wide variety of unconsolidated particles of inorganic or organic (biogenic) origin. The **grain size** of a sedimentary deposit reflects the energy of the wind, water, or ice that transported the particles, as well as the environment that allowed the particles to be deposited. For example, sand and pebbles are deposited close to shore in the surf zone. Although much of this sediment may be moved again by storm waves and longshore currents, turbulence is too great for the finer grained particles (silt, clay) to accumulate.

The sediment found along a rocky coastline is characterized by the largest grain sizes: boulders, cobbles, and pebbles, which are derived from the erosion of sea cliffs or exposed bedrock. Beaches consisting of pebbles or sand develop in pockets between the higher energy rocky exposures. In some areas, such as along the coast of Maine, additional coarse-grained material comes from the debris left by retreating ice sheets during the last episode of continental glaciation. Along sandy shorelines, beaches are typically composed of rounded sand-size rock fragments, mineral grains such as quartz and feldspar (the two most common rock-forming minerals in the Earth's crust), or biogenic particles such as whole or broken shells. A beach is actually made of whatever sedimentary particles are locally available from river runoff or coastal erosion (see section 5.7). These grains are rounded smooth by the pounding they receive from wave action in the high-energy surf zone. The **mud** found in estuaries, marshes, and bays is composed of **clay and silt-sized** particles together with variable amounts of **organic detritus**.

We will look at the details of beaches and the movement of sediment in later sections.

boulders → cobbles → pebbles → sand → silt → clay
high energy → ***low energy***

Much of the sand and mud of the coastal zone is delivered to the ocean by rivers. Some sediment is derived from the erosion of coastal areas, such as rocky headlands, sea cliffs, and ancient sedimentary deposits. **Erosion** of the coast is caused by pounding surf, tides, severe storms, strong winds, and rising sea level. In addition, the wind delivers sand and finer material to the coast but plays a much more important role in the redistribution of sand in a natural give-and-take between the beach and dunes.

Transportation of sediment in the coastal zone occurs by a number of processes including wind, currents, tides, and gravity. Sand is transported parallel to shore via **longshore currents** (Fig. 5.15). The movement of sand down the coast is called **longshore drift** or **longshore transport**. Once sand is deeper than about 10 m (~30 ft.), it is lost from the longshore transport system. The sand is then transported by storm waves and gravity to deeper parts of the continental shelf and beyond. The finer grained mud (silt and clay) is more easily held in suspension and is therefore typically transported parallel to the shore or offshore as sediment plumes.

Deposition of sand in high energy environments like beaches, barrier islands, and spits is mostly temporary; much of the sand is shuffled between the beach, dunes, and offshore sand bars in a natural seasonal cycle that maintains the profile of the shoreline provided the supply of sand has not been severed or disrupted by man-made structures such as dams on rivers, or by jetties, groins, break-waters, or seawalls along the coast. Deposition of sand and mud also occurs in deltas where sedimentation rates are high, and in quieter water settings such as salt marshes, estuaries, and bays (Fig. 5.15). Mud also accumulates offshore on the continental shelf, beyond the reach of the high energy surf zone.

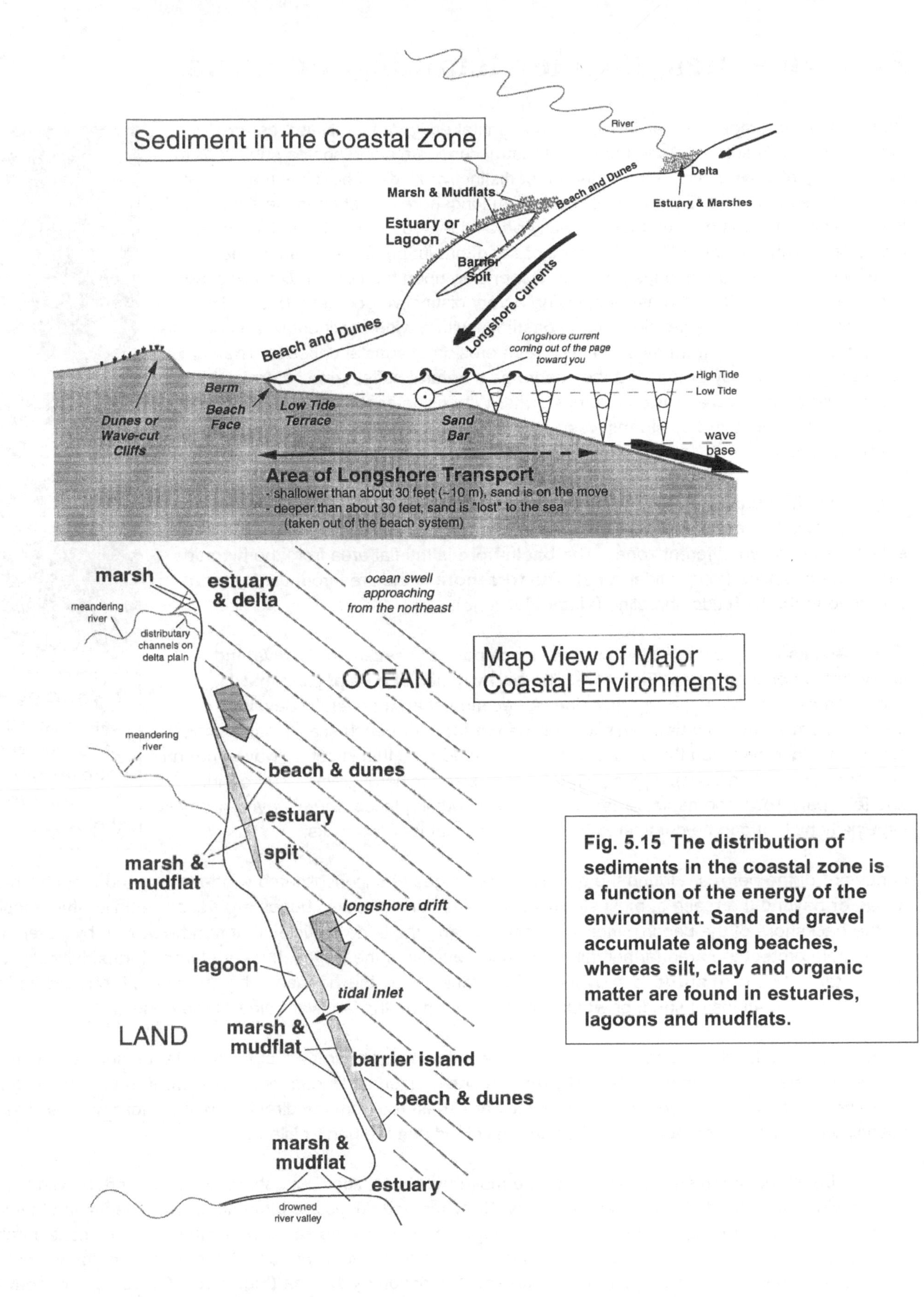

Fig. 5.15 The distribution of sediments in the coastal zone is a function of the energy of the environment. Sand and gravel accumulate along beaches, whereas silt, clay and organic matter are found in estuaries, lagoons and mudflats.

■5.7 Beaches, Barrier Islands, and Spits

Beaches are the most familiar feature of the coastal environment. **Beaches** are deposits of unconsolidated sand or gravel that accumulate along shores subject to the high energy of wave action. One of the most distinctive kinds of beach is the barrier beach or barrier island. These are formed when longshore drift shapes the sediments into low-lying ribbons of sand that generally parallel the coastline. Related landforms are spits, which are finger-like extensions of sand that jut out from the shoreline parallel to the direction of longshore drift. Depending upon the current directions, spits can often curve back on themselves, giving a very distinctive geometry (Fig. 5.16). Barrier islands and spits develop along coastlines with a wide continental shelf and an ample sand supply from river runoff or from erosion of coastal deposits. They are flood-prone and easily eroded but they serve as a natural buffer zone by protecting the mainland from wave erosion during storms. With rising sea level, these features migrate ("roll") landward as storms wash over the barriers and deposit sand on their landward sides.

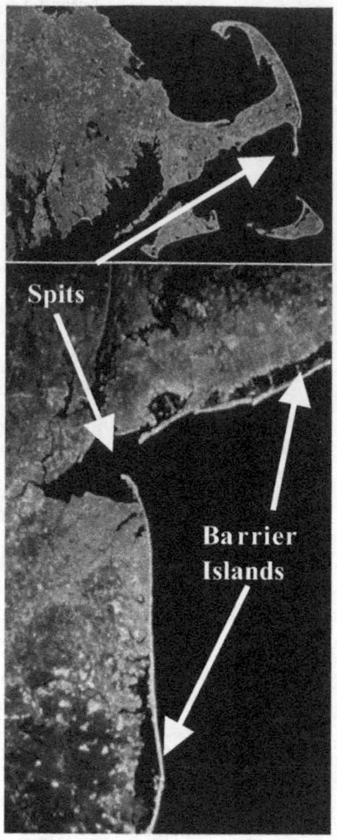

Fig 5.16 Barrier-beach coastlines of Massachusetts (above) and New York-New Jersey (below).

In general, the **coastline** refers to the highest elevation on the continent affected by storm waves. The **shore** is the area from the low tide line to the coastline. This is subdivided into two different zones. The **backshore** is the flat area from the high tide line to the coastline (=supratidal zone). The **foreshore** is the area from the low tide shoreline to the high tide shoreline (=intertidal zone).

The beach itself is a complex system that is composed of several distinctive and important subenvironments (Fig. 5.17). The **berm** is the flat area of sand that accumulates just above the high tide line. A second flat area generally develops on the foreshore as the **low tide terrace**. The **beach face** (or beach scarp) is the sharply inclined surface between the berm and the low tide terrace that is cut by waves during high tide. Typically a beach is composed of sand-sized mineral grains (e.g., quartz and feldspar), rock fragments, or broken-up shells, but in places where wave energy is especially high, it can be dominated by pebbles or cobble-sized rocks.

Landward of the berm are found the **dunes**, linear ridges of unconsolidated wind-blown sand that accumulate above or beyond the reach of most storm waves. The sand grains in dunes are usually smaller than those found on the backshore of the beach, since wind cannot carry the large particles that can be moved by water. The dunes help protect the area farther inland from the effects of the waves, but very large storms, typically those associated with **storm surge**, can over-run the dunes. When this happens, the dunes are breached and fan-shaped accumulations of sand, or **washover fans**, form on the landward side of the dunes.

Landward of the barrier beach and dunes there are the low-lying areas that form marshes and tidal mudflats. These low-energy environments typically receive fine grained sediments and water from the washover fans, and they are very biologically productive, since they are sheltered from the direct impact of storm waves. They are associated with a bay or lagoon between the mainland and the barrier island.

Sand in beach environments is always on the move by waves, tides, longshore currents, and the wind. The free movement of sand absorbs ocean energy. Beaches and dunes are dynamic environments; in other words, they are always changing. These depositional features may look the same year after year, but considerable movement and recycling of sand occurs during the course of a year. Seasonal changes in the beach profile actually help to protect the coast from erosion and inundation by the sea (Fig. 5.18). As we venture seaward of the beach environment, we enter into the nearshore zone between the low tide shoreline and where the breakers form; also called the "surf zone". Sand bars are found here. These linear ridges of unconsolidated sand often serve to "trip" the incoming waves to start breaking; they are typically dynamic, shifting location and changing shape daily or seasonally. In the summer, the sand bars are closer to the shore. The breakers are gentler and move sand toward the beach. In the winter time, the sand bars form farther away from the beach, tripping the breakers to reduce the force that large breakers exert on the beach.

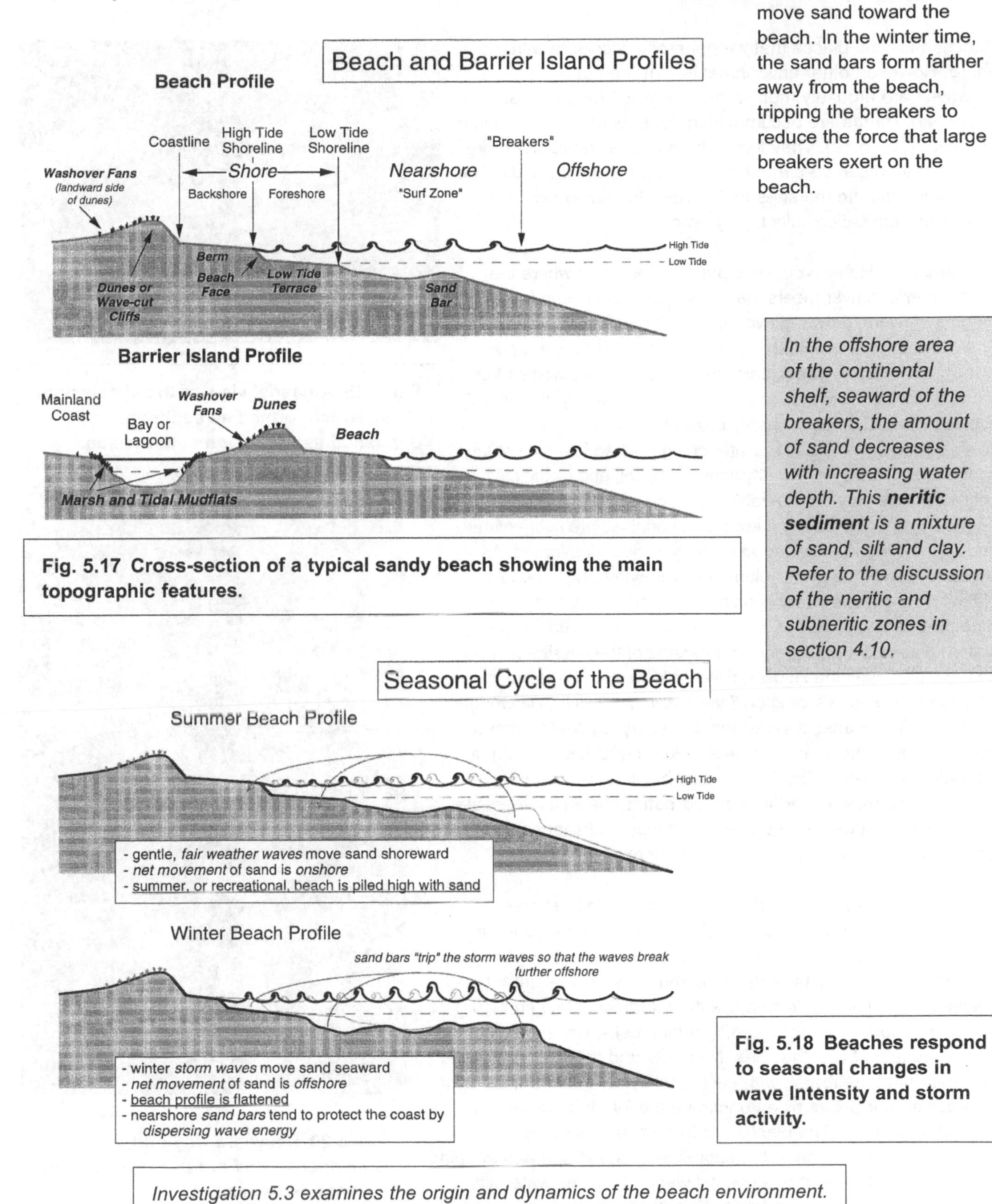

Fig. 5.17 Cross-section of a typical sandy beach showing the main topographic features.

*In the offshore area of the continental shelf, seaward of the breakers, the amount of sand decreases with increasing water depth. This **neritic sediment** is a mixture of sand, silt and clay. Refer to the discussion of the neritic and subneritic zones in section 4.10.*

Fig. 5.18 Beaches respond to seasonal changes in wave Intensity and storm activity.

Investigation 5.3 examines the origin and dynamics of the beach environment.

■5.8 Deltas, Estuaries, and Salt Marshes: Fertile Oases

Beaches are the places that we generally associate with the shore. However, other environments that are not dominated by waves are arguably much more important for the balance in the ocean. **Deltas** are accumulations of sediment at the mouth of a river (Fig. 5.19). They form where a river transports more sediment than can be carried away by longshore currents. The flood plain and the marshes that border the distributary river channel(s) are biologically highly productive.

Fig. 5.19 An aerial view of the Mississippi Delta, which formed as sediment is deposited as the river meets the sea.

Estuaries are highly productive areas of the coast where the fresh water of a river meets the salt water of the ocean (e.g., mouths of rivers, drowned river valleys, bays, fjords) (Fig. 5.20). The salinity of the **brackish waters** (mixture of fresh and salt water) in an estuary varies daily and seasonally, as well as from top to bottom or from side to side across the estuary. In general, circulation in estuaries is characterized by low salinity water flowing seaward over saltier water being pushed into the estuary by the tides. However, the physical, chemical, and biological characteristics vary considerably from one estuary to another (Fig. 5.21). Two of the most important variables are river_volume and tidal mixing. A **salt-wedge estuary** is river-dominated. As a consequence of the great volume of river water and minimal impact of tidal mixing, the estuary is highly stratified by a well-developed **halocline**, a sharp change in salinity between the surface and bottom waters of the estuary. The mouths of the Mississippi River on the Gulf Coast, the Hudson River in New York City, and the Columbia River in Washington State are examples of salt-wedge estuaries. By contrast, a **well-mixed estuary** is tide-dominated. During times of the year when river volume is low, the mouth of the Columbia River at the Oregon-Washington border becomes a well-mixed estuary. A **partially mixed estuary** is an intermediate between the salt wedge and well-mixed types. Chesapeake Bay, San Francisco Bay, and Puget Sound are examples.

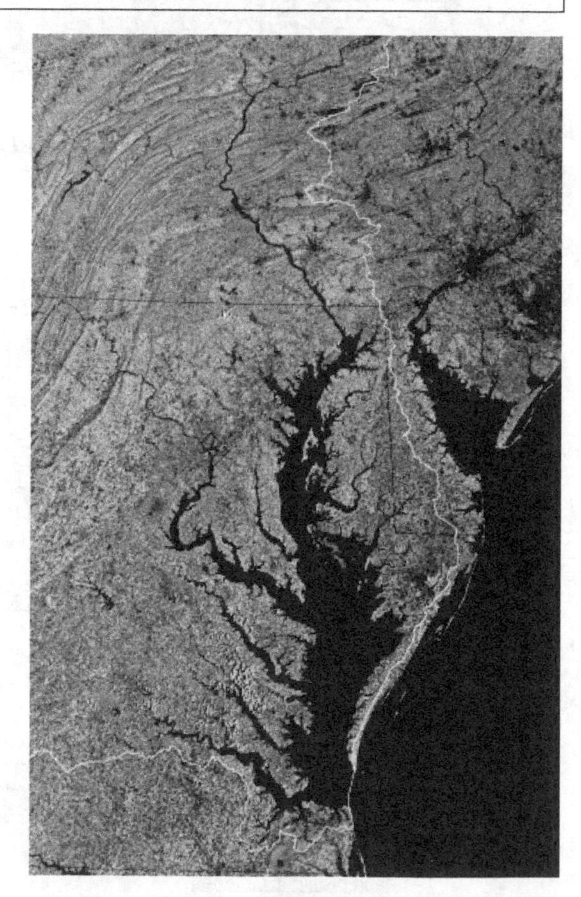

Fig. 5.20 Delaware Bay and Chesapeake Bay are prime examples of large estuaries.

Salt marshes are vegetated tidal flats found along shores protected from the pounding surf (Fig. 5.22). Marshes border estuaries and develop at the edges of bays and lagoons behind barrier islands and spits. A dense community of salt-tolerant grasses and other plants colonize the intertidal marsh surface. The marsh surface is dissected by tidal creeks, which conduct the daily flood and ebb of the tides. Nutrients and detritus are flushed into and out of the marsh with each tidal cycle. In the tropics and subtropics, **mangrove trees** dominate the intertidal vegetation instead of grasses. The plant roots in both salt marshes and mangrove swamps extend the shoreline by stabilizing and trapping sediment. In addition, these coastal wetlands act as water filters by absorbing pollutants and as baffles by dissipating storm energy.

Estuaries

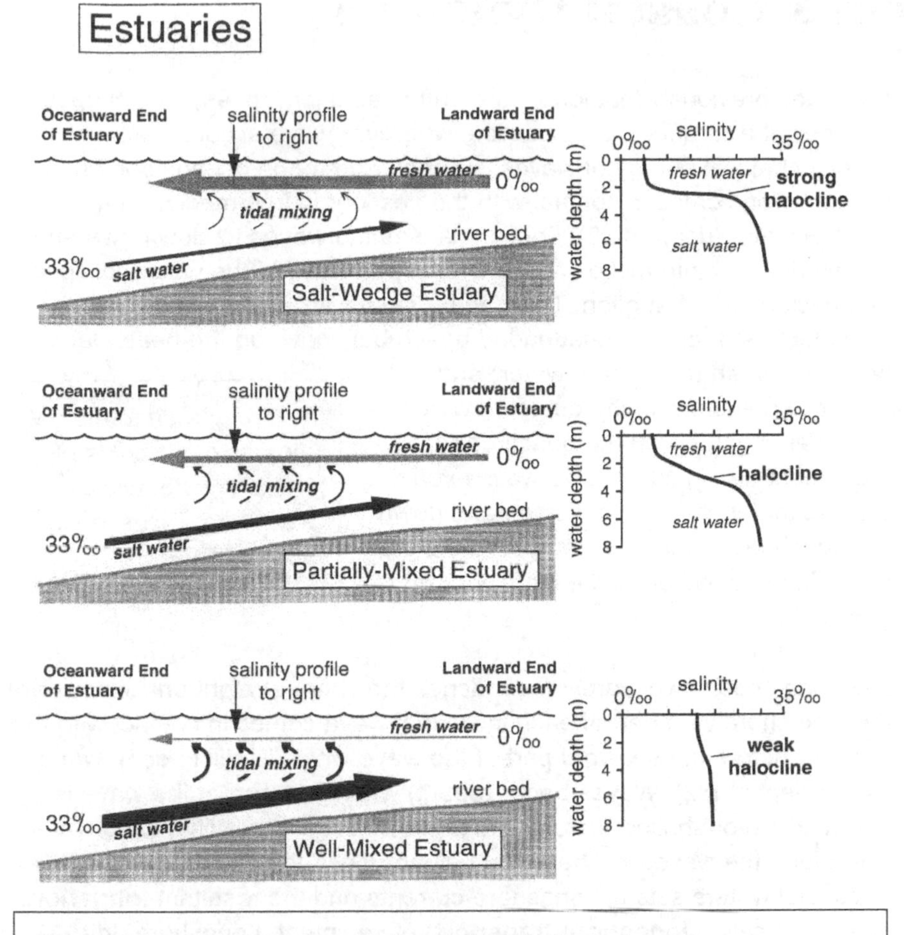

Fig. 5.21 Estuaries occur where river valleys have been drowned by rising sea levels. They have variable environments depending upon the balance between the flow of fresh water and sea water into the system.

The abundance of nutrients and sunlight, and the daily tidal mixing stimulates very high biological productivity in estuaries and marshes. Refer to section 4.9 for information about the ecology of these environments. The amount of organic matter produced is 4–10 times greater than an equivalent size cornfield. These rich waters support many coastal and oceanic food webs by providing spawning grounds and nurseries for many species of fish. For example, >75% of commercial fish spend at part of their life in coastal waters. Coastal waters provide food, employment, tourism and recreation. Fishing contributes ~$111 billion to the nation's economy every year. Collectively, coastal industries account for ~28 million jobs and >30% of the Gross National Product is generated in coastal counties in the U.S. About 45% of all endangered or threatened species of birds and mammals rely on coastal waters.

Salt Marshes

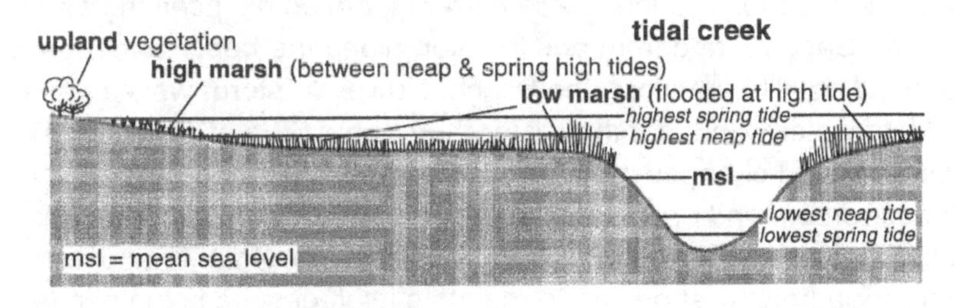

Fig. 5.22 Salt marshes are highly productive environments that are protected from the harsh action of waves by barrier beaches on their seaward side.

Investigation 5.4 examines circulation patterns in estuaries in greater detail.

■5.9 Longshore Drift & Coastal Dynamics

Groins trap sand along a beach showing the direction of longshore drift.

We noted previously that longshore drift is a major process that shapes beaches; it also affects the coastline wherever wave action is present. The mechanical energy of waves is transferred to the ocean floor when wave motion comes in contact with the seafloor in intermediate and shallow water (depth <L/2). Friction causes the waves to slow down and sediment is put into motion as the orbital pathways of the water collapse into back-and-forth motion. This can be seen with each breaking wave as water, sand, and an unattended beach ball move up the beach face with the **swash** (up-rush of water) and then back down again with the outgoing water. However, if you watch the beach ball's movement during successive waves you will see that it not only moves up and down the beach face, but it also moves along the shore in the direction of the longshore drift (Fig. 5.23).

You may wish to review the basic principles of shallow-water waves that were discussed in section 5.2.

Incoming ocean swell rarely approaches the shore straight on. Because of this, the shoreward part of each individual wave comes in contact with the seafloor before the seaward part of the wave which is still in deep water (water depth >L/2). Waves bend (refract) whenever part of the wave is in intermediate or shallow water while part of the wave is still in deep water. Therefore, the waves will bend as they approach the shore. Wave energy in coastal waters sets up longshore currents and the resultant **longshore drift** (also called **longshore transport**) of sediment. Longshore drift occurs in the **surf zone**, the area between the shore and the breakers, and can be thought of as a "river of sand" moving down the coast.

The processes of wave refraction and longshore drift are important influences on coastal **dynamics**, particularly those that deal with the ever-changing conditions along the beach. Wave action causes coastal erosion, which together with the materials brought down to the sea by rivers, supply the sediment (mostly sand) necessary to establish and maintain beaches, dunes, and barrier islands. The free movement of sand down the coast, and among the beach, dunes, and sand bars, is a natural buffer against storms and the energy of the ocean because unconsolidated sand absorbs wave energy in the surf zone. The longshore currents, driven by incoming swell or storms, distribute the sediment along the shore. Sand eroded from one location along the beach is deposited farther down the beach front, maintaining a general equilibrium along the beach. However, storm waves can drag beach sand farther offshore, and if it is moved into water with a depth greater than about 30 feet (10 meters), then the sand will be lost to the beach system. Seasonal changes in wave energy along the coast result in net erosion of the beach during the winter and deposition of sand on the beach during the summer, although this regular cycle rarely produces major changes in the year-to-year beach profile. The mobility of sand, and its continuous supply down the coast, is necessary for a healthy shoreline to maintain itself despite rising sea level or severe storms. Coastal environments are adaptable and will retain their overall profile as they move landward with rising sea level.

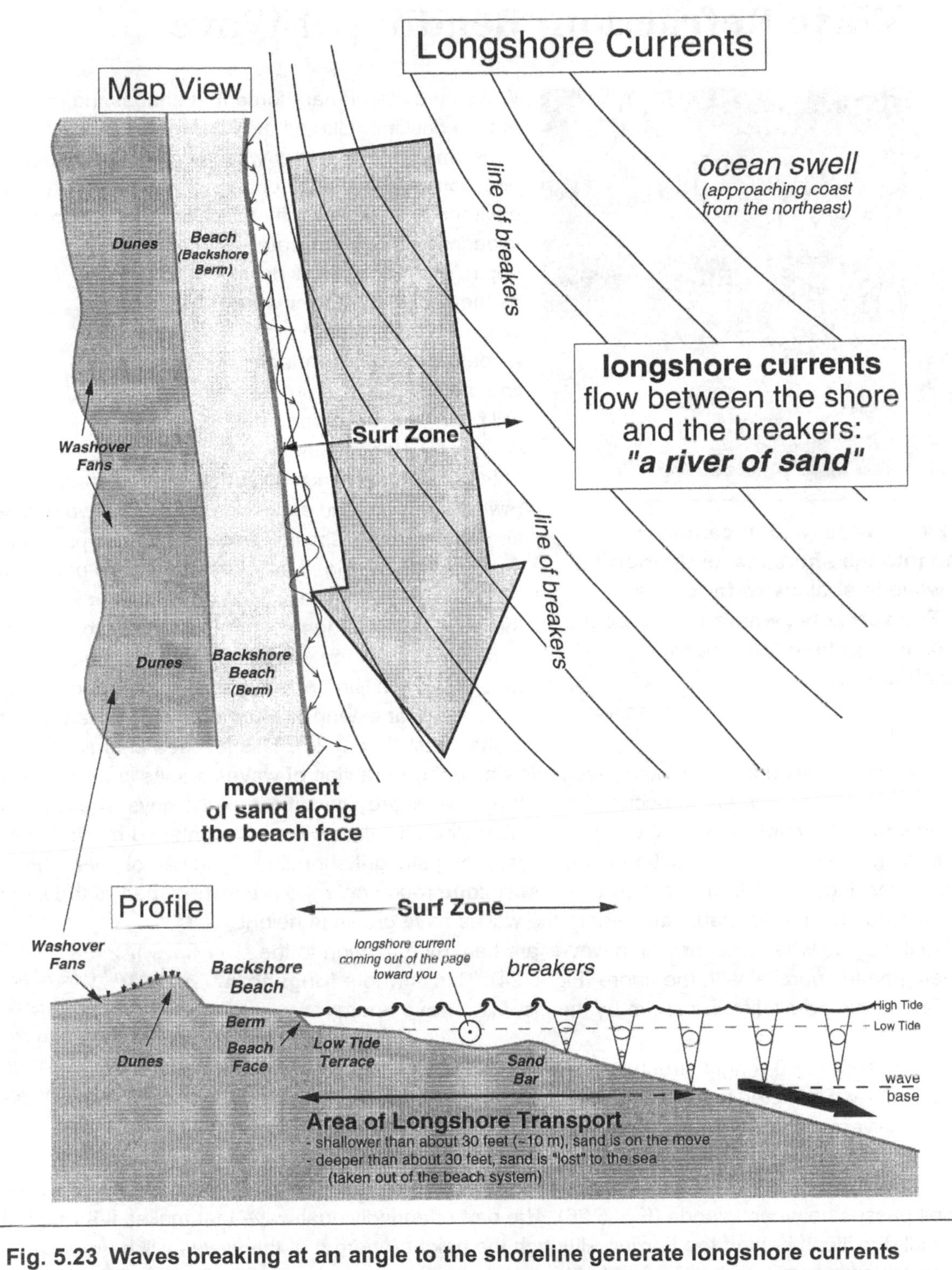

Fig. 5.23 Waves breaking at an angle to the shoreline generate longshore currents that cause net movement of sand in a preferential direction parallel to the coast.

Investigation 5.5 looks at the process of longshore drift and how it affects the coastline.

■5.10 Wave Refraction: Bending of Waves

Fig. 5.24 Wave refraction causes waves to bend into the shoreline as the portion of the wave in shallow water slows down. The surf zone, where waves begin to break, is visible in this photograph of the beach at Cancun.

Waves are the primary force that shapes the many features of the coastline. Like other types of waves (sound waves or seismic waves), water waves can alter their speed or direction in response to changes in the surrounding physical environment. The velocity (or celerity) of shallow-water waves is dependent only on water depth, and waves slow down as they enter shallower water. Since the water depth along a coastline is quite variable, a line of waves seen from above will often appear to bend as they encounter shallow water. This bending is called **refraction**. As the crests of waves (swell) approach the shore, the part of the wave closest to the shore encounters shallow water before the part of the wave further offshore (Fig. 5.24). The shoreward part of the wave begins to slow down and "pile up" while the seaward part of the wave is still in deep water (i.e., where the water depth is greater than half the wavelength, depth > L/2). This bending results in a focusing of wave energy on **headlands**, parts of the coast that extend out further into the sea than other parts of the coast (Fig. 5.25). This focused energy results in erosion of the headlands. Between the headlands are bays where the refraction of waves results in dispersed energy. In this way, it is easier for sediment to accumulate in the lower energy conditions of the bays where the deposition of sand can form a "**pocket beach**". Over geologic time, the coastline will be straightened by continued wave erosion on the headlands and deposition in the bays. Along straight shorelines, you can observe the distinctive zone where breaking waves form. This so-called **surf zone** represents the area where part of the incoming swell has slowed down appreciably and where the waves have grown in height. This is also the place where the incoming waves are bent by refraction to the point of being nearly parallel with the shore (Fig. 5.24). This is where **longshore currents** are set-up parallel to the shore by the incoming wave energy.

You may wish to review the basic principles of shallow-water waves that were discussed in section 5.2.

Waves will also **reflect** off a rigid structure like a seawall or the hull of a ship with little loss of energy. Reflected waves may then collide with on-coming waves to create larger waves and greater turbulence by way of constructive interference.

We will examine the consequences of wave refraction and reflection on beach communities in a subsequent section.

Diffraction happens when waves pass through narrow openings, such as through a gap in a breakwater or as ocean swell passes between islands (Fig. 5.26). The part of an individual wave that makes it through the opening radiates in all directions behind the barrier, although the height (energy) of the waves will be reduced. In this way, waves will appear to bend around or between natural irregularities along the coast.

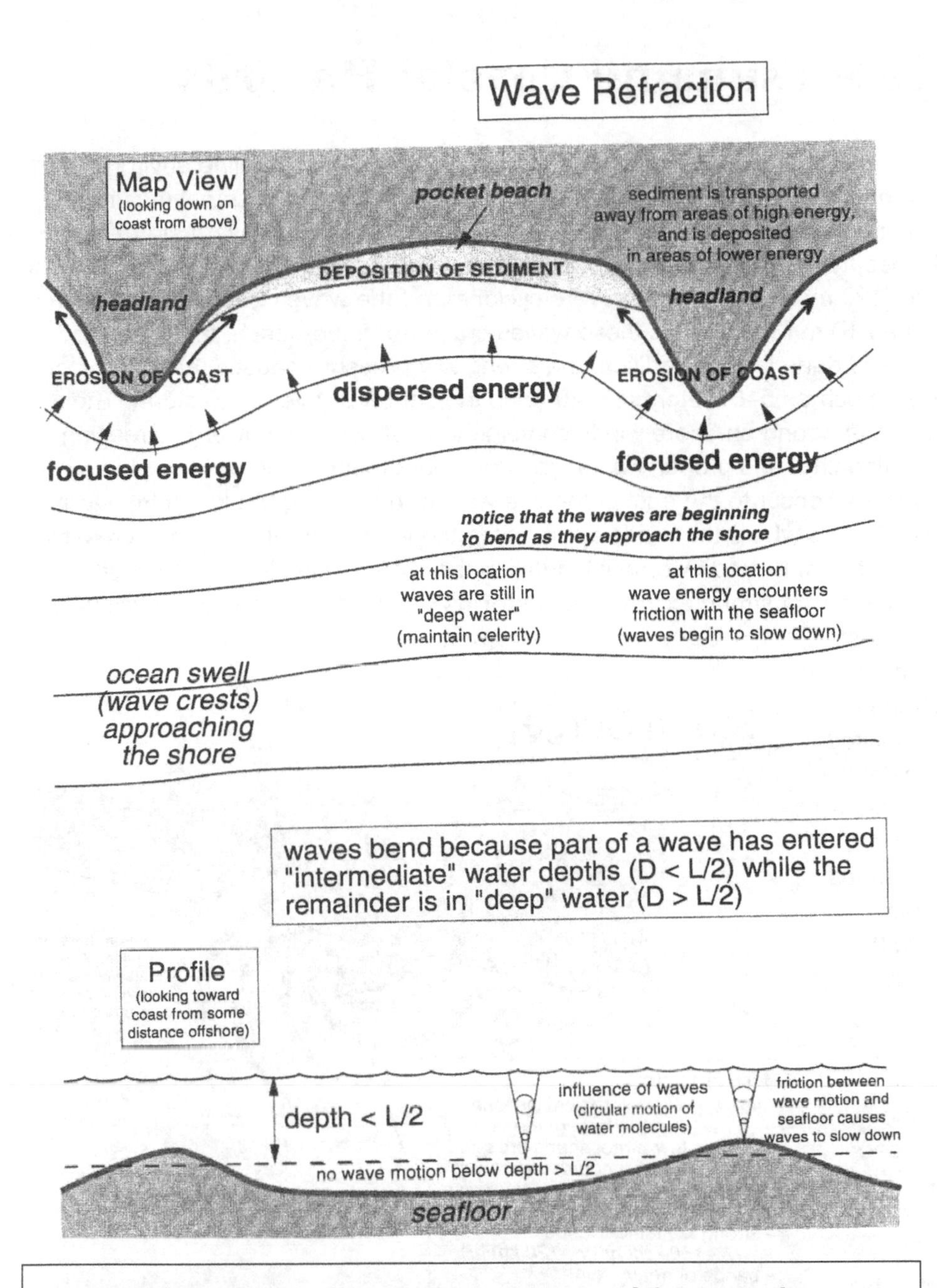

Fig. 5.25 Wave refraction results when parts of the wave slow down as they enter shallower water. This concentrates energy of the waves at different parts of the coastline.

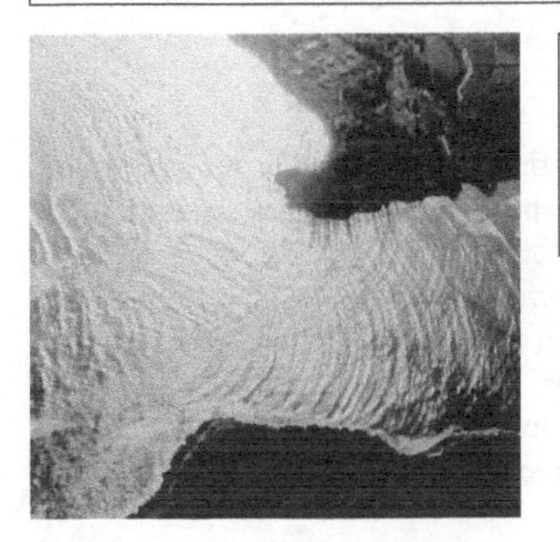

Fig. 5.26 Waves entering a narrow channel undergo diffraction.

Investigation 5.6 examines the processes of coastal erosion in greater detail.

■5.11 Storm Surge & Tsunami: Coastal Hazards

Wave action is responsible for almost all of the changes we see at the beach and other shoreline environments. Much of the time the changes are gradual so that the difference from one year to the next is sometimes hardly noticeable. However, the coastline can be altered dramatically in a matter of hours when a severe storm strikes the shore. Tropical cyclones (hurricanes, typhoons) are strong storms characterized by intense low atmospheric pressure. Winds can reach 200 km/h (120 mph) in the most severe cyclone and the waves generated by such winds can reach heights of greater than 10 m (33 feet). As these waves crash upon the beach, they can erode huge volumes of sand from the berm and dune line. In addition, the strong low pressure causes the surface of the ocean to be drawn upwards by as much as 5–6 meters (17–20 ft.) in the center or eye of the storm. The doming of the ocean surface coupled with strong on-shore winds combine to push water landward increasing the amount of beach erosion, coastal flooding, and property damage. This phenomenon is known as **storm surge** and the most serious consequences occur to the east of the eye wall, or on the "right" side of the storm as it is viewed from space (Fig. 5.27). This is where the winds are pushing the water onto the shore, increasing the energy of the advancing water. The threat is made worse if landfall of the storm coincides with high tide (Fig. 5.28). Storm surge is also associated with strong **extratropical storms** that form outside the tropics, like the "nor'easters" that occur along the East Coast during the winter. During storm surge, water and waves can breach the barrier dunes causing sand to be deposited in **washover fans** on the landward side of the dunes. This is an important process in shoreline retreat that pushes the beach landward as it adjusts to sea-level changes and all the other coastal environments retain their original position relative to the beach as they all move gradually farther inland.

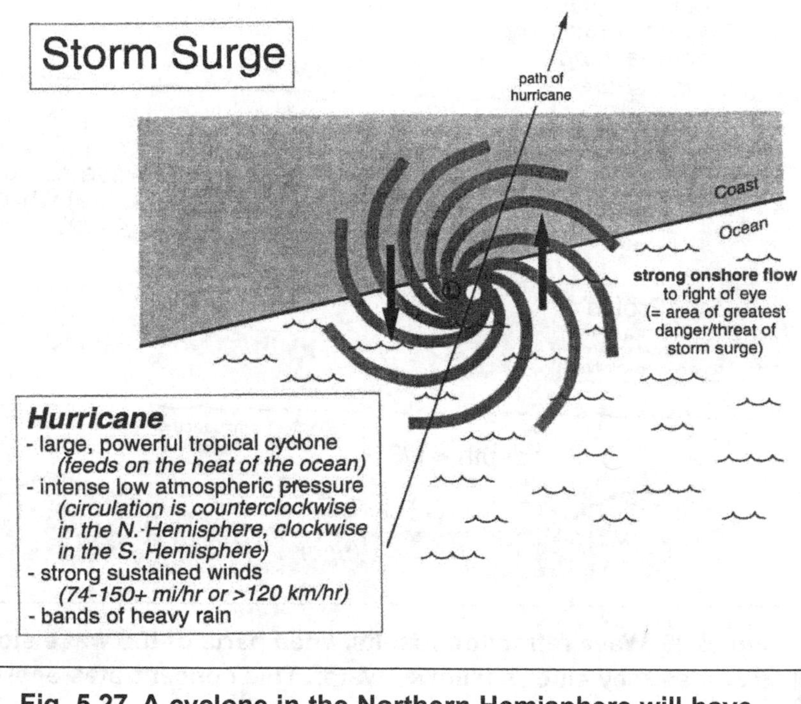

Fig. 5.27 A cyclone in the Northern Hemisphere will have its greatest destructive power on the side of the storm where the winds blow onshore.

Tsunami (a Japanese word meaning "harbor wave") represent another serious threat to some coastal communities (see section 2.10). They have sometimes erroneously been called "tidal waves", but they have nothing to do with tides. These large waves are most often generated by major earthquakes associated with the subduction of oceanic crust (see section 2.13). Therefore, communities around the rim of the Pacific, or islands in the Pacific, are particularly at risk.

Tsunami are affected by the same physical processes that influence the movement and behavior of wind waves (see sections 5.1 and 5.2). When they are initially created by the undersea earthquake, they have a very long wavelength (L > 200 km or 124 mi). Often the height of these at the outset is low, perhaps only a meter or two. However because of their long wavelength they can move very fast (~ 700 km/hr or ~400 mi/hr) and behave as intermediate and shallow-water-waves almost immediately. They slow down as they move away from the epicenter, but, as in the case of all shallow-water waves, their height increases. As they encounter the shallower waters of the continental margins, the waves slow down even more and grow to very large size. These waves "feel the bottom" far out to sea and can churn up the seafloor for a great distance away from shore, carrying incredible amounts of sand and other debris shoreward. The net result is that the force of the moving water is amplified by the scouring action of the entrained debris. The coastal devastation that results from the impact of a tsunami is extreme (Fig. 5.29), and it can all occur within a matter of minutes.

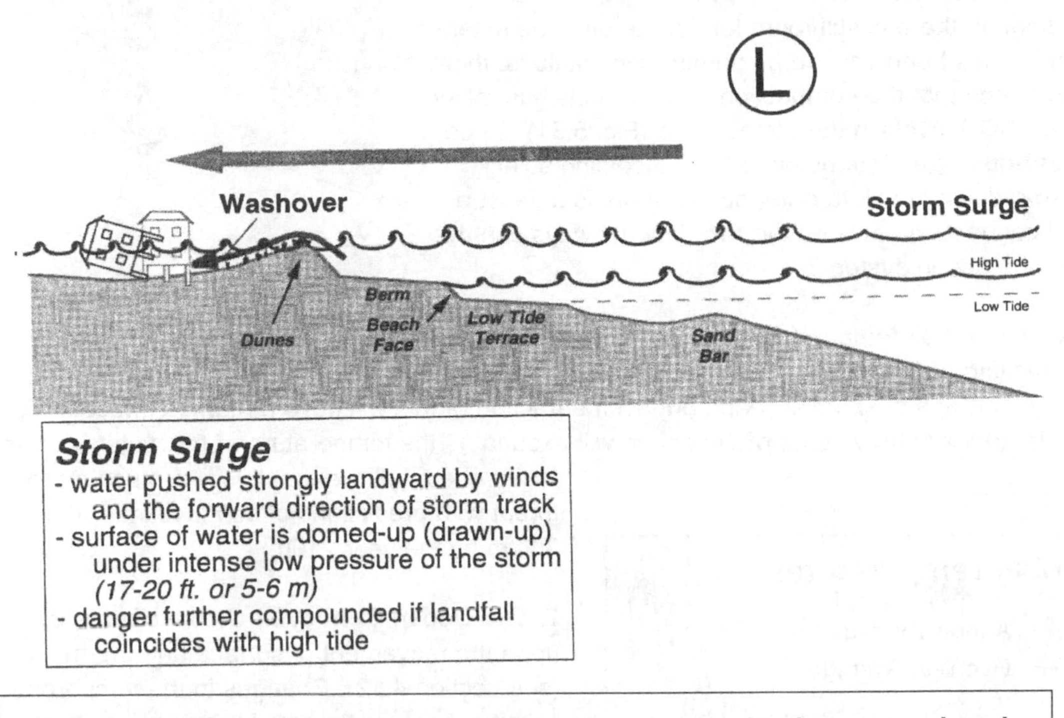

Fig. 5.28 The intensity of a storm surge can reach over the dunes on a beach, causing widespread erosion and property destruction.

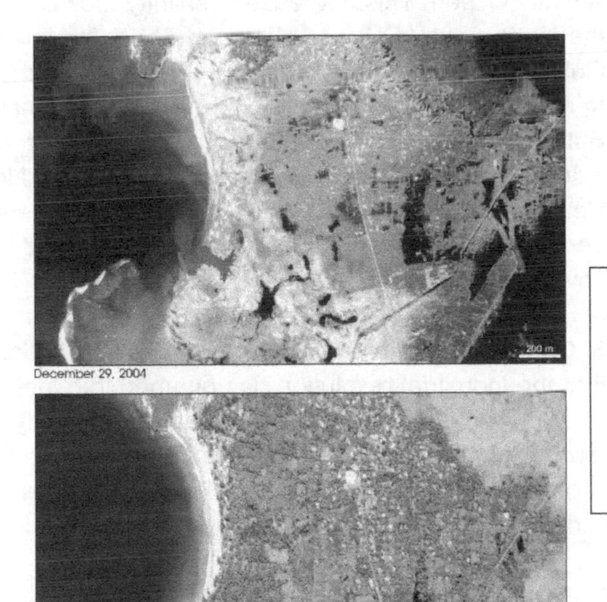

Fig. 5.29 The coastline of Banda Aceh, Sumatra, Indonesia, before (bottom) and after (top) the tsunami of December 26, 2004. Vegetation (dark area in bottom photo) has been completely denuded, and the only building left standing is a mosque (white square).

■5.12 Global Warming and the Ocean System

Most scientists agree that the average temperature at the surface of the Earth has increased measurably over the past century (Fig. 5.30). Although there is still room for debate over the extent that this warming has been caused by human contributions, there is also firm evidence that the combustion of fossil fuels has raised carbon dioxide (CO_2) levels in the atmosphere (Fig. 5.31). Since CO_2 is a **greenhouse gas** that helps to keep incoming solar energy from re-radiating back to outer space, there is at least a circumstantial connection between the two. In what ways can this process affect the ocean system?

1. Sea Level Rise. As air temperature warms, the polar ice caps will melt. The amount of water that results from the complete melting of the Greenland Ice Sheet could raise sea level by as much as 7 meters. This is likely to occur gradually, perhaps over 1000 years, but even a fraction of this will have a marked effect on our coastal communities. In addition the volume of the ocean will expand as the temperature of the water increases. Many researchers believe that this is a much more serious threat with predictions of sea level rise of as much as 30 cm by the year 2100.

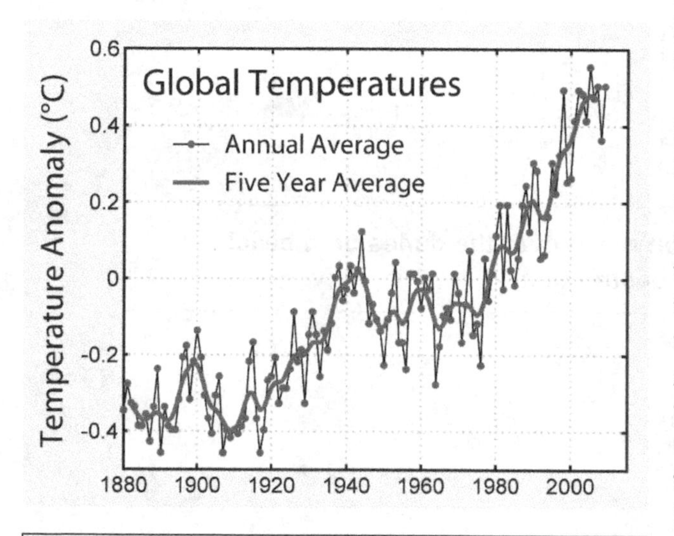

Fig. 5.30 Global temperature measurements from the past century indicate a rapid rise in temperature that is higher than any time in the previous 1000 years as estimated from environmental records such as tree rings and sediments.

2. The Ocean Conveyor. Global climate is dependent upon the movement of surface and thermohaline currents (see section 4.12). Changes in the temperature or salinity of sea water could have major effects upon the world climate system. In one scenario, the melting of the Greenland ice sheet will cause a layer of cold fresh water to spread over the ocean surface in the polar North Atlantic Ocean. This decrease in salinity may cut off the sinking of NADW and slow down or divert the warm Gulf Stream water that flows along the ocean surface to replace it. Such a change could make the climate of Europe and eastern North America much colder; in an extreme case, a new Ice Age could begin in the Northern Hemisphere. Recent data show that there has been a decrease in the salinity of the North Atlantic over the past several years (Fig. 5.32).

3. Ocean Chemistry. About half of the carbon dioxide that the industrial revolution has pumped into the atmosphere has "disappeared." That's not exactly the right term; we know where it has gone: it has dissolved in the ocean. At first glance, this might be the way to solve the greenhouse gas problem, but dissolving carbon dioxide in sea water is not without consequences. When carbon dioxide dissolves in water it forms carbonic acid:

$$CO_2 + H_2O \Rightarrow H_2CO_3 \Rightarrow H^+ + HCO_3^-$$

in atmosphere *carbonic acid (a weak acid)*

Too much of this in sea water could lower the pH of the ocean. In fact, recent measurements in the Pacific Ocean indicate that the pH of the surface has decreased by 0.025 units since the early 1990's. While this may not seem like much, remember that pH is an exponential scale. That is, a pH decrease of 1 unit is a tenfold increase in acidity level. Many marine organisms build their shells from calcium carbonate ($CaCO_3$), and surface ocean water today allows this mineral to be stable. However, if the pH drops too much, then these shells will dissolve more quickly and threaten the viability of the entire marine ecosystem as we know it.

Trying to minimize the effects of increasing atmospheric carbon dioxide is an area that requires continual research and public action.

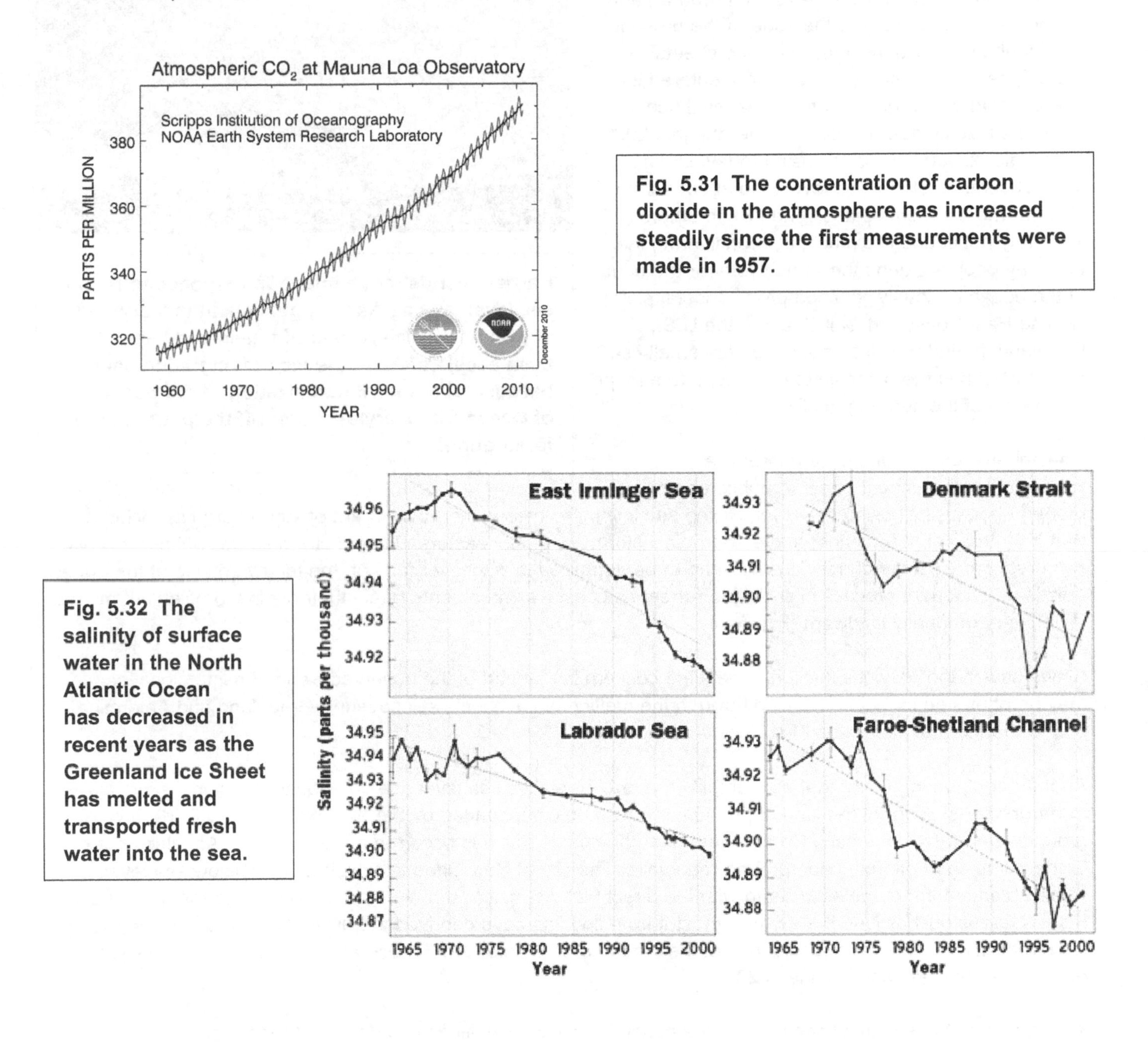

Fig. 5.31 The concentration of carbon dioxide in the atmosphere has increased steadily since the first measurements were made in 1957.

Fig. 5.32 The salinity of surface water in the North Atlantic Ocean has decreased in recent years as the Greenland Ice Sheet has melted and transported fresh water into the sea.

Investigation 5.7 examines the greenhouse effect and some consequences for the ocean environment.

■5.13 Sea Level Rise & Shoreline Retreat: A Real Threat

Barrier islands move inland in response to rising sea level, as has Assateague Island in Maryland, shown here. The retreat of this island has been accelerated by the lack of migrating sand because of the hard stabilization of the beach of Ocean City Maryland, just off the photo in the foreground.

Global sea level has not remained constant through time. The most recent episode of continental-scale glaciation reached its maximum extent of ice-sheet growth 18,000 years ago. As a consequence, global sea level was lowered by 120–130 m (~400 ft.) and the shoreline was out near the edge of the present continental shelf. As these massive ice sheets melted, sea level rose as these waters entered the ocean basin. Although the rate of sea level rise since the last ice age has slowed over the last 2000 years, global sea level is still rising today. During the last century, global sea level rose about 15 cm (0.5 ft.), more in some places and less in others. This may not sound like much, but considering that so many people around the world live near the edge of the ocean on low-lying, flood-prone coastal plains like the East Coast and Gulf Coast of the U.S., Bangladesh, and the Netherlands, a very small rise of sea level has the potential to translate into a major inundation of the sea (Fig. 5.33).

Coastal erosion and shoreline retreat are increasingly becoming a threat to public and private property because of rising sea level. Rising sea level also means a greater threat of storm surge associated with both tropical (hurricanes) and extratropical storms (e.g., nor'easters). During storm surge, water and waves can breach the barrier dunes causing sand to be deposited in washover fans on the landward side of the dunes. This is an important process in shoreline retreat as coastal environments retain their original profiles but migrate ("roll") very gradually landward (Fig. 5.34).

As we saw in the previous section, a genuine concern is that part of the observed trend of rising global sea level may be attributed to global warming through the melting of ice sheets still covering Greenland and Antarctica, and to the thermal expansion of surface waters.

Another contributing factor that may amplify the rate of relative sea level rise on a local or regional scale is **subsidence** (sinking) of the land, a problem that can be compounded by the extraction of pore fluids such as groundwater or hydrocarbons (oil and gas) near the coast. This has occurred around the Los Angeles area due to the pumping of oil from underground reservoirs. The city of New Orleans, which is at or below sea level, is vulnerable to storm surge associated with the direct hit by a major hurricane, or flooding along the Mississippi River. Levees built around the city to protect it from flooding have deprived the area of sediment that is needed to counteract the impact of subsidence of the land and rising sea level. These are reasons why the city was so devastated by Hurricane Katrina in 2005.

A reduction in the supply of sediment to the coastal zone can significantly contribute to the problem of shoreline retreat. Dams on our rivers provide vital hydroelectric power, flood control, and drinking water supplies, as well as recreation, but dams also deprive the coast of much needed sediment which becomes trapped in the reservoirs. Without mud, coastal wetlands, and particularly the salt marshes that border estuaries and bays may not be able to keep pace with rising sea level and drown, thereby contributing to the loss of these highly productive and vital coastal ecosystems. Without an ample supply of sand to the longshore transport system, there will not be enough material to maintain the natural give-and-take between the beaches, dunes, and offshore bars that occur seasonally and protect the coast from flooding and erosion. Rising sea level and shoreline retreat are but two of a number of challenges that many coastal communities, businesses, and individual property owners will face during the twenty-first century.

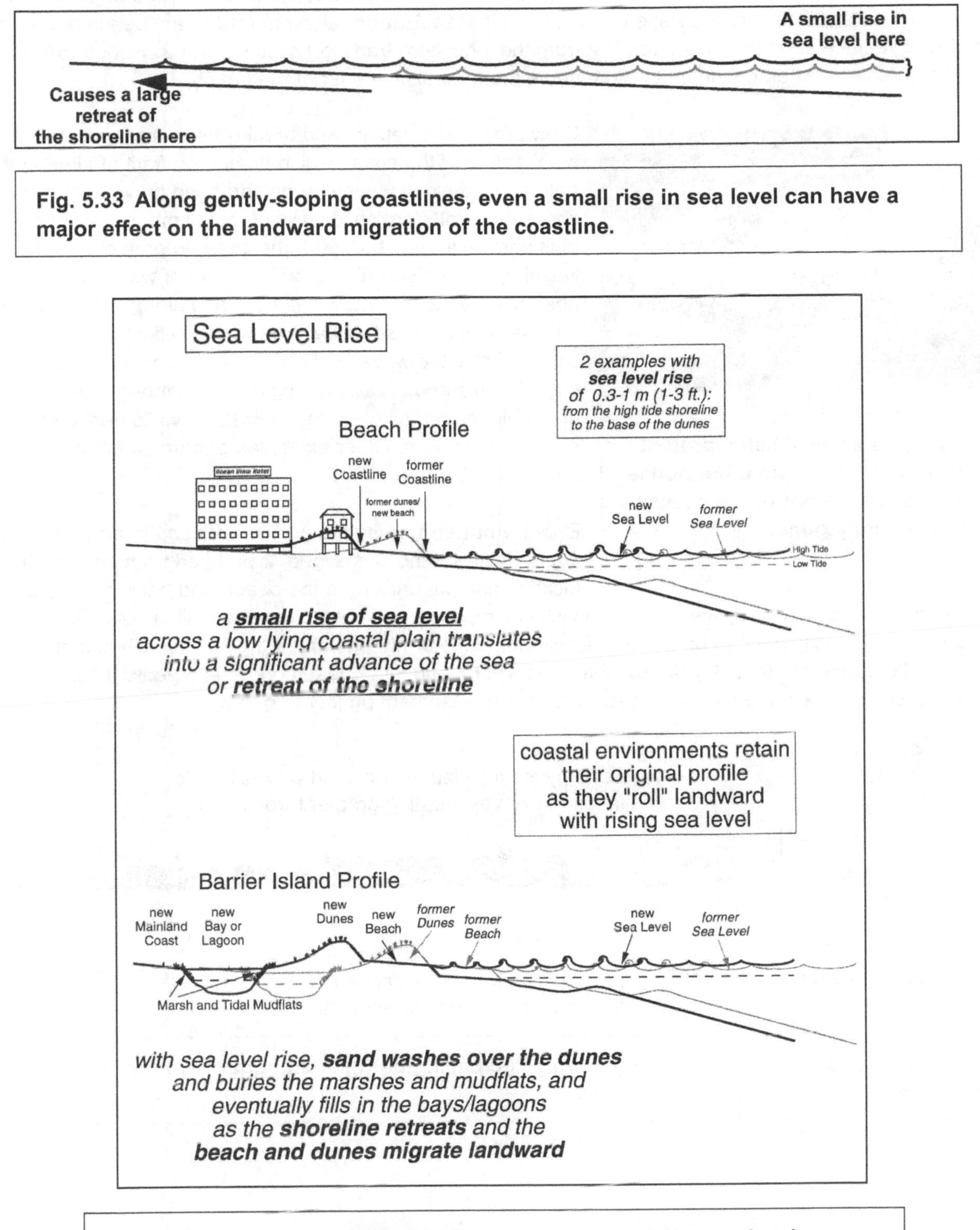

Fig. 5.33 Along gently-sloping coastlines, even a small rise in sea level can have a major effect on the landward migration of the coastline.

Fig. 5.34 The response of coastal environments to rising sea level.

■5.14 Options in the Face of Rising Sea Level

We can see from our discussions that rising sea level, subsidence of the land, storm surge, and coastal erosion are growing threats to many coastal communities around the world. There are a number of different options available to protect coastal homes, businesses, and beaches. There are three general categories: 1) **hard stabilization**, or the "armoring" of the coast with rocks and manmade structures, is designed to protect the coast from erosion, trap sand, or redirect wave energy, 2) **soft stabilization**, also referred to as "beach nourishment", is intended to replace sand that has been lost from the longshore transport system, and 3) **relocation** of a structure or structures is an option that will preserve the natural character of the beach.

Fig. 5.35 This seawall helps protect the property from erosion, but notice that the beach in front of the seawall is almost entirely gone.

Seawalls, groins, jetties, and breakwaters are examples of hard stabilization of the coast, which have the effect of altering the natural dynamic of wave energy and sand movement along the shore. **Seawalls** are solid walls of rock, timbers, or concrete built parallel to the shore with the intent to protect buildings from washing into the sea (Fig. 5.35). Instead of wave energy being absorbed by the free movement of sand along the shore, the rigid seawall causes the wave energy to reflect back towards the ocean. Reflected waves collide with incoming waves creating larger waves and greater turbulence. Eventually, the walls will be undermined and fall over (Fig. 5.36). Seawalls destroy beaches over the long-term. Other examples of hard stabilization are summarized in (Fig. 5.37).

Beach nourishment is the addition of sand to an eroding beach. Typically, this sand is dredged or pumped from an offshore location and put back onto the beach and back into the active longshore transport system. However, this process is temporary and costly. Several millions of dollars could be invested by a community, only to be lost in a single hurricane or nor'easter. Of the U.S. beaches that have been replenished, 26% last less than 1 year, 62% last 1–5 years, and ~12% last more than 5 years. Miami Beach is one of the best examples of a highly successful beach nourishment project (Fig. 5.38).

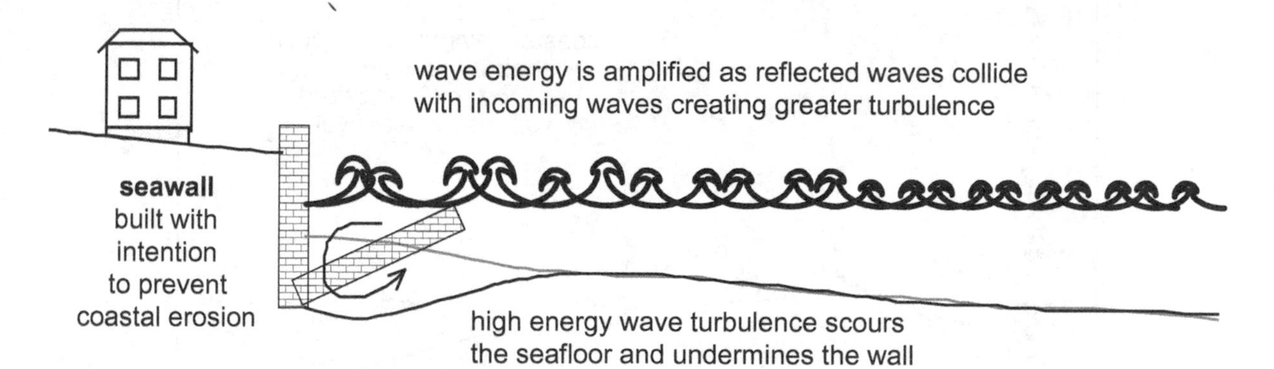

Fig. 5.36 Seawalls can collapse during storms, increasing both the amount of erosion and resulting property damage.

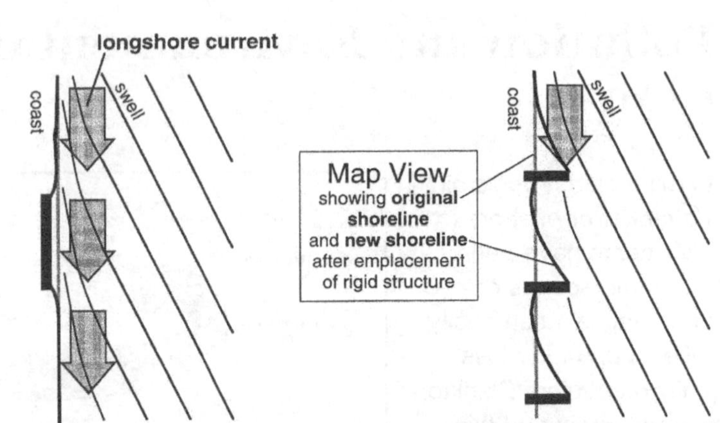

seawalls - solid walls built parallel to shore
purpose: protect manmade structures and buildings from washing into the sea with rising sea level
result: incoming wave energy reflects off wall; reflected waves crash with incoming waves causing bigger waves and greater turbulence; eventually, walls will be undermined and fall over; seawalls destroy beaches over the long-term

groins - short structures built perpendicular to the shore, part-way across the surf zone
purpose: trap sand from longshore transport system and widen an eroding beach
result: sand will accumulate on the up-drift side and cause erosion on the down-drift side; may lead to construction of more and more groins down coast ("groin field")

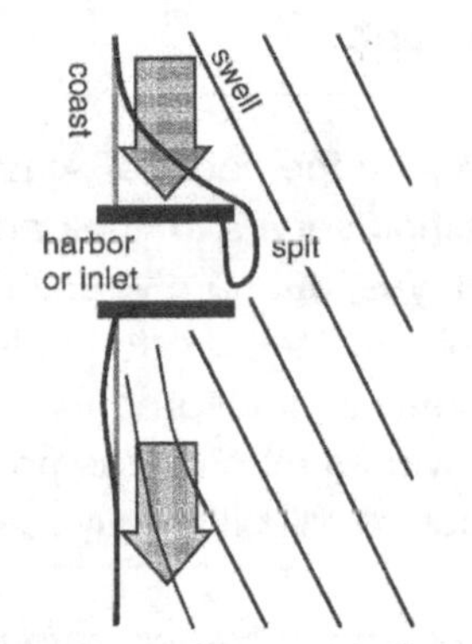

jetties - long structures built perpendicular to the shore.
purpose: protect harbor or channel inlet from incoming swell.
result: sand accumulates on the up-drift side and a sand spit will develop at end of jetty; must be dredged to prevent inlet from being filled with sand.

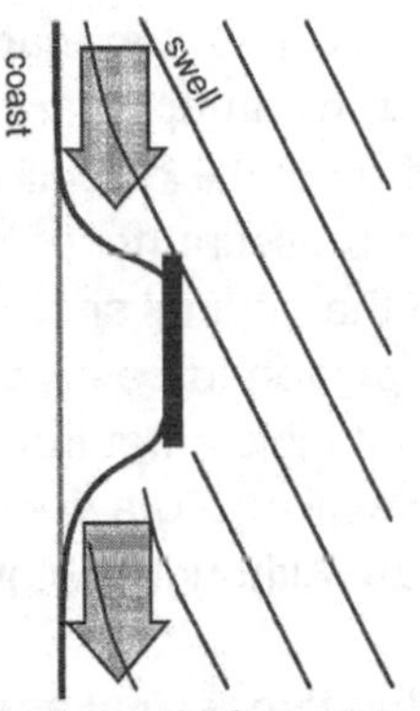

breakwaters - rigid structures built a short distance from, and parallel to, the shore.
purpose: provide quiet water for boat anchorage.
result: disrupts incoming swell which provides the energy to move sand via longshore drift; sand accumulates in quieter water behind the breakwater; must be dredged.

Fig. 5.37 Various kinds of hard stabilization of the coast are only temporary solutions to the problem of beach erosion.

Fig. 5.38 Miami Beach before (left) and after (right) successful beach nourishment.

Investigation 5.8 looks at other aspects of the coean environment related to issues of climate change.

■5.15 Marine Pollution and Environmental Degradation

Marine pollution often brings to mind catastrophic oil spills from accidents involving a tanker or offshore platform. Indeed, some of the accidents have been spectacularly large (Table 5.2) and the scenes of oil-soaked shore birds and marine animals can easily spark outrage. Moreover, the effects upon the less visible marine ecology are equally damaging. Plankton in the oil-spill areas are damaged severely and this will disrupt the local food chain. Many organisms that are filter feeders or scavengers, such as mussels and crabs, will ingest the oil, which can poison the organisms or, at the very, least, render them unfit for human consumption. Matters are often made worse during the well-meaning clean-up effort. For example, the shoreline clean-up of the oil spill from the Exxon *Valdez* off the coast of Alaska in March, 1989 was accomplished using high pressure hoses of hot water. This method serves to cook and blast away any living organism that survived the original shock of the spill. Cleaned, yes, but hardly restored! Detergents used to disperse the oil have also proven to be as damaging as the petroleum itself. Fortunately, we have learned our lessons over the years that oil is a natural compound and is ultimately biodegradable. The best techniques to use involve containing the spill, using a suction apparatus to recover as much oil as possible, and wiping up some of the remaining residue. Although it may take many years, nature will ultimately restore the environment.

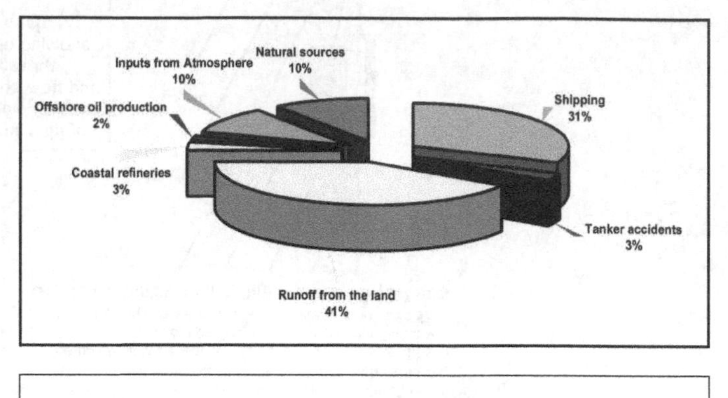

Fig. 5.39 Sources of oil entering the marine environment.

Unfortunately, spills are not the largest leakage of oil into the sea. Much of it comes from us! In our daily driving of cars, we drip oil and gas onto roadways and driveways. This flows to rivers and streams, and ultimately reaches the coastline. Boats also contribute to this chronic flow. The amount of this oil dwarfs that of tanker accidents (Fig. 5.39). Fortunately, the concentration is low and the petroleum compounds will often degrade without causing a serious problem.

Table 5.2 The 10 Worst Major Marine Oil Spills.

Location	Incident	Date	Size (Gallons)
Persian Gulf	Gulf War Oil Fields Sabotage	March 19-21, 1991	400+ million
Gulf of Mexico	Deepwater Horizon Well Blowout	April 20 – July 15, 2010	205 million
Gulf of Mexico	Ixtoc Well Blowout	March 6, 1979	140 million
Tobago and Barbados	Tanker Collision (*Atlantic Empress, Aegean Captain*)	July 19 – August 2, 1979	87 million
North Sea	Ekofisk Well Blowout	April 22-25, 1977	81 million
Persian Gulf	Norwuz Well Blowout	April 2, 1983	80 million
South Africa	Tanker Accident (*Castillo de Bellver*)	June 8, 1978	78.5 million
Brittany Coast, France	Tanker Accident (*Amoco Cadiz*)	March 16, 1978	68.7 million
Newfoundland	Tanker Accident (*Odyssey*)	November 10, 1979	43 million
Genoa, Italy	Tanker Accident (*Haven*)	April 11, 1991	42 million
Angola	Tanker Accident (*ABT Summer*)	May 28, 1991	40? million

The much-publicized Exxon Valdez spill off Alaska on March 24, 1989 discharged 10 million gallons.

The slow leak of oil points to a larger problem. As the human population of the Earth grows, and especially since more people are living closer to the ocean, increasing pressure is put upon the coastal environment in many ways. Runoff from urban areas and agricultural regions contains heavy metals, pesticides, sewage, and fertilizer that enter into some of the most biologically productive regions of the ocean. Some of these contaminants are absorbed by sediment particles and settle to the sea floor. This is not necessarily a good thing, since scavengers and deposit feeders can ingest these and incorporate them into their own flesh. Even if these levels cause no harm to the organism, these creatures are often near the bottom of the food chain, and the toxins can be concentrated as they are consumed and passed to higher trophic levels. This is the process of biomagnification (Fig. 5.40). This is why mercury has reached high levels in many kinds of tuna and swordfish.

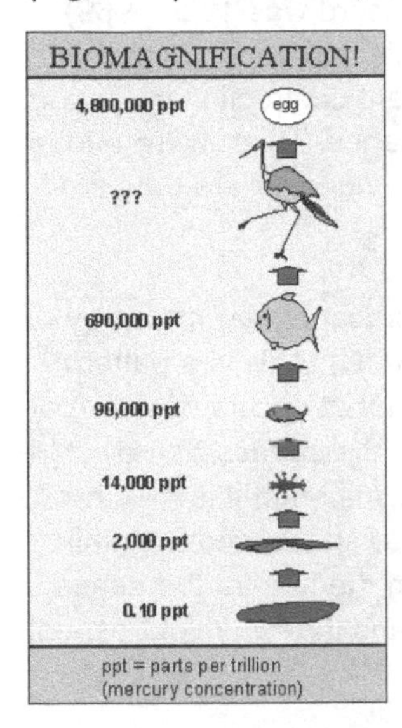

Fig. 5.40 Chemicals are concentrated in the flesh of organisms at higher trophic levels in the food chain.

Excessive nutrients from agricultural and urban runoff also cause problems. "Blooms" of microorganisms can occur in areas where nutrients are abundant. Many of these, such as the dinoflagellates responsible for causing "red tides," are undesirable. Since these microorganisms are often heterotrophic (that is, they consume food and oxygen rather than photosynthesize) these blooms can deplete the dissolved oxygen in the water to the extent that other organisms have difficulty surviving. In recent years there has been a noticeable expansion of the "dead zone" in the shoreline region of the Gulf of Mexico (Fig. 5.41), which is attributed to the nutrient supply from the Mississippi River.

However, there are some notable success stories in cleaning up damaged coastal environments. In 1985 Boston Harbor was an environmental disaster area as a result of decades of raw or poorly-treated sewage entering the harbor from antiquated treatment plants. Through a combination of court orders, political courage, and environmental advocacy, a new sewage treatment plant was completed on Deer Island in the harbor in 2000. The result is that the harbor, if not pristine, ranks as one of the cleanest urban coastal regions in the nation (Fig. 5.42). Numerous native fish species, including smelts, winter flounder, bluefish, herring, and striped bass have returned to the harbor, and the outer islands are home to harbor seals and porpoises. It has been a remarkable transformation and a testimony to what can be accomplished with the right mix of leadership and public cooperation.

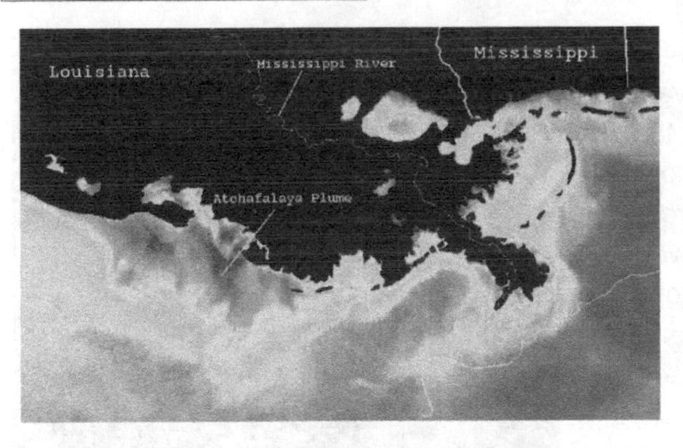

Fig. 5.41 Bloom of microorganisms (light shading) caused by excessive nutrients coming from a tributary of the Mississippi River.

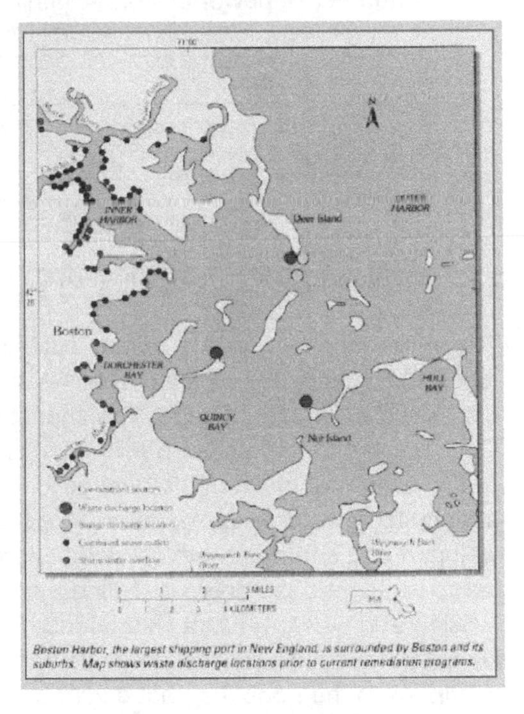

Fig. 5.42 Sewage discharge into Boston Harbor (small dots) was eliminated when the Deer Island treatment plant was established, which restored the health of the harbor.

Investigation 5.9 looks at some of the issues surrounding marine pollution.

■ *Oceanography in Action*

The Hurricanes of 2004 and 2005

Hurricane Katrina, which struck New Orleans in the summer of 2005, will be remembered for many years as one of the most devastating storms to strike the eastern United States. However, Katrina was only one of several large storms to form during the 2005 Atlantic hurricane season, which has also gone into the record books as the season with the most storms since records were being kept. There were 28 named storms (exceeding the previous record of 21 set in 1933) of which 12 achieved hurricane status (the previous record was 12 in 1969). Four major hurricanes (Dennis, Katrina, Rita, and Wilma) reached the U.S. coastline. This hurricane season followed on the heels of 2004, which also had several major storms that caused significant destruction in Florida. Nine tropical storms affected the United States during this year, of which six were hurricanes. There were a total of 15 named storms and nine of these reached hurricane status. Were these two years a fluke, or are they the start of a pattern that will be with us for some time?

You may wish to review how hurricanes form as we examined it in section 4.7.

Many researchers believe that the frequency and intensity of hurricanes are driven by a phenomenon called the **Atlantic Multidecadal Oscillation (AMO)**. This is a pattern of alternating warm and cool phases of the North Atlantic Ocean that occurs over approximately 20- to 40-year cycles. During the warm episodes, the surface of the ocean can be as much as 1°F warmer than during cool phases. Although this may not sound like much, it is sufficient to affect the ability of the ocean to spawn and maintain tropical storms, since storms start and intensify by drawing upon the heat of the ocean surface. The evidence indicates that we are just entering a new warm phase, which means that we might expect a large number of powerful storms within the next decade.

Year	*2001*	*2002*	*2003*	*2004*	*2005*	*2006*	*2007*
Named Storms	15	12	15	15	28	9	17
Hurricanes	9	4	7	9	12	5	5
Total affecting U.S.	3	9	6	9	9	3	4
Hurricanes affecting U.S.	1	4	3	5	4	0	1

The implications for coastal communities are perilous. During 2004, four major hurricanes crossed over the state of Florida causing over $35 billion dollars in damage. The impact of Hurricane Katrina on the Gulf Coast in 2005 has been estimated to be as much as $60 billion. At the coastline, much of the destruction came from the storm surge as already high water levels generated by the storm's low pressure were whipped into enormous waves as the storm made landfall. The storm surge re-shaped the entire coastline by accelerating the processes of erosion and washover that characterize the natural beach processes. Despite these experiences, the development of beachfront areas continues in the hope that that engineering solutions can somehow mitigate the effects of the natural movement of water and sand in coastal areas. In addition, the hurricane seasons of 2006 and 2007 were relatively quiet, leading some to think that the

Images of Gulfport. Mississippi before (top) and after Hurricane Katrina in 2005. Arrows point to identical structures in both photos.

previous high hurricane frequencies were a short-lived anomaly. But were they? Considering the scale of the destruction that the hurricanes of 2004 and 2005 inflicted upon coastal communities, this hope may well be misplaced. The truth remains that should hurricane frequency and intensity increase, the only sure way to avoid massive property damage is to reduce the development along the coast.

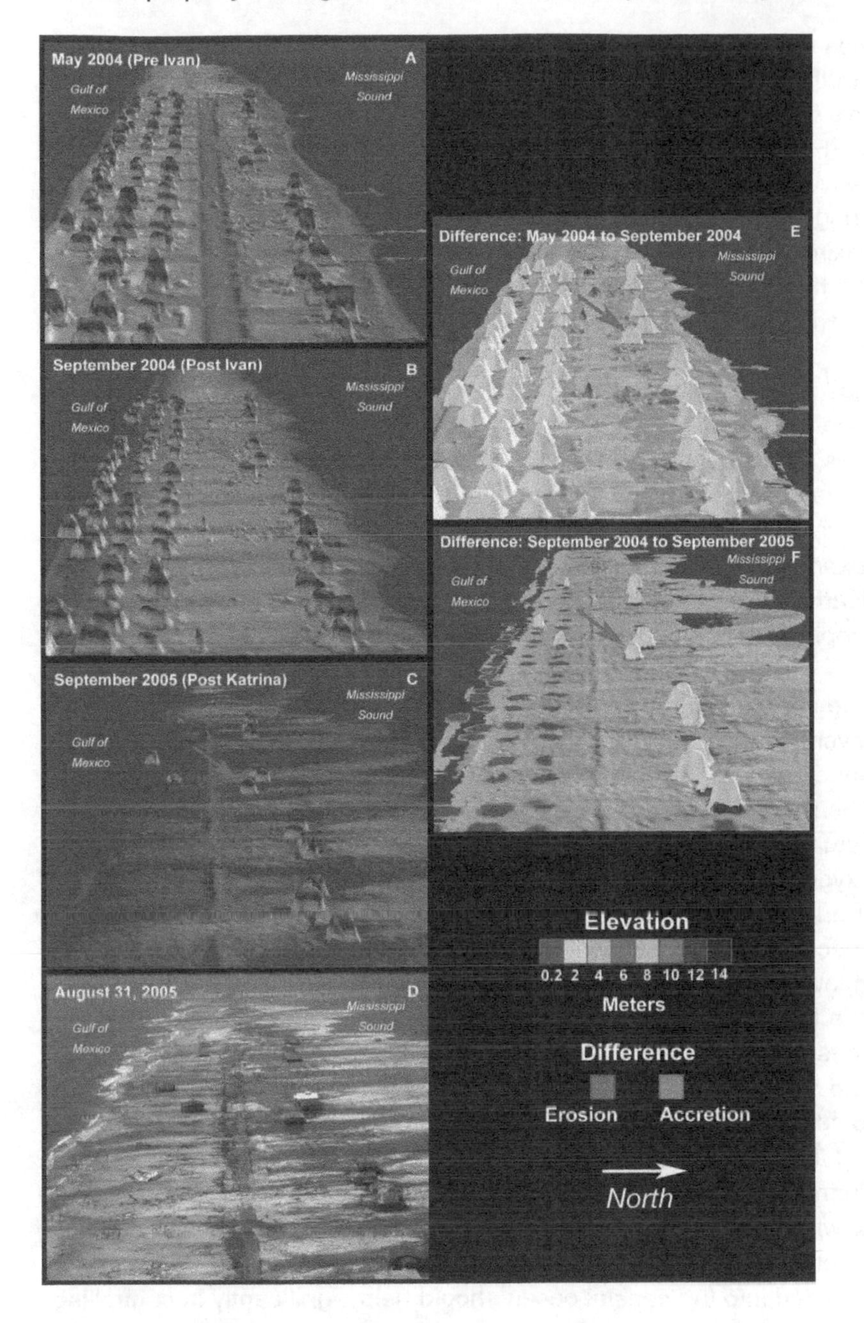

Changes in the barrier beach of Dauphin Island, Alabama resulting from the hurricanes of 2004 and 2005. A and B show the actual topography before and after Hurricane Ivan. E shows the difference between the two. Note that sand was removed from the beach front (pink area in E) and deposited as washover (the green area). Hurricane Katrina did even more damage in 2005. The digital image in C is based upon the oblique aerial photograph in D. Note the much greater erosion and the deposition of sand much farther into Mississippi Sound. This shows how beaches move landward during these storm episodes. Dark spots in illustration F show houses that were totally destroyed. Arrow points to the same house in each panel.

Further Reading

"In Hot Water" National Geographic Magazine, August, 2005, p.72–85. http://www7.nationalgeographic.com/ngm/0508/feature4/index.html

"Atlantic Climate Pacemaker for Millennia Past, Decades Hence?" Science, v. 309 (2005), p. 41–43 http://www.sciencemag.org/cgi/content/full/309/5731/41

"NOAA Reviews Record-Setting 2005 Atlantic Hurricane Season" NOAA News Online (2005) http://www.noaanews.noaa.gov/stories2005/s2540.htm

■ *Oceanography in Action*

Red Tides

During the spring of 2005, fishing communities in New England region were in a panic. The authorities had prohibited the harvesting of any shellfish from the entire coastline because of an unusually severe red tide. Many samples of clams, oysters, and mussels from the region had been found to contain toxins that could cause serious neurological problems if eaten. Fishermen who harvest shellfish were out of work, restaurants and seafood stores scrambled to find alternative supplies, and the summer tourist season was threatened. At the same time, a similar problem was occurring of the west coast of Florida. An extensive red tide there was depleting the oxygen in the water, and the toxins were killing tons of fish as well as sea turtles, manatees, and dolphins. This particular red tide also affected humans by emitting noxious vapors in the sea spray that was very irritating to the lungs and hazardous to those with respiratory problems.

What causes the phenomenon of the red tide? At times, the growth of microscopic algae (protists), typically dinoflagellates, is so rapid, and the abundance of cells in the water so great, that the water turns a reddish color, but the color is not diagnostic. Some "red tides" are green or brown, or show no coloration at all, depending upon which organism is undergoing the bloom. Some species of dinoflagellates produce toxins that become ingested by filter-feeding shellfish, such as clams or mussels. This is what happened in the New England outbreak, which was largely a bloom of the dinoflagellate *Alexandrium* sp. The toxins then become concentrated in the tissues of the shellfish in a process called **biomagnification**. When humans eat these infected shellfish, they can become severely ill. Unlike bacterial contamination, cooking does not destroy the shellfish toxins. Toxins can also kill fish.

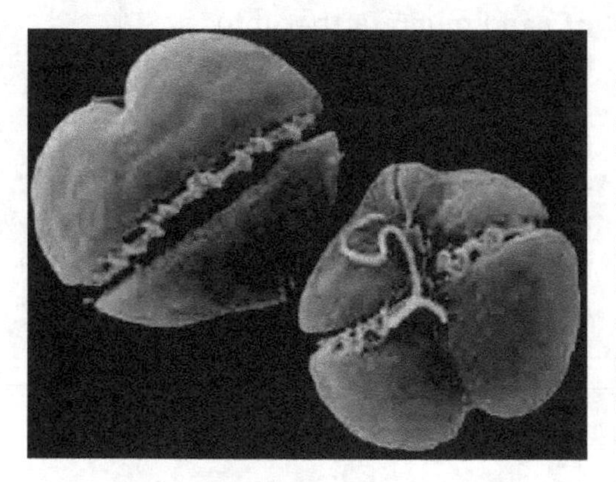

Photomicrograph of Karenia brevis, the organism that commonly causes the red tide outbreaks along Florida's Gulf Coast.

The red tides in the Gulf of Mexico were caused by *Karenia brevis* a very common dinoflagellate in subtropical waters. Fish are also affected by the density of algal cells, which can lead to suffocation. The short-lived abundance of organic matter then settles in the estuary or bay where it decomposes and consumes the dissolved oxygen further affecting fish and benthic animals. *Pfiesteria piscicida* is another particularly nasty heterotrophic fish killing dinoflagellate species in the coastal waters of the U.S. Most of the time it occurs in low abundances or lies dormant in resting cysts at the bottom of a bay or estuary waiting for optimum conditions to emerge. Red tides occur naturally due to the right combination of nutrient-levels and stratification. However, nutrient loading in coastal waters due to sewage, fertilizers, or other agricultural runoff can also stimulate red tides. Red tides appear to be increasing in number and intensity during the past several decades. It is not clear if this is a real increase or whether we are just paying more attention to conditions in the water as our coastal population grows, but reducing the level of nutrients expelled into the coastal ocean should help significantly in controlling the problem.

Further Reading

"Red Tide Shuts Shellfish Areas in New England, New York Times, June 4, 2005.

"Persisitent Red Tide Takes Toll on Florida Sea Life and Tourism", New York Times, October 8, 2005.

"Red Tides", Scientific American, v. 271, No. 2,(1994), pp. 62–69.

Name ______________________________

First three letters of last name

Investigation 5.3 **Beaches**

1). In the diagram below, indicate some possible locations where the sand on the beaches might come from. Does the sand stay in one place? Indicate by arrows how the sand might move and explain why.

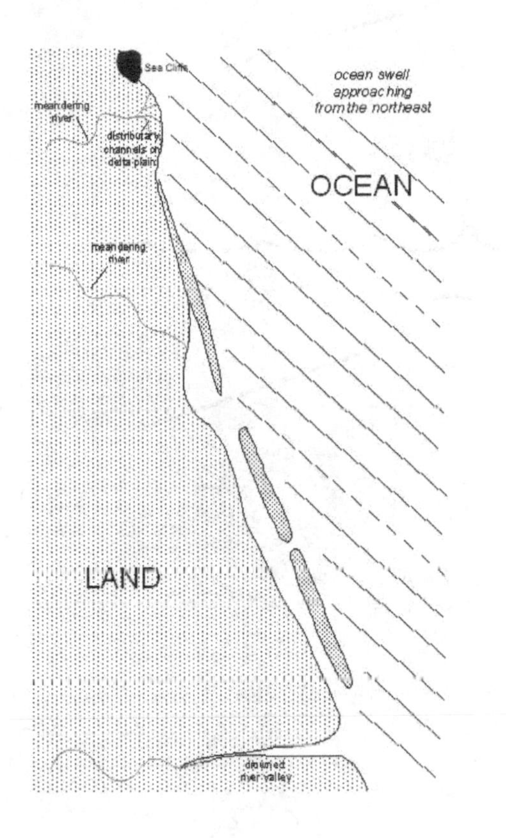

2). What is a barrier beach? Why are there so many of them along the eastern coast of North America?

3). The sketches below are profiles of a typical beach in the summer and winter. Describe the seasonal changes that occur, such as areas of erosion and deposition (you may do this with a sketch). What causes these seasonal changes?

a. summer profile:

b. winter profile:

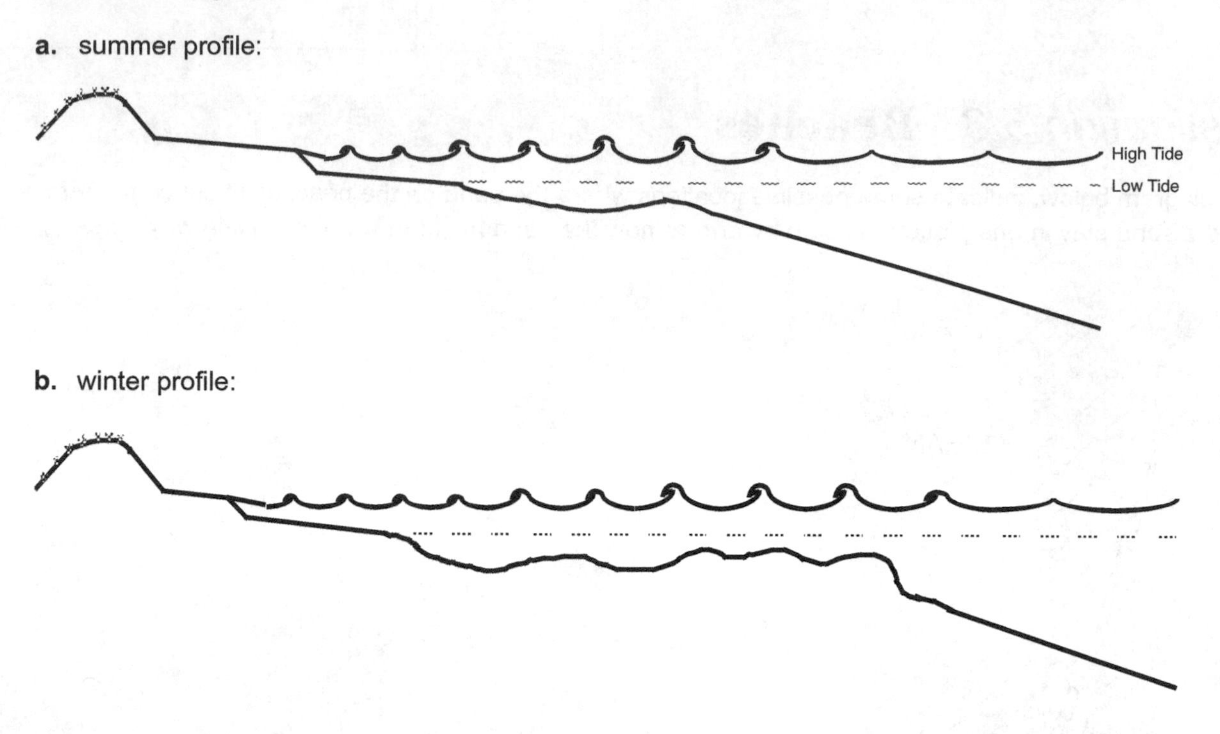

c. cause of seasonal changes:

Name ____________________________

First three letters of last name

Investigation 5.4 **Estuaries**

An estuary is a place where fresh water meets seawater. A common example is the mouth of a river, or the distal end of a river valley that flows to the sea. Using the three profiles below and on the back of this page, predict what might happen when river water (0‰) meets saltwater (33‰) in one type of estuary. Use arrows to depict the flow of each. Using the graph of salinity vs. depth on the right of each profile, plot the predicted salinity profile through the oceanward side of the estuary, the middle of this estuary, and the landward side of the estuary. For each diagram use the arrow as an indicator where to draw the graph. Specify the type of estuary you are illustrating.______________

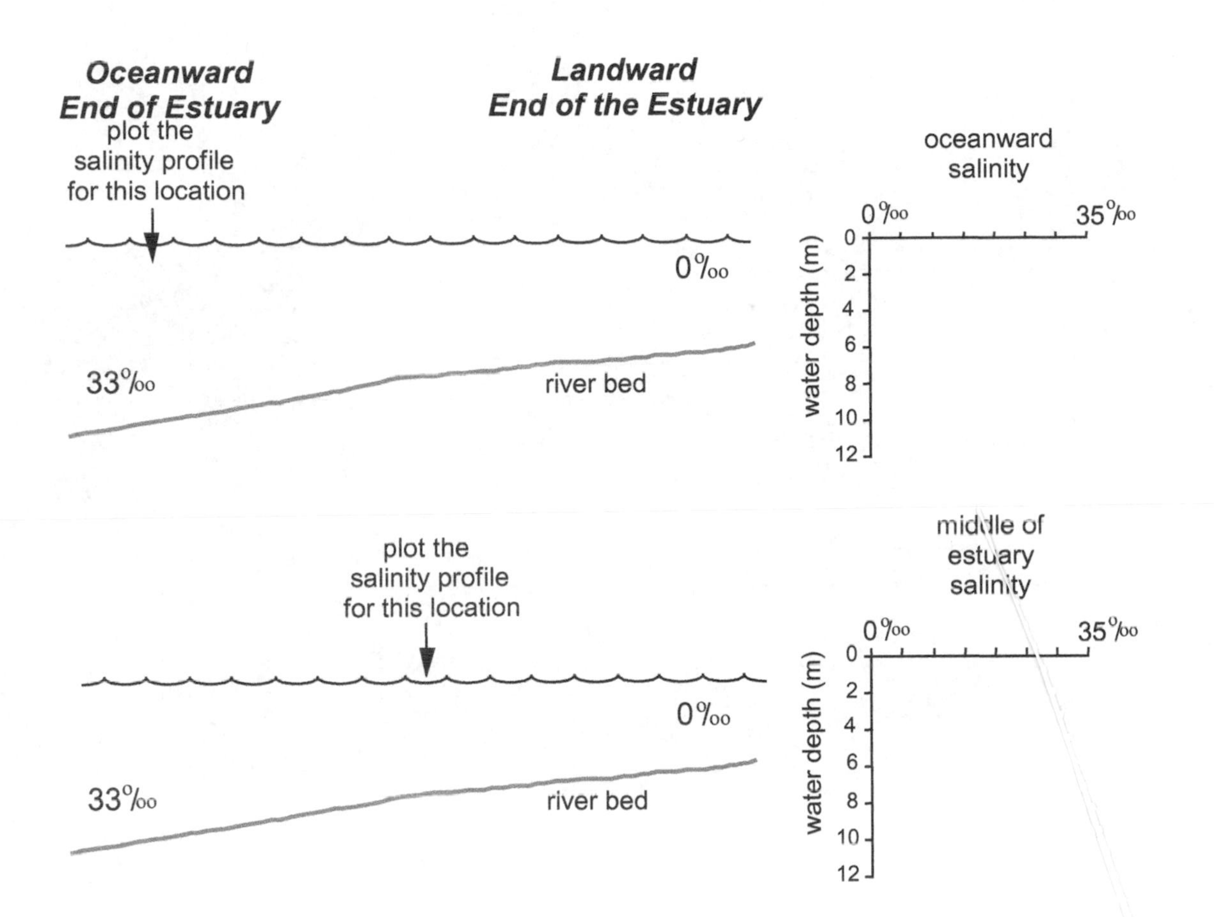

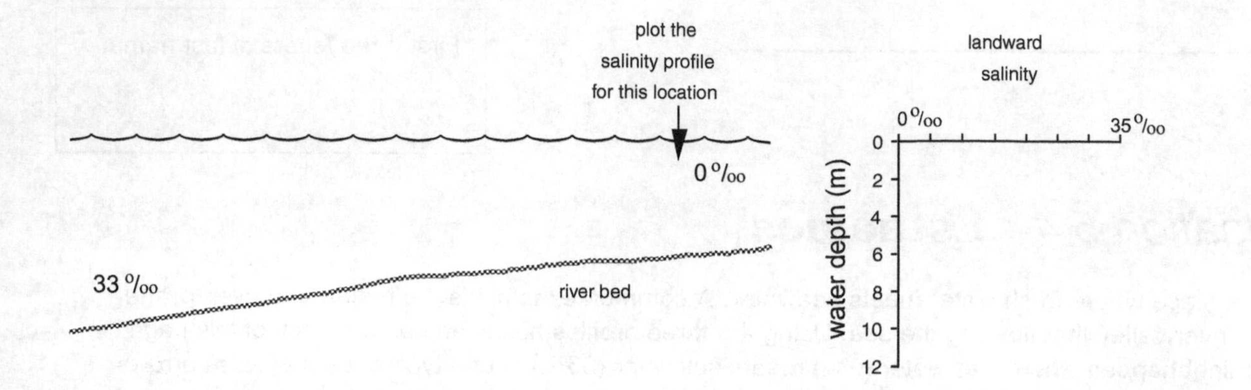
plot the
salinity profile
for this location
0 ‰
33 ‰
river bed
landward
salinity
0 ‰
35 ‰
water depth (m)
0
2
4
6
8
10
12

Name ______________________________

First three letters of last name

Investigation 5.6 Coastal Erosion

During more than 350 years of European settlement, the coast of Cape Cod has been inundated by strong storms 84 times! During the winter of 1978, and again during the "Perfect Storm" of 1991 when powerful nor'easters pounded the coast. The effects were widespread and devastating, but out of sight and out of mind of many "summer people".

1). The map below shows the location of cliffs and sandy beaches along the Cape Cod shoreline. Identify the areas where erosion is the dominant process and explain why.

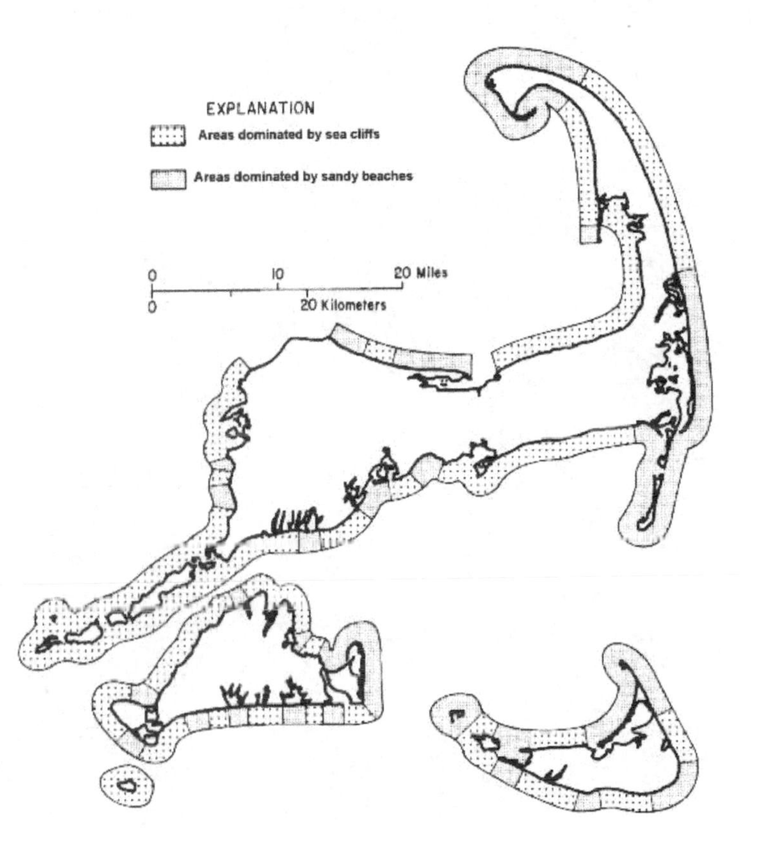

2). Sand dunes are a common feature on Cape Cod and other barrier beaches. Where are dunes usually located with respect to the beach? Can they be of value in preventing beach erosion?

Minute paper An increasingly large population in North America and the world is living directly on the coast. Many communities are being damaged time and again by storms as well as by slower processes of coastal erosion. Are there effective measures against coastal erosion? What can be done to address the problem? In the space below, write down your ideas on some remedies that may work and others that are likely to fail.

Name ______________________________

First three letters of last name

Investigation 5.7 Greenhouse Effect

Greenhouse gases such as carbon dioxide (CO_2) and methane (CH_4) trap long-wavelength solar radiation in the atmosphere. There is strong evidence that average global temperatures are slowly rising. A likely cause of global warming is the clear trend of increasing concentrations of greenhouse gases due to the burning of fossil fuels. The plot below shows the monthly mean concentration of as measured near the summit of Mauna Loa in Hawaii since 1958 (the International Geophysical Year).

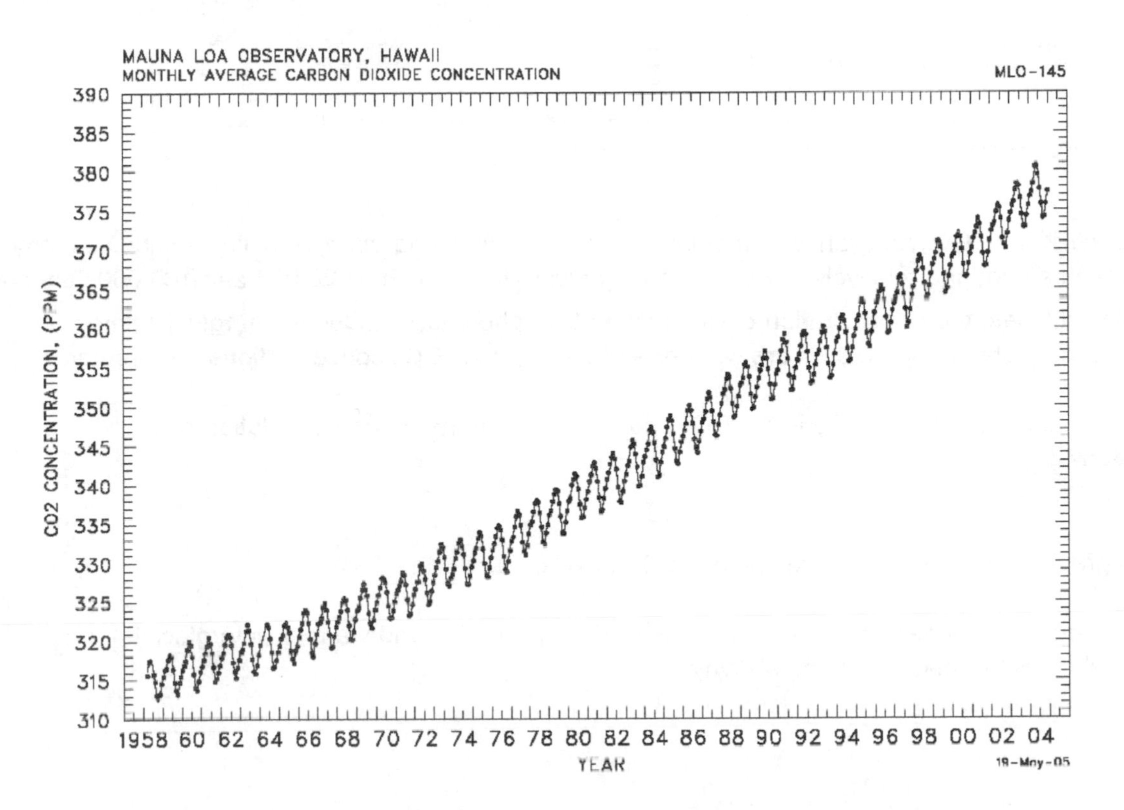

Source: Carbon Dioxide Information Analysis Center, Oak Ridge National Laboratory.

1). Describe the trend of CO_2 over the last 40 years. Has CO_2 changed at a constant rate?

2). What is responsible for the distinctive "saw-tooth" (zig-zag) pattern superposed on the overall long-term trend of rising CO_2?

The plot below shows trends in CO_2 concentrations and temperature as determined from ice cores collected in Antarctica.
(Source: http://www.epa.gov/climatechange/science/pastcc.html).

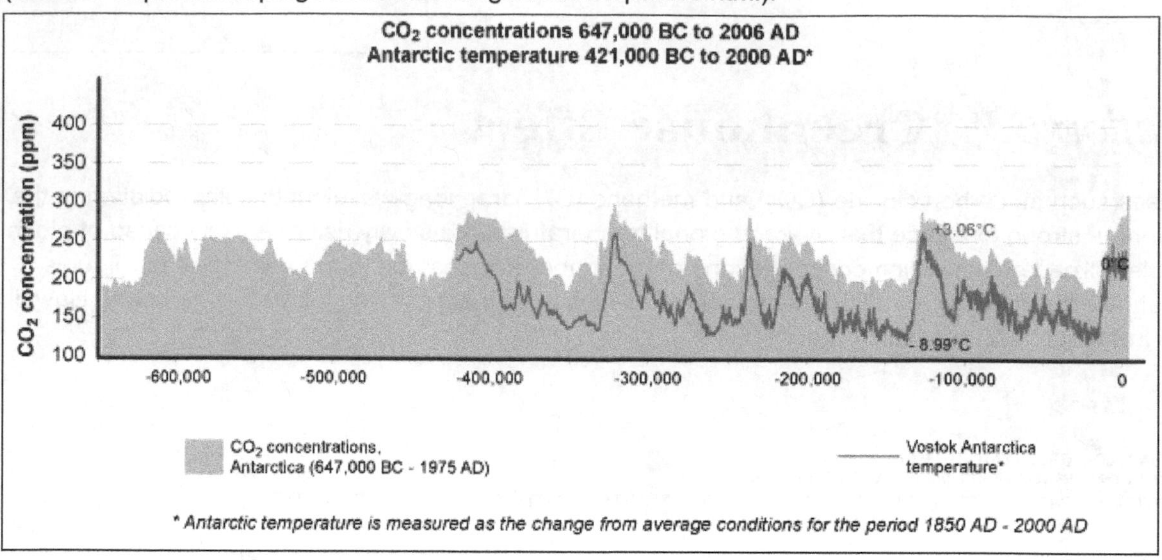

- The concentration of CO_2 has varied from relatively high values during *interglacial* times such as today and ~130,000 years ago, and relatively low values during *glacial* times such as 20,000 and 160,000 years ago.
- During glacial times, the concentration of CO_2 in the atmosphere is low. During interglacial times like today, average global temperatures are warmer and atmospheric CO_2 concentrations are greater.

3). What is the natural range of variability in the CO_2 prior to growth of the human population and industrialization?

4). Label on the graph where today's concentration of CO_2 would be.

5). Indicate on the graph the times when the Earth was colder (glaciation) and warmer (interglacials). What would sea level be like during these times? Why?

Name ______________________________

First three letters of last name

Investigation 5.8 Global Warming and the Ocean

1). The graph below shows the estimated annual carbon dioxide emissions from the burning of fossil fuels. The total injected into the atmosphere since 1850 is 315 billion tons.

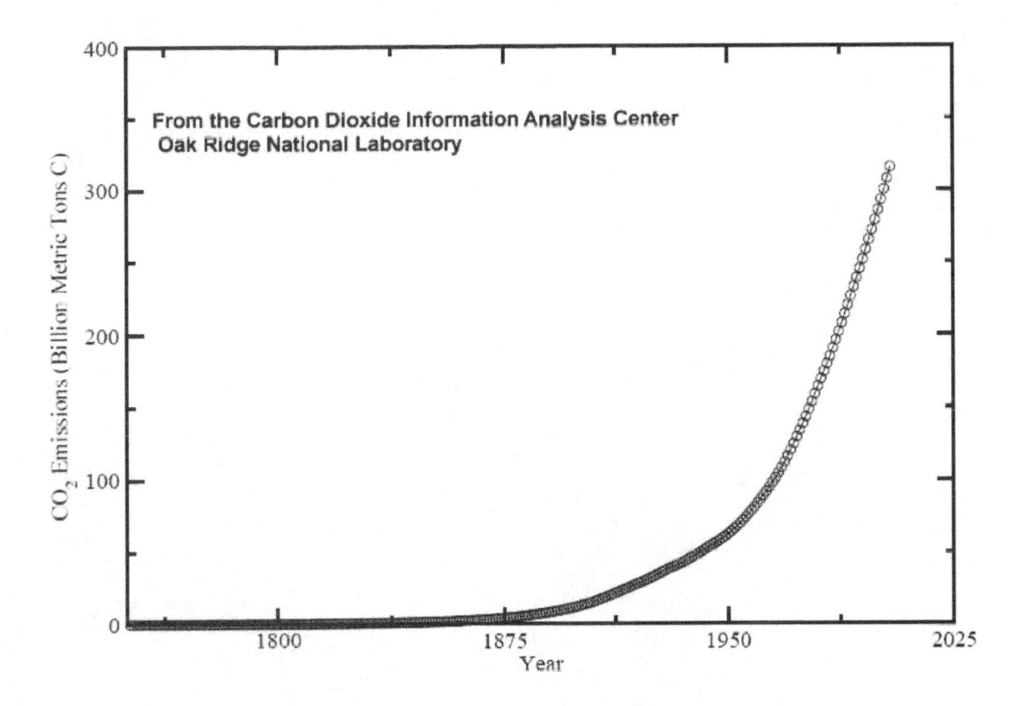

During the same period of time, from 1850 to the present, the concentration of CO_2 in atmosphere has increased to 369.5 ppm from 288 ppm. It takes 2.13 billion tons of CO_2 to increase the concentration in the atmosphere by 1 ppm.

a. Calculate the total mass of CO_2 in the atmosphere today.______________

b. What is the difference between this number and the total CO_2 put into the atmosphere by fossil-fuel burning since 1850?_________

c. How can you account for the difference between the two numbers?

2). Based upon your answer to 1c, what effects might this CO_2 have on the chemistry of the ocean?

Name ______________________________

First three letters of last name

Investigation 5.9 **Marine Pollution**

1). List 10 things that can pollute the ocean environment. Indicate by numbering which three you think are the greatest problems (#1, #2, #3).

____

____

____

____

____

____

____

____

____

____

2). Explain the reasons behind your choice of the three greatest marine pollution problems.

3). For each of the following, explain the connection with marine pollution or a contamination problem.

a. Minimata disease

b. Paralytic shellfish poisoning (PSP)

c. “Dead zone” in the Gulf of Mexico

d. Tuna in sushi

e. Coral reef decline

Additional Resources

The investigations in this book are designed to be flexible, so that they can be used in conjunction with a wide array of electronic, print and audiovisual resources. We have found some videos that can be used especially well with certain exercises.

Investigation 2.3: Continents and Ocean Basins. Video clips that can be used for this investigation are available at https://udrive.oit.umass.edu/rfyureti/Continents%20%26%20Ocean%20Basin%20Videos
A CD-ROM with these video clips can be requested from the authors.

Investigation 3.1: Polar and Non-polar Liquids. A video showing a suitable experiment is being developed by the authors.

Investigation 3.2: Temperature and Heat Capacity. Video clips that can be used for this investigation are available at http://www.vimeo.com/15311766
A CD-ROM with these video clips can be requested from the authors.

Investigation 3.6: Density. A video showing a suitable density experiment is being developed by the authors.

Investigation 3.9: The Seasons. A video about misconceptions of the causes of the seasons, *A Private Universe* (1987, Harvard-Smithsonian Astrophysical Observatory) can be helpful to a discussion.

Investigation 3.11: The Coriolis Effect. A video demonstrating the Coriolis Effect is being developed by the authors.

Investigation 4.5: Coastal Ecology. *Where the Bay Becomes the Sea* (1985, National Film Board of Canada) provides an excellent framework for discussion.

Investigation 4.6: The Intertidal Zone. *The Intertidal Zone* (1985, National Film Board of Canada) is a good source.

Investigation 4.8: Overfishing. The video *The Last Hunters: the Cod War* (1990, Films for the Humanities and Sciences) is a stimulating source for debate.

Investigation 4.9: Environment of the Gulf Stream. The video *Gulfstream* (1982, National Film Board of Canada) is highly recommended.

Investigation 4.10: Marine Mammals. The introductory parts of the video. *If Dolphins Could Talk* (1990, National Audobon Society) provides some good background on the characteristics of marine mammals.

Investigation 5.1: Waves. A video of the physics of water-wave motion is available from http://www.vimeo.com/16231885 and http://www.vimeo.com/16231931
A CD-ROM with these video clips can be requested from the authors.

Investigation 5.3: Beaches. The film or video *Beach: A River of Sand* (1965, EBF) remains a very good summary.

Investigation 5.6: Coastal Erosion. *Portrait of a Coast* (1980, Circle Films) provides a comprehensive overview of the effects and remedies of the problem.

Investigation 5.9: Marine Pollution. *The Ocean Sink* (1990, Films for the Humanities and Sciences) states some of the issues very well.

Glossary

Abyssal hills: low volcanic peaks usually found in deeper parts of the ocean.

Abyssal plain: extensive flat area of the deep ocean adjacent to continental margins.

Accretionary prism: deformed sediments found on the landward side of a deep-sea trench or subduction zone.

Active continental margin: a coastline that is close to the boundary of two colliding tectonic plates.

Ammonites: a group of extinct marine animals related to the modern nautilus. They are recognized as fossils in rocks by distinctive coiled shells.

Anadromous: fish that spend their adult lives in the ocean but then migrate up rivers to breed in fresh water.

Anaerobic bacteria: single-celled organisms without a nucleus that do not need oxygen to survive.

Aphelion: the point in the Earth's orbit when the planet is farthest from the sun (152×10^6 km), which occurs around July 6 each year.

Aphotic: the depth region in the ocean where light does not penetrate.

Aquaculture: the process of raising fish for food consumption in coastal farms.

Arctic (Antarctic) Circle: imaginary circles that surrounds the Earth at a latitude of 66.5°N (S). It marks the northernmost (southernmost) limit of solar radiation in the winter.

Asthenophere: the upper region of the Earth's mantle that deforms plastically. Circulation in the asthenosphere drives the motions of plate tectonics.

Atolls: circular coral reefs formed when the volcanic island the reefs surround sinks below sea level.

Authigenic sediment: ocean deposits that are precipitated directly from seawater. Manganese nodules are an example.

Autotroph: an organism that can produce its own food by photosynthesis or some other mechanism of primary productivity.

Bacterioplankton: single-celled floating organisms that are members of the Kingdom Monera.

Ballast water: sea water that tanker ships use to balance their load when they are not full of cargo.

Barrier islands: long, linear beaches that are separated from the mainland by a shallow lagoon or tidal marsh.

Basalt: A magnesium- and iron-rich rock that is produced by volcanic activity. This is the rock type that is produced at oceanic ridges and is the rock type the makes up the oceanic crust.

Bathymetric map: a representation of the physical features of the sea floor based on depth measurements.

Bathymetry: measurement of depth below sea level; the topography of the ocean floor.

Bathymetry: the depth of the seafloor below the ocean surface.

Beach nourishment: the process of pumping sand from deeper water to the shoreline in order to replenish sand lost by erosion.

Beach: an extended deposit of sand or gravel that results from the action of waves on a shoreline.

Benioff zone: earthquakes that occur at progressively increasing depths on the landward side of a deep-sea trench that marks the location of plate subduction.

Benthic: refers to the environment on the sea floor.

Berm: the flat area of a beach that is just above the high tide line.

Biogenic sediment: deposits on the sea floor that are composed of the shells of marine organisms.

Biological productivity: the amount of new organic matter that is created by the process of **photosynthesis**.

Biological pump: the breaking down of organic matter into CO_2 and nutrients by bacteria in deep water masses that pave the way for increased biological productivity at the surface in zones of upwelling.

Biomass: the total amount of living organisms within a specified area in the ocean.

Bottom trawling: fishing using nets that drag along the seafloor and catch a wide variety of groundfish but can damage the benthic ecology in the process.

Brackish: a general term for salinity that is less than that of sea water because of mixing with fresh water.

Calcareous ooze: fine-grained deep sea sediment that consist primarily of the shells of microscopic organisms made from calcium carbonate ($CaCO_3$).

Cap rock: a sedimentary rock, usually shale or salt, that is found at the top of a subsurface oil reservoir. The rock layer is impermeable and allows the liquid to accumulate beneath it.

Capillary waves: small ripples that form on the smooth surface of the ocean by the friction generated from wind energy.

Carbonate compensation depth (CCD): the level below the ocean surface at which calcium carbonate ($CaCO_3$) dissolves.

Celestial navigation: the process of determining latitude and longitude by the position of the sun and stars.

Chemical weathering: the process by which rocks and soils on the continents are broken down by wind and rain and are partially dissolved into groundwater and river water.

Chemosynthesis: the process by which organisms can produce their own food using the energy in dissolved chemical compounds such as sulfate (SO_4^{2-}).

Chronometer: a precise clock that can keep time accurately on board a ship.

Coastal upwelling: ocean currents parallel to the coastline are deflected offshore by the Coriolis Effect and offshore winds, stimulating the rise of nutrient-rich water from greater depths.

Conduction: the process of transferring heat from one object to another by direct contact. Some heat energy is transferred from the ocean to the atmosphere in this manner.

Continental rise: on passive continental margins, it is the area adjacent to the abyssal plains where ocean crust transitions into continental crust.

Continental shelf: a long, gently sloping area of shallow water that starts at the coastline and continues until a water depth of approximately 200 meters. They are more developed along passive continental margins.

Continental slope: a steeper part of the continental margin that lies between the shelf and continental rise. It is cut by submarine canyons.

Contour lines (isobaths): connect points of equal elevation (or equal depth below the ocean surface).

Convection: the process by which heat is transferred by fluid motion. Mantle convection is the driving force behind plate tectonics.

Convergence: the process of moving masses or fluids coming together.

Cyanobacteria: a class of single-celled organisms without a nucleus that can produce their own food through photosynthesis.

Deep-sea fans: accumulation of terrigenous sediments at the mouth of a submarine canyon that spreads out over the abyssal plain in the shape of a fan.

Deep-sea trench: a narrow and arc-shaped canyon on the deep-sea floor that usually trends parallel to a coastline. Trenches mark the location of convergent plate boundaries and are the deepest parts of the ocean.

Delta: a fan-shaped deposit of sediment that is formed when a river slows down as it enters the ocean.

Density stratification: a condition that exists when warm, fresh (less dense) water overlies cold, salty (more dense) water and effectively prevents mixing of the layers.

Deposition: the geological process by which sediment accumulates at a particular location.

Detritus: particles of inorganic and organic matter that settle through the ocean water.

Diffraction: the process by which waves appear to curve as they pass through a narrow opening or inlet.

Diffusion: the slow mixing of salts or other chemical substances caused by the random thermal motion of the molecules.

Dipolar structure: in reference to the water molecule, which has one end with a net positive charge and the other end with a negative charge, owing to the distribution of electrons around the atoms in the molecule.

Dispersion: the process by which waves are sorted according wavelength as they move away from the storm-generating area of the ocean. Longer-wavelength waves move faster than shorter-wavelength waves.

Diurnal tide: one high tide and one low tide every day, with a period of 24 hours and 50 minutes between successive high tides.

Divergence: the process of moving masses ore fluids moving apart from each other.

Divergent plate boundary: the location where two lithospheric plates are moving away from each other. These are marked by a mid-ocean ridge with associated volcanic activity.

Downwelling: the sinking of cold, dense water in the polar regions to form deep water masses.

Dunes: accumulations of fine sand resulting from wind action that is found on the landward side of a beach or barrier island.

Dynamic positioning: the process by which a drilling ship is kept on station by computer-controlled thrusters in the hull.

Dynamical model: the prediction of tides that takes into account the actual geographic featuers of the coastlines and the observed patterns of tidal movement.

Dysphotic: the depth region in the ocean with a very low level of light energy.

Eccentricity: the amount by which the orbit of the earth deviates from a perfect circle. The eccentricity of the Earth's orbit is very small.

Echo sounding: a method that uses sound waves reflected by the sea floor to determine the depth of water beneath a moving boat.

Ekman spiral: surface ocean currents decrease in velocity with depth and shift direction as influenced by the Coriolis Effect, giving rise to a "circular staircase" of moving water.

Ekman transport: the net motion of ocean currents that is at 90° to the direction of the prevailing wind caused by the Coriolis Effect.

El Niño (also called El Niño Southern Oscllation or ENSO): a pattern of ocean circulation in the equatorial Pacific that involves the westward expansion of warm water along the equator and reduced upwelling of cold, nutrient-rich water off the coast of western South America. The strength of the Trade Winds also decreases; El Niño events generally occur every 3 to 7 years.

Epicenter: the geographic location of an earthquake.

Epifauna: benthic organisms that live on the surface of the sea floor or attached to rocks and seaweed.

Equator: an imaginary circle that splits the Earth into northern and southern hemispheres. It is used as the reference for measuring degrees of latitude.

Equilibrium model: the prediction of tides based entirely on the relative positions of the sun and moon with respect to the Earth.

Equilibrium waves: deep-water waves reach a maximum height when the frictional force of the wind that piles the water into waves is equally balanced by the force of gravity that pulls the water back down to the ocean surface.

Equinox: the points in the Earth's orbit when the most intense rays of the sun are received at the Equator. This occurs twice a year (spring and autumn).

Erosion: the geological process by which soil or sediment is removed from an area by the action of wind or water.

Estuary: the lower part of a river valley that has been filled with salt water as a result of rising sea level or a subsiding coastline.

Eukaryote: cells that contain a distinct and identifiable nucleus.

Euphotic zone: the upper layer of the ocean where light energy is >1% of the light energy that impacts the surface; it is usually the upper 100m of the water.

Euryhaline: refers to organisms that can tolerate a wide range of variation in salinity.

Eurythermal: refers to organisms that can tolerate a wide range of variation in temperature.

Evaporite minerals: salts, such as sodium chloride (NaCl), that are precipitated from sea water as it is concentrated or dried out by evaporation.

Exclusive economic zone (EEZ): the area of the ocean floor that extends 200 nautical miles from the coastline of a nation.

Extratropical storm: a strong low-pressure center that forms over the ocean in high latitudes; the Atlantic "nor'easter" is a typical example.

Fecal pellets: spherical particles of digested food excreted by marine organisms that are commonly found in marine sediments.

Fore-arc basin: a relatively deep area of accumulating marine sediments that is found on the seaward side of an island arc along a convergent plate boundary.

Fracture zone: region of long cracks in the ocean floor that cut oceanic ridges at right angles.

Gabbro: an igneous rock with the same composition as basalt but with much larger mineral grains, indicating that it cooled slowly at great depth within the crust.

Geostrophic flow: the horizontal large-scale circulation of surface currents in the ocean that is a balance between the Coriolis Effect, which tends to cause water to pile up in the middle of an ocean basin, and gravity, which forces the water back down slope.

Glacial marine sediment: deposits on the sea floor or near the coastline that were left by retreating masses of ice.

Global conveyor: the integrated circulation of the ocean that includes sinking of cold dense waters at the polar Atlantic Ocean, subsurface transport around the world and upwelling in other ocean basins.

Global Positioning System (GPS): navigation aid that uses the distance from several orbiting satellites to determine geographic location anywhere on Earth.

Grain size: refers to the diameter of sedimentary particles. Sand is greater than 2 millimeters across, silt is between 2 and 0.063 mm, and clay is less than 0.063 mm.

Granite: a potassium- and aluminum- and silicon-rich rock that cooled from a molten magma. It has visible mineral grains and it generally represents the composition of continental crust.

Greenhouse gas: a gaseous compound in the atmosphere that keeps infrared radiation from returning space and thereby contributes to warming the atmosphere.

Greenwich Mean Time (Universal Time): the time of day at the Prime Meridian in Greenwich, England. Abbreviated GMT or UT.

Guyots: flat-topped mountains that rise from the sea floor. Their flat surfaces were formed by wave action when these volcanoes extended to the ocean surface.

Half-life: the time it takes for an isotope undergoing radioactive decay to be reduced to one-half its original mass.

Headland: part of the coast that juts farther out into the ocean and receive more wave energy as a result.

Heat capacity: the heat energy (in calories) that it takes to raise the temperature of 1 gram of a substance by 1 degree Celsius.

Heat flow: the energy that is being transferred from the interior of the Earth to the surface. The rate of this transfer is controlled by geologic processes.

Hemipelagic sediment: sea-floor deposits that are a mix of material brought to the ocean by rivers and the shells of microscopic marine organisms.

Heterotrophic: organisms that must consume other organisms or organic matter in order to grow and develop.

Hot spot: a location where hot material from deep within the Earth is rising to the surface and causing extensive volcanic activity.

Hydrogen bond: the interaction of the positive (hydrogen) end of water molecules with the negative (oxygen) end of neighboring molecules. Hydrogen bonds affect the physical properties of water.

Hydrologic cycle: the general circulation of water at the Earth's surface involving the processes of evaporation, condensation, precipitation, infiltration, and runoff.

Hydrophone: a device that can listen for sounds generated underwater.

Hydrothermal circulation: the process by which seawater is circulated through oceanic ridges and emerges as hot springs or smokers.

Hypertonic: solutions that have a higher salinity than the surrounding fluid.

Hypotonic: solutions that have a lower salinity than the surrounding fluid.

Igneous rocks: rocks that are formed by crystallization of minerals from a high-temperature liquid state known as magma or lava.

Infauna: benthic organisms that live by burrowing into sediment or the sea floor.

Insolation: the amount of incoming solar radiation received by a point on the Earth's surface.

Internal wave: energy that moves along the interface between two subsurface water masses of different density.

Intertidal zone: in coastal areas, it is the sea bottom between high and low tides; also known as the littoral zone.

Intertropical Convergence Zone (ITCZ): the meteorological equator where the Northeast and Southeast Trade Winds come together. The ITCZ will shift north during summer in the Northern Hemisphere and south in the winter.

Invasive species: non-native plants or animals that are inadvertently transported to other locations where they can often damage the ecological balance.

Invertebrate: animals without a backbone or internal skeleton.

Ion: an atom that has lost or gained one or more electrons. Positively-charged ions are cations; negatively-charged ions are anions.

Island arc: a curved chain of volcanic islands that is usually found on the landward side of a deep-ocean trench.

Isostasy: the condition of equilibrium or balance that is controlled by the thickness of the lithosphere and the density difference between the lithosphere and the underlying asthenosphere.

Isotonic: solutions that have similar salinity and are therefore in equilibrium with each other.

Isotope: an atom of an element that has a particular number of neutrons in the nucleus.

Latent heat of condensation: the energy released by a substance when it changes from a vapor to a liquid.

Latent heat of fusion: the energy released by a substance when it crystallizes into a solid from a liquid.

Latent heat of vaporization: the energy absorbed by a substance when it changes from a liquid into a vapor.

Latent heat: the energy that is required for changing the phase of a substance, e.g., from liquid to gas, but does not change the temperature.

Latitude: location on Earth referenced to degrees north or south of the Equator (0°).

Lava: molten rock that is emitted from volcanoes. It will ultimately cool at the Earth's surface to form volcanic igneous rock.

Liquefaction: occurs when a water-saturated solid loses its rigidity during shaking. This process is a common cause of catastrophic ground failure and building collapse during earthquakes.

Lithosphere: the uppermost zone of the Earth that consists of the crust plus the upper part of the mantle. This zone behaves rigidly and comprises the tectonic plates of the Earth.

Littoral zone: in coastal areas, it is the sea bottom between high and low tides; also known as the intertidal zone.

Longitude: location on Earth referenced to degrees east or west of the Prime Meridian (0°).

Longshore currents: the net motion of water that is parallel to shore that results from waves breaking at an angle to coastline.

Longshore drift: the transportation of sand parallel to shorelines by currents generated by breaking waves.

LORAN: Long Range Navigation that uses radio beacons from shore-based stations as reference points to locate position by triangulation.

Low-velocity zone: the region beneath the base of the lithosphere where the velocity of seismic (earthquake) waves decreases.

Magma: molten rock that remains within the interior of the Earth. When magma cools slowly it forms igneous rocks with visible crystals (plutonic igneous rocks).

Manganese nodules: round objects found on the deep-sea floor that are made up of manganese and other metallic elements. They are believed to form as direct precipitates from sea water.

Marine snow: (see also **detritus**) settling particles of organic matter and pelagic sediments in the deep ocean that reflect artifical light and resemble falling snowflakes.

Maximum sustainable yield: the total amount of fish that can be safely removed from the ocean without damaging the future growth of the stock.

Meroplankton: pelagic organisms that are the larval (young) stages of common marine animals.

Methane hydrate: a solid formed at low temperatures when methane (CH_4) combines with ice. This solid is unstable as the temperature rises and sublimes (evaporates) to form gaseous methane.

Methane: the simplest hydrocarbon made up of one carbon atom and four attached hydrogen atoms (CH_4), It occurs as a gas and is produced during the anaerobic (oxygen-free) breakdown o organic matter.

Mixed layer: the upper part of the ocean, usually up to 100 m depth, where winds, waves and surface currents keep the water well-stirred.

Moho: also called the Mohorovicic Discontinuity, this is a seismic boundary that separates the less dense crust from the underlying upper mantle.

Monsoon: the reversal of the prevailing winds that primarily occurs in the Indian Ocean as a result of the seasonal migration of the Intertropical Convergence Zone (ITCZ).

Mud: a general term for fine-grained sediment composed mostly of silt and clay particles.

Neap tide: the tide that occurs about twice each month when the tidal range is at a minimum.

Nekton: marine organisms that are able to swim freely in the water.

Neritic sediment: deposits of sand, silt, and clay on the continental shelf that are brought there from the continents by rivers.

Neritic zone: the region of sea water that overlies the continental shelf.

Neutral buoyancy: the equilibrium achieved when the density of a substance is exactly the same as its surrounding medium.

Neutron: one of the particles in the nucleus of an atom that carries no electrical charge.

Ocean ridge: an elongated, continuous mountain chain that rises from the sea floor. These are the centers of sea-floor spreading and the creation of new oceanic crust.

Oceanic divergence: upwelling that occurs when the Coriolis Effect forces parallel currents to move in opposite directions and deeper water rises to the surface. This occurs in the polar regions and also along the Equator.

Opaline silica: a hydrated form of silicon dioxide ($SiO_2 \cdot H_2O$) that microorganisms such as radiolarian and diatoms produce to make their shells.

Organic detritus: the remains of organisms that have been broken down into particles the size of silt and clay.

Osmosis: the movement of water through membranes, usually from zones of low salinity to zones of higher salinity.

OTEC (Ocean Thermal Energy Conversion): an experimental process to use the vastly different temperature between warm surface water and cold deep water.

Oxygen compensation depth: the depth in the ocean at which photosynthesis is exactly balanced by respiration; the net productivity is zero.

Passive continental margin: a coastline that is in the middle of a tectonic plate where oceanic crust is connected directly to continental crust.

Pathogens: harmful bacteria and other microorganisms.

Pelagic sediment: deposits on the deep sea floor that form as particles settle through the overlying water column.

Pelagic: refers to the environment of the water column in the ocean.

Perihelion: the point in the Earth's orbit when the planet is closest to the sun (147×10^6 km), which occurs around January 3 each year.

Phosphorite: a rock that forms from the accumulation of phosphate-bearing minerals.

Photic zone: the layer of the ocean that where sunlight is present. The maximum depth is about 1000 m.

Photosynthesis: the process by which autotrophic organisms convert carbon dioxide and water into sugar using the energy of sunlight.

Physical and chemical weathering: the processes by which rocks on the continent are decomposed into soils and sediments.

Phytoplankton: single-celled algae and bacteria that photosynthesize and live in the upper part of the pelagic zone.

Placer deposits: an accumulation of an ore that forms when rivers concentrate large particles of the material in one place on the river bed.

Plane of the ecliptic: the imaginary flat surface that contains the orbit of the Earth about the sun.

Plankton: marine organisms that float in the water column and do not have an active swimming capability.

Plate tectonics: the theory that proposes the Earth is divided into numerous pieces of rigid lithosphere that are constantly in motion with respect to one another.

Prevailing winds: the large-scale global winds that are generated by the heating and cooling of air masses in the atmosphere and divide the Earth into latitudinal climate zones or belts.

Primary productivity: new growth in biomass that is created by photosynthesis or chemosynthesis.

Prime Meridian: an imaginary line running north-south through Greenwich, England that is the reference for measuring degrees of longitude.

Prokaryote: cells that do not have a nucleus, typical of bacteria and other members of the Kingdom Monera.

Protists: single-celled organisms with a nucleus.

Proton: one of the particles in the nucleus of an atom that carries a positive electrical charge.

P-waves: earthquake (seismic) waves where the wave energy travels in the same direction as the wave. These are also called "primary" or "pressure" waves, and they are in principle similar to sound waves.

Pycnocline: the layer in the ocean where density increases rapidly with depth. The pycnocline is a barrier to mixing of deep and shallow water.

Pyroclastic flow: an eruption of hot, dense volcanic ash and gases that travels at high speed down the slopes of volcanoes and leaves a deposit of ash in its wake.

Radioactive decay: the spontaneous breakdown of neutrons in the nucleus of an atom that produces heat and nuclear radiation.

Radioactive: the production of alpha, beta, and gamma radiation by the spontaneous decay of particles in the nucleus of an unstable isotope.

Rayleigh waves: earthquake (seismic) waves that travel along the surface in a fashion similar to ocean waves.

Red clay: a type of pelagic sediment found in the deepest part of sea floor composed of dust particles that have settled through the entire water column.

Reentry cone: a device used in ocean drilling that permits the drill string to re-enter a hole after the drill bit has been changed.

Refraction: the process by which waves appear to bend because they slow down as they enter shallow water.

Reservoir: an economic accumulation of petroleum that occurs when oil and gas fill the pore spaces in a sandstone or other rock.

Residence time: the average amount of time water or a dissolved substance remains in a reservoir. It can be calculated by dividing the amount in the reservoir by the rate of input or output.

Ridge push: a mechanism for sea-floor spreading whereby the formation of new crustal material in ocean ridges causes the two halves of the ridge crest to move away from each other.

Rift: a valley often along the crest of an ocean ridge where the volcanic activity associated with sea-floor spreading is found.

Rogue wave: an unusually high wave that often occurs in storm situations.

Salinity: the total amount of salt dissolved in water, expressed in units of parts per thousand (‰).

Salt marsh: a vegetated tidal flat found in low-energy areas of coastlines.

Seafloor spreading: the process of the expansion of the ocean floor by the cooling of basaltic magma in the ocean ridge.

Seamounts: extinct volcanoes rising from the sea floor that have not reached the ocean surface. They often occur in linear chains.

Sedimentary rocks: formed by the accumulation, burial, and lithification of sand, silt, clay, and calcium carbonate in marine or non-marine environments.

Seismic: relating to earthquakes.

Semidiurnal tide: two high tides and two low tides every day, with a period of 12 hours and 25 minutes between successive high tides.

Sensible heat: energy absorbed or released by a substance that will change the temperature of that substance.

Sextant: an instrument that can be used to measure the angle of the sum or stars above the horizon.

Shadow zone: regions on Earth distant from an earthquake epicenter where no seismic waves are detected on seismographs.

Shallow-focus earthquakes: earthquakes occurring in the crust at depths of less than approximately 60 km.

Side-scan sonar: an echo-sounding method that uses sound waves that blanket a wide area to determine the detailed bathymetry of the sea floor.

Sigma tee (σ_t): shorthand units used to indicate the density of sea water: σ_t = [density (in g/cm^3) –1.000] x 1000.

Siliceous ooze: pelagic sediment that is composed predominantly of the shells of microorganisms made from opaline silica.

Slab pull: a mechanism for sea floor spreading whereby the dense old crustal material sliding down subduction zones (trenches) is causing new crust to be added at ocean ridges.

Solar radiation: energy derived from the sun.

Sounding: determining the depth of water at a point in the ocean.

Source rock: an organic-rich sedimentary rock that provides the raw material for the formation of petroleum.

Spreading center: another term for an ocean ridge that emphasizes its role in the formation of new ocean crust.

Spring tide: the tide that occurs about twice each month when the tidal range is at a maximum.

Stenohaline: refers to organisms that can tolerate only a narrow range of salinity.

Stenothermal: refers to organisms that can tolerate only a narrow range of temperature.

Storm surge: high water produced by large waves and the effects of low atmospheric pressure that travels far inland in coastal regions.

Strike-slip: movement along a fault that is primarily horizontal. It is also known as transverse movement.

Subduction zone: the region of the sea floor where old ocean crust is returned to the mantle. The location marked by a deep-ocean trench.

Sublittoral zone: the area of the sea floor in shallow water that is below low tide but can still be affected by the water motion of waves.

Submarine canyon: a deep valley carved into the continental shelf and slope that runs approximately perpendicular to the coast. It is formed by the action of rivers and turbidity currents that erode the shelf floor in these areas.

Subneritic zone: the seafloor of the continental shelf that lies below the depth affected by the motion of waves.

Suboceanic province: the area of the seafloor that is at a greater depth than the continental shelf.

Subsidence: refers to the sinking of land masses or coastal areas with respect to sea level.

Subtropical gyre: the dominant pattern of surface ocean circulation in the low- to mid-latitudes that describe a circular pathway in the ocean basin: clockwise in the Northern Hemisphere, counter-clockwise in the Southern Hemisphere.

Summer solstice: the point in the Earth's orbit when the most intense rays of the sun are received at the Tropic of Cancer at 23.5° North latitude.

Supratidal zone: along coastalines, this is the area above high tide but within the reach of sea spray from breaking waves.

Surf zone: the area between the beach and offshore where waves begin to break.

Surface tension: the cohesion of the molecules of a liquid that allow it to stick together to form droplets. Water has a high surface tension.

Suture zone: an area on the continent, usually a mountain range, that marks the collision of two tectonic plates.

Swash: the water that runs up a beach face after the waves break.

S-waves: earthquake (seismic) waves where the energy is transmitted perpendicular to the direction of the wave motion. Also called "secondary" or "shear" waves.

Symbiosis: two organisms living together in an ecological relationship that benefits both of them.

Taxonomy: classification organisms according to similarities in their biological structure.

Terrigenous sediment: deposits in the ocean that are derived from the weathering and erosion of rocks on the continent and transported to the sea by rivers.

Thermocline: the layer in the ocean where temperature decreases rapidly with depth. The thermocline is a barrier to the mixing of cold, deep water with warm, shallow water.

Thermohaline circulation: the sinking, subsurface movement, and rising of water masses throughout the world ocean that is controlled by temperature and salinity (density) differences in the water.

Tidal range: the height difference between high and low tides at a given location.

Topography: the height of the land surface above sea level.

Transform fault: a type of strike-slip fault that represents the boundary between two tectonic plates.

Transportation: the movement of sediment from one location to another by wind or water.

Trilobites: extinct marine organisms found as fossils in sedimentary rocks. They were abundant creatures in the ocean from about 540 million to 200 million years ago.

Trophic pyramid: a representation of a heirarchy in a food chain that shows primary producers on the bottom and carnivores on the top.

Tropic of Cancer (Capricorn): imaginary circle that surrounds the Earth at a latitude of 23.5°N (S). It marks the northernmost (southernmost) limit of the most intense rays of the sun.

Tropical cyclones: areas of intense low pressure that form over low-latitude regions of the ocean as a result of evaporation of sea water from the warm ocean surface. Winds spiral counterclockwise in the Northern Hemisphere into these low-pressure areas.

Tsunami: large wave generated by undersea movement such as an earthquake or volcanic eruption.

Turbidity currents: flows of sediment-laden water that rush down the continental slope at high velocity and deposit sand, silt, mud, and organic matter onto the abyssal plains.

Ultramafic: a type of igneous rock that is relatively low in silicon and high in magnesium and iron. It is typical of rocks found in the upper mantle.

Upwelling: the general process by which cold, nutrient-rich deep-ocean waters rise to the surface.

Viscosity: a measure of the degree to which fluid resists flowing when a force is applied.

Volcanic emissions: gases, dust, and other particles that are introduced into the atmosphere by eruptions of volcanoes.

Volcaniclastic sediment: material that accumulates on the land surface or sea floor as a result of a volcanic eruption.

Washover fan: a deposit of coarse sand pushed inland by storms that have overtopped the dunes along a beach and spread out into the lagoon.

Wave base: the depth of water that wave action will affect.

Westward intensification: the result of the Coriolis Effect and geostrophic flow that causes ocean currents on the western side of ocean basins are narrow and swift.

Winter solstice: the point in the Earth's orbit when the most intense rays of the sun are received at the Tropic of Capricorn at 23.5° South latitude.

Zooplankton: heterotrophic organisms that live in the pelagic zone but have no swimming capability.

Zooxanthellae: photosynthetic algae that reside within the flesh of coral animals and provide food for the coral with the excess carbohydrate they synthesize.

INDEX

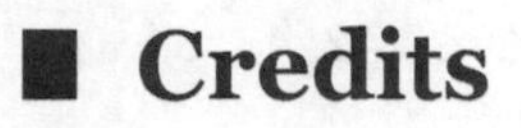

Credits

Front Cover: NASA
Back Cover: NOAA (Walter F. Smith)
Inside Front Cover: US Coast and Geodetic Survey
Inside Back Cover: NASA/JPL; U.S. Geological Survey

Part 1: Introducing the Ocean
Opener: NASA
p.2: NASA
p.4: Reports of the *HMS Challenger* expedition
1.3: McGraw-Hill Digital Asset Library
1.7: McGraw-Hill Digital Asset Library
p.12: Garmin Corporation
1.11. Nautical chart from US Coast and Geodetic Survey
1.12. Aerospace Corporation
1.24: NOAA
1.15: US Geological Survey
1.16, 1-17: NOAA/Woods Hole Oceanographic Institution
1.18: NOAA
1.19: NASA/JPL and NOAA/NGDC
1.20: National Marine Fisheries Service
p.18: McGraw-Hill Digital Asset Library
1.21: McGraw-Hill Digital Asset Library
p.22: http://en.wikipedia.org/wiki/File:H1_low_250.jpg (Phantom Photographer)
p.24: map modified from www.wikipedia.org (Central Intelligence Agency)
p.25. http://en.wikipedia.org/wiki/File:Ernest_Henry_Shackleton_Nadar.jpg
p.27: http://en.wikipedia.org/wiki/Concept_map
p.34: Nautical chart from the US Coast and Geodetic Survey

Part 2: Geology and the Ocean
Opener: NASA
2.6: McGraw-Hill Digital Asset Library
2.11: McGraw-Hill Digital Asset Library
p.54: NASA
p.58: McGraw-Hill Digital Asset Library
2.17: McGraw-Hill Digital Asset Library
2.18: NASA
2.20: a) NASA b) U.S. Geological Survey c) base map from NOAA
2.22: U.S. Geological Survey
2.23, 2.24: Takeuchi et al, 1967, Debate about the Earth (permission requested)
2.25: McGraw-Hill Digital Asset Library
2.27: a) McGraw-Hill Digital Asset Library b) base map from NOAA
2.28: NOAA
2.29: U.S. Geological Survey
2.34: Sverdrup, Duxbury, and Duxbury (2006) Fundamentals of Oceanography (Fig. 4.17)
2.36: McGraw-Hill Digital Asset Library
p.76, 77, 78: U.S. Geological Survey
p.79: http://en.wikipedia.org/wiki/File:2004-tsunami.jpg; http://en.wikipedia.org/wiki/File:US_Navy_050102-N-9593M-040_A_village_near_the_coast_of_Sumatra_lays_in_ruin_after_the_Tsunami_that_struck_South_East_Asia.jpg

p.80, 81: Ocean Drilling Program
p.82: NASA
p.83: McGraw-Hill Digital Asset Library
p.88: McGraw-Hill Digital Asset Library'
p.94: NOAA (Walter F. Smith)
p.95: U.S. Geological Survey
p.98: University of California, Berkeley; Smithsonian Institution
p.102: NOAA (Walter F. Smith)
p.106: NOAA (Walter F. Smith)

Part 3: Water and the Ocean-Climate System
3.4: Sverdrup and Armbrust, 2009, Introduction to the World's Ocean (Fig. 5.5)
p.112: NASA
3.8: McGraw-Hill Digital Asset Library
p.132: National Hurricane Center
p.138: Dr. Robert Mariano, Univ of Miami
p.140: http://en.wikipedia.org/wiki/File:Corrientes-oceanicas.gif
p.142, 143: NASA
p.148: National Science Foundation
p.173: NASA/JPL

Part 4: Life in the Sea
Opener: McGraw-Hill Digital Asset Library
4.1: Lynn Margulis and Louise Armstrong
p.177: (2 photos) McGraw-Hill Digital Asset Library
4.4: Sverdrup and Armbrust, 2009, Introduction to the World's Ocean (Fig. 16.5, 16.8, 16.10)
4.5: Sverdrup and Armbrust, 2009, Introduction to the World's Ocean (Fig. 17.11, 17.13, 17.14)
4.6: Sverdrup and Armbrust, 2009, Introduction to the World's Ocean: (Fig. 18.7)
p.188: McGraw-Hill Digital Asset Library
4.19: U.S. Geological Survey
4.21: Sverdrup and Armbrust, 2009, Introduction to the World's Ocean (Fig. 18.4)
4.22: Sverdrup and Armbrust, 2009, Introduction to the World's Ocean (Fig. 18.8)
4.24: Sverdrup and Armbrust, 2009, Introduction to the World's Ocean (Fig. 18.7)
4.25: Sverdrup and Armbrust, 2009, Introduction to the World's Ocean (a. Fig. 16.5; b. Fig. 16.12; c, d. Fig. 16.10; e. Fig. 17.11; f. Fig. 16.15; g. Fig. 17.14; h. Fig. 17.3)
4.26: McGraw-Hill Digital Asset Library
4.30: a), b), e), h), i), j) McGraw-Hill Digital Asset Library;
c) University of Hawaii SOEST;
d) http://en.wikipedia.org/wiki/File:Bathocyroe_fosteri.jpg
f) Sverdrup and Armbrust, 2009, Introduction to the World's Ocean (Fig.17.14)
g) http://en.wikipedia.org/wiki/File:Eurypharynx_pelecanoides.jpg
4.32: NOAA Ocean Explorer
4.33: a) McGraw-Hill Digital Asset Library;
b) http://en.wikipedia.org/wiki/File:Nur04505.jpg (C. Van Dover, OAR/National Undersea Research Program)
4.34: Dr. Ransom Myers, Dalhousie University (http://ram.biology.dal.ca/~myers/depletion/images/famcolor3no.jpg)
4.35: United Nations Food and Agriculture Organization
4.36: Greenpeace
4.37: Earthsave.org
4.38: NOAA
4.39: http://en.wikipedia.org/wiki/File:Abalone-farm1web.jpg, and NOAA
4.40: United Nations Food and Agriculture Organization

Part 5: Waves, Tides, and the Coastal Environment
Opener: NASA
p.234: McGraw-Hill Digital Asset Library
5.10, 5.11: Sverdrup and Armbrust, 2009, Introduction to the World's Ocean (Fig. 11.11, 11.2)
5.12: Energy Information Service, Minerals Managements Service
5.14: National Renewal Energy Laboratory
5.16: U.S: Geological Survey
5.19: NASA MODIS
5.20: U.S. Geological Survey
p.248: McGraw-Hill Digital Asset Library (Doug Sherman)
5.24: McGraw-Hill Digital Asset Library
5.29: NASA
p.254: McGraw-Hill Digital Asset Library
5.30: NASA GISS
5.31: NOAA ESRL, Dr. Pieter Tans
p.256: McGraw-Hill Digital Asset Library
5.35, 5.38: McGraw-Hill Digital Asset Library
5.40: U.S. Geological Survey
5.41: NOAA
5.42: Massachusetts Water Resources Authority
p.273: U.S. Geological Survey
p.275: Oak Ridge National Laboratory
p.276: U.S. EPA
p.277: Oak Ridge National Laboratory